PUBLICATIONS OF THE UNIVERSITY OF MANCHESTER

ECONOMIC HISTORY SERIES
No. II

IRON AND STEEL IN THE INDUSTRIAL REVOLUTION

IRON AND STEEL IN THE INDUSTRIAL REVOLUTION

THOMAS SOUTHCLIFFE ASHTON, M.A.

Professor of Economic History in the University of London

" For even iron too which locks up all
other treasures, comes out of England."
—Henry Belasyse, 1657.

MANCHESTER UNIVERSITY PRESS

First Published . . 1924
Second Edition . . 1951
Third Edition . . 1963

Published by the University of Manchester
at the UNIVERSITY PRESS
316–324 Oxford Road, Manchester, 13

CONTENTS

BIBLIOGRAPHICAL NOTE TO THE 1963 EDITION

FEW books on economic history can have stimulated a greater amount of further research than Professor T. S. Ashton's *Iron and Steel in the Industrial Revolution*, first published as long ago as 1924. Ever since the book's appearance the industries with which it dealt have exercised a powerful and fruitful fascination over economic historians, over historians of technology, and over a considerable section of the interested public. Naturally Ashton's account has been modified in detail, but in spite of the vast amount written on the subject during the past forty years it still remains the basic and most readable authority. The purpose of the following bibliographical note is to guide the student through recent work, and to indicate its significance. A few books published before 1924 are also mentioned.

On the earlier period H. R. Schubert's massive *History of the British Iron and Steel Industry from c. 450 B.C. to A.D. 1775* (1957) is indispensable on the technological side, but much less satisfactory on the commercial and entrepreneurial aspects of the industry. A list of charcoal blast-furnaces (with some omissions) is given on pages 366–92, and there are many other useful appendices. It is unfortunate that the book contains such a large number of small misprints. M. W. Flinn's *The Iron Industry in Sixteenth-Century England* (1951) is a useful short account. This originally appeared in *Edgar Allen News* (Sheffield) for January, March, April and May 1951, and was subsequently issued as a separate pamphlet. Mr. B. G. Awty's work on the account books of Sir Richard Shireburn (1526–94) shows how the operator of a bloomery could attempt to make profits from the less marketable kinds of timber by using them in ironworks ("Sir Richard Shireburn's Esholt ironworks," *Bradford Antiquary*, new ser., part xl, May 1960, pp. 243–54).

E. N. Harley's *Ironworks on the Saugus: the Lynn and Braintree Ventures of the Company of Undertakers of the Ironworks in New England* (University of Oklahoma Press, 1957), dealing with the history of the first two blast-furnaces set up by Englishmen in North America, contains much of interest to students of the seventeenth-century iron industry in England. Professor Ashton's account of the attempts by interested parties in the Mother Country either to control or to liberate the iron industry in the American plantations is now supplemented by A. C. Bining, *British Regulation of the Colonial Iron Industry* (Philadelphia, 1933). For attempts by Boyle and Sir Charles Coote to establish an Irish charcoal-iron industry in the first half of the seventeenth century, see H. F. Kearney, " Richard Boyle, ironmaster " (*Journal of the Royal Society of Antiquaries of Ireland*, vol. lxxxviii, part ii, 1953, pp. 156–62).

Mr. B. L. C. Johnson has shown (" The charcoal iron industry," *Geographical Journal*, vol. cxvii, part ii, June 1951, pp. 169–77, and " L'influence des bassins houillers sur l'emplacement des usines à fer en Angleterre avant circa 1717," *Le Fer à travers les Ages, Annales de l'Est*, Nancy, 1956, pp. 217–23) that, owing to the use of coal in the secondary processes of the iron industry, the coalfields, with their associated iron ore measures, were already exercising a powerful influence upon the location of blast-furnaces, forges and iron manufacturing work-shops long before the discovery and spread of the coke-smelting process from 1709 onwards:

". . . Ashton a suggéré que les changements techniques ont encouragé les usines de fer à se redistribuer. Il écrit que l'introduction de l'usage du coke créa de nouveaux fourneaux plus grands, qui surgissaient non pas dans les bois silencieux, mais dans les agglomérations industrielles que les terrains houillers avaient développés. A mon avis, cette image, quoique vraie dans une certaine mesure, insiste trop sur le déplacement. Je soulignerai plutôt la continuité de l'industrie du fer déjà établie sur bien des terrains houillers, souvent assez loin des bois silencieux."

Mr. Johnson has also published the following regional studies of the charcoal industry:

(a) " New light on the iron industry of the Forest of Dean," *Trans. Bristol and Gloucestershire Archaeological Society*, vol. 72, 1953, pp. 129–43. '

(b) " The Stour Valley iron industry in the late seventeenth century," *Trans. Worcestershire Archaeological Society*, vol. xxvii (for 1950), pp. 35–46.[1]

(c) " The Foley partnerships: the iron industry [of the Midlands] at the end of the charcoal era," *Economic History Review*, 2nd ser., vol. iv, no. 3, 1952, pp. 322–40.

(d) " The Midland iron industry in the early eighteenth century: the background to the first successful use of coke in iron smelting," *Business History*, vol. ii, no. 2, June 1960, pp. 67–74.

(e) " The iron industry of Cheshire and North Staffordshire, 1688–1712," *Trans. North Staffordshire Field Club*, 1953–4, pp. 32–55.

Other important studies of the charcoal iron industry include:

(a) E. W. Hulme, " A statistical history of the iron trade in England and Wales, 1717–1750," *Trans. Newcomen Society*, vol. ix, 1928–9, pp. 12–35. This article contains lists of blast-furnaces and forges in 1717, 1720, 1736 and 1750 with a valuable critical commentary.

(b) A. Raistrick and E. Allen, " The South Yorkshire iron-masters, 1690–1750," *Economic History Review*, vol. ix, 1939, pp. 168–85.[2]

(c) C. R. Andrews, *The Story of Wortley Ironworks* . . . *Eight Centuries of Yorkshire Iron-making*, 1st edn. 1950, 2nd rev. edn. 1956.

(d) R. F. Butler, *The History of Kirkstall Forge through Seven Centuries, 1200–1945 A.D.*, 1st ed. 1945, 2nd rev. edn. 1954. This book contains much material on the coke-smelting era as well.

1. See also R. L. Downes, " The Stour Partnership, 1726–36: a note on landed capital in the iron industry," *Economic History Review*, 2nd ser. vol. iii, 1950–1, pp. 90–6.
2. H. G. Baker, " Blast furnace construction and costs in 1740," *Trans. Newcomen Society*, vol. xxiv, 1943–5, pp. 113–20, also based on the Spencer Papers, refers to the South Yorkshire furnaces.

(e) I. Edwards, "The charcoal iron industry of East Denbighshire, 1630–90," *Trans. Denbighshire Historical Society*, vol. 9, 1960, pp. 1–31.

(f) I. Edwards, "The charcoal iron industry of Denbighshire, c. 1690–1770," *ibid.*, vol. 10, 1961, pp. 1–49.

(g) I. Edwards, "The early ironworks of North-West Shropshire," *Trans. Shropshire Archaeological Society*, vol. lvi, part ii, 1959, pp. 185–202.

(h) R. A. Mott, "The Shropshire iron industry," *Trans. Shropshire Archaeological Society*, vol. lvi, part i, 1957–8, pp. 69–81.

(i) A. S. Davies, "The early iron industry in North Wales," *Trans. Newcomen Society*, vol. xxv, 1945–7, pp. 83–90.

(j) B. G. Awty, "Charcoal ironmasters of Cheshire and Lancashire, 1600–1785," *Trans. Historic Society of Lancashire and Cheshire*, vol. 109, 1957, pp. 71–124.

(k) G. G. Hopkinson, "The charcoal iron industry in the Sheffield region, 1500–1775," *Trans. Hunter Archaeological Society*, vol. viii, pt. 3, 1961, pp. 122–51.

One of the most important recent contributions to the history of the charcoal iron era is by M. W. Flinn (" The growth of the English iron industry, 1660–1760," *Economic History Review*, August 1958, pp. 144–53—see, in particular, the useful list of references at the end of his article). Mr. Flinn shows cogently that this period was not, as invariably stated, one of general decline and stagnation in the iron industry. In a few areas, e.g. the Weald,[1] decline did indeed take place, but for the West Midlands, South Wales, South Yorkshire and Furness, it was one of expansion. Mr. Flinn also demonstrates that the effect of rising charcoal prices on the location of the industry

---

1. For the Wealden iron industry, see E. Straker, *Wealden Iron* (1931) and the same author's " Westall's Book of Panningridge," *Sussex Archaeological Collections*, vol. lxxii, 1931, pp. 253–60. This article concerns the earliest surviving detailed expenditure account for an English blast-furnace (1546). For the earliest printed (1646) descriptions of blast-furnace operation and charcoal burning in the Weald (at Barden), see " The Diary of Sir James Hope . . ." (*Publications of the Scottish History Society*, 3rd ser., vol. L (Miscellany, ninth volume)), 1958, pp. 146–52.

has been exaggerated. The charcoal most suitable for making iron was obtained from young trees of about twenty years' growth. Therefore thinnings from carefully-managed woodlands (interest in economic silviculture was growing among landed proprietors and their estate stewards between 1660 and 1760) could be used in charcoal burning, leaving the remaining trees to provide the heavier timber required for constructional purposes in the future, e.g. house- and ship-building.

Mr. Flinn has also added to knowledge by his studies of the activities and works organization of Sir Ambrose Crowley (1658–1713); first by his edition of *The Law Book of the Crowley Ironworks*, Surtees Society, vol. 167 for 1952, pub. 1957, and secondly, by his *Men of Iron: the Crowleys in the early Iron Industry* (1962), which traces the Crowleys and their iron and steel manufacturing interests from the seventeenth to the nineteenth centuries.[1]

Much valuable information on the merchanting side of the charcoal iron industry in Furness from the 1680's to the 1740's may be gleaned from *The Autobiography of William Stout, of Lancaster, wholesale and retail grocer and ironmonger, a member of the Society of Friends, A.D. 1665–A.D. 1752* (ed. J. Harland, 1851), which was for long neglected by historians. Alfred Fell quoted from it in his *Early Iron Industry of Furness* (1908); the first professional economic historian to refer to it extensively, however, appears to have been the late Ephraim Lipson in the revised third edition (1943) of vol. ii of his *Economic History of England*.[2] The sections devoted to the Furness charcoal iron industry by J. D. Marshall in his *Furness and the Industrial Revolution* (1958), pp. 19–41, should also be noted.

Professor Ashton, in demonstrating that it was Abraham Darby I (1678–1717) who first achieved success with the coke-smelting process as early as 1709 (see *infra*, pp. 24–38, 249–52), cast doubt on the claims of " Dud " Dudley to have smelted iron ore successfully with coal to produce merchantable bar

1. See also M. W. Flinn, "Industry and technology in the Derwent valley of Durham and Northumberland in the eighteenth century," *Trans. Newcomen Society*, vol. xxix, 1953–5, pp. 255–62, and "The Lloyds in the early English iron industry," *Business History*, vol. ii, no. 1, Dec. 1959, pp. 21–31.
2. Pages 155, 161, 472, 479–81, 495, 502, 503. A new edition of Stout is in preparation from the original manuscript.

iron in the first half of the seventeenth century. These doubts
have now been confirmed by Dr. R. A. Mott:

" Dr. Mott submitted to chemical analysis samples of the
small coal from the thick seam of the Dudley area which
Dud Dudley tells us he used at his furnace and forge. It
was found that this coal had a sulphur content too high to
allow of its use, in the raw state, to produce sound pig-iron,
let alone merchantable bars. Some of the sulphur can be
removed by coking. But Dud Dudley makes no mention
of coking, and Dr. Mott has shown that the small coal from
this seam cannot be turned into any form of coke that could
be used in the blast-furnace. (It is what is now called a non-
coking coal.) The controversy about Dud Dudley has been
settled not in the library or the muniment room, but in the
laboratory." [1]

In addition, it was shown by the same methods that the
Shropshire " clod " coal used by Darby has the necessary
qualities for producing suitable blast-furnace coke. [2]

There is now a good deal more in print on the origins of the
coke-smelting process than there was when the second edition
of this book appeared in 1951. In 1953 Dr. Arthur Raistrick
published an excellent full-scale study of the Coalbrookdale
Iron Company, *Dynasty of Iron Founders: the Darbys and Coalbrookdale,* based upon the surviving records of the firm. [3]

The whole question of the date of the invention of coke

1. Professor T. S. Ashton, in the preface to the second edition of *Iron and
Steel in the Industrial Revolution,* 1951, p. vii. Dr. Mott's findings are in his
article " Dud Dudley and the early coal-iron industry," *Trans. Newcomen
Society,* vol. xv, 1934–5, pp. 17–38. See also R. A. Mott and G. J. Greenfield
(ed.), *A History of Coke Making and of the Coke Oven Managers' Association*
(1936). For additional material on the early history of cokemaking, see
J. U. Nef, *The Rise of the British Coal Industry,* vol. i, 1932, pp. 216, 248–50,
and W. H. Walton, " Early use of coke in Derby," *Journal of the Derbyshire
Archaeological Society,* vol. liv, 1934, pp. 16–18.

2. See also W. H. Chaloner, " Further light on the invention of the
process for smelting iron ore with coke," *Economic History Review,* 2nd ser.,
vol. ii, no. 2, 1949, pp. 185–7.

3. See also Dr. R. A. Mott's " Coalbrookdale: the early years," *Trans.
Shropshire Archaeological Society,* vol. lvi, part i, 1957–8, pp. 82–93, and his
article, in two parts, entitled " The Coalbrookdale Group Horsehay Works "
in *Trans. Newcomen Society,* vol. xxxi, 1957–9, pp. 271–87, and vol. xxxii,
1959–60, pp. 43–56.

smelting was reopened in 1957 by Dr. R. A. Mott's two articles
(" The earliest use of coke for iron making," *Gas World*, Coking
Section, Jan. 5th, 1957, pp. 7–18, and " Abraham Darby (I and
II), and the coal-iron industry ", *Trans. Newcomen Society*,
vol. xxxi, 1957–9, pp. 49–94). Briefly, Dr. Mott argues that
there occurred at Coalbrookdale a sharp and successful transition in January 1709 from the smelting of iron ore with charcoal
to the smelting of iron ore with coke, i.e. without a transitional
and experimental period of some years (1709–11 or even
1709–13) suggested by Samuel Smiles[1] and Professor Ashton,
during which coke was used with varying admixtures of charcoal. Mr. Flinn has summed up the controversy as follows:

" Dr. Mott's argument in favour of the year 1709 con-
founds the reader by its monumental scale (each of the two
articles quoted above runs to some 12,000 words), and by the
intricacy of its detail. However, his material is the same
as that available to all other investigators—the surviving
records of the Darby firm—but his approach is quite different,
being that of the analytical scientist. He begins by satisfy-
ing himself that *coles* may be safely interpreted as mineral
fuel, though, as has been argued above, other contemporary
records of the iron industry do not justify this assumption.
He then shows that had Darby used charcoal in 1709, the
iron he made would have cost more to produce than he sold
it for, indicating that it was unlikely that charcoal was
used. This calculation is based, not on Darby's costs in
1709, for which all the relevant figures are not available,
but on the cost of cordwood in Coalbrookdale in 1718, the
consumption of charcoal per ton of pig iron in Yorkshire
in 1742 and on transport costs in Coalbrookdale after 1720.
Without going more deeply into the question of general
price movements, this is shaky ground on which to build,
particularly when it leads to calculations running to three
decimal places. There is, moreover, no justification for
assuming that the surviving accounts of 1709 are complete,
and that the quantities of raw materials and sales recorded
there are complete. Perhaps it would be wiser to admit

1. *Industrial Biography: Ironworkers and Toolmakers*, 1908 edn. p. 83.

that the Darby account book of 1708–9 does not contain sufficiently detailed information to establish beyond dispute the use of one fuel or another. Dr. Mott makes a great deal of use of the accounts for the period after 1718, when the use of coke is undisputed, in order to illuminate the 1709 account, but this dangerous form of extrapolation is based on innumerable minor assumptions, very few of which would stand careful scrutiny. Analysis of this kind, relevant to twentieth-century technology, can at best only be acceptable for the early eighteenth century when it is corroborated by other documentary evidence: it can never be accepted to the point of overriding conflicting evidence, least of all when the latter is well founded." [1]

An article of interest to students of the charcoal era and the coke era is R. A. Lewis's discussion of " cricking," or the provision of horses and carts for carriage of materials to and from ironworks (" Transport for eighteenth-century ironworks," *Economica*, 1951, new ser., vol. xviii, pp. 278–84), based on the Knight MSS. at Kidderminster.

The efforts of the notorious William Wood (d. 1730) and his sons to make iron using pit coal have been examined at some length by M. W. Flinn in a paper read to the Newcomen Society on January 31st, 1962 (" William Wood and the coke-smelting process "). As Mr. Flinn remarks: " Very little is known yet, unfortunately, about the diffusion of Darby's coke-smelting process. Only three furnaces outside Coalbrookdale are known for certain to have attempted to smelt with coke before 1750," i.e. Redbrook (1716–17) in the Forest of Dean, Bersham (1721–2) in North Wales, and Little Clifton (1723) in Cumberland.

1. M. W. Flinn, " Abraham Darby and the coke-smelting process," *Economica*, new series, vol. xxvi, no. 101, Feb. 1959, pp. 56–7. The whole article occupies pp. 54–9. In his reply Dr. Mott points out that the quantities of the " coles " brought to Coalbrookdale in 1709 are expressed in measures normally applied to coal and not to charcoal. And the men who carried the " coles " were those who were regularly employed in transporting coal from the pits (R. A. Mott, " ' Coles ': weights and measures, with special reference to Abraham Darby and the coke-smelting process ", *Economica*, new series, vol. xxvi, no. 103, Aug. 1959, pp. 256–60). It seems probable, therefore, that Darby was using mineral fuel (whether alone or in conjunction with charcoal) as early as 1709. Whether the product was good saleable pig or cast iron as early as this year it is unfortunately impossible to determine.

The period from the 1750s onwards is comparatively well-documented by recent research. A. H. John has edited *Minutes relating to Messrs. Samuel Walker & Co., Rotherham, Iron Founders and Steel Refiners, 1741–1829* (Business Archives Council, 1951) and the same author's *The Industrial Development of South Wales, 1750–1850* (1950) contains new material on the finance of the rising iron industry in that area, which may be supplemented by D. J. Davies, *The Economic History of South Wales prior to 1800* (1933), and Sir Lewis Namier's " Anthony Bacon, M.P., an eighteenth-century merchant " (*Journal of Economic and Business History*, vol. ii, no. 1, November 1929, pp. 20–70). Several studies have been made of the great iron firms of South Wales:

(a) J. P. Addis, *The Crawshay Dynasty: a study in Industrial Organization and Development, 1765–1867*, 1957.

(b) J. D. Evans, " The Uncrowned Iron King (the first William Crawshay)," *National Library of Wales Journal*, vol. vii, no. 1, summer 1951, pp. 12–32.

(c) M. Elsas, *Iron in the Making: Dowlais Iron Company Letters, 1782–1860*, 1960—a careful selection of some 650 items out of 563,000 now available to scholars.

(d) E. L. Chappell, *Historic Melingriffith: an account of Pentyrch Iron Works*, 1940.

The earlier portions of W. E. Minchinton's *The British Tinplate Industry: a history* (1957) should also be consulted. L. J. Williams has written a useful study of Robert Morgan's operations at Carmarthen blast-furnace based on his letter-book for 1759–62 in " A Carmarthenshire ironmaster and the Seven Years' War," *Business History*, vol. ii, no. 1, Dec. 1959, pp. 32–43. A. H. Dodd's *The Industrial Revolution in North Wales* (1933) contains a detailed and well-documented section on the iron industry (pp. 132–52) and W. H. Chaloner has traced the career of Isaac Wilkinson (d. 1784) who, originally connected with the charcoal-iron industry, converted Bersham furnace, near Wrexham, to coke-smelting (1754–6) in " Isaac Wilkinson, potfounder," *Studies in the Industrial Revolution presented to T. S. Ashton*, ed. L. S. Pressnell (1960), pp. 23–51. For the rise of the Scots iron industry the account given in

H. Hamilton's *The Industrial Revolution in Scotland* (1932) is now supplemented by R. H. Campbell's *Carron Company* (1961), a detailed bicentenary history of the first coke-smelting ironworks in Scotland,[1] a similar concern to the great South Wales firms of the period, which depended very largely, like Carron, on English capital and technical skill.

W. H. B. Court's *The Rise of the Midland Industries, 1600–1838* (1938), surveys in masterly fashion the iron trade of this area and its connections with the coal industry and iron manufacturing (pp. 78–114, 149–216). The Boulton and Watt papers, so fruitfully used in the present volume, have formed the basis for many other studies, of which the following list contains the most significant:

(a) E. Roll, *An Early Experiment in Industrial Organisation, being a history of the firm of Boulton Watt, 1775–1805*, 1930.

(b) H. W. Dickinson and Rhys Jenkins, *James Watt and the Steam Engine*, 1927.

(c) H. W. Dickinson, *James Watt*, 1935.

(d) H. W. Dickinson, *Matthew Boulton*, 1936.

(e) W. K. V. Gale, *Soho Foundry* (W. &. T. Avery Ltd.), 2nd edn. 1948.

(f) A. E. Musson and E. Robinson, " The early growth of steam power," *Economic History Review*, 2nd ser. vol. xi, no. 3, 1959, pp. 418–39.

(g) Particular reference must be made to J. E. Cule's somewhat neglected article on " Finance and industry in the eighteenth century: the firm of Boulton & Watt " (*Economic History: a supplement of the Economic Journal*, vol. iv, no. 15, Feb. 1940, pp. 319–25) which discredits the widely-held legend that Watt was a dreamy inventor only saved from ruin by the able and efficient business-man, Boulton.

There is no full-scale study of Henry Cort,[2] but E. Wyndham Hulme's " Henry Cort, founder of the iron puddling process,

1. See also J. M. Norris, " The Struggle for Carron: Samuel Garbett and Charles Gascoigne," *Scottish Historical Review*, vol. xxxvii, no. 124, Oct. 1958, pp. 136–45; and A. Birch, " Carron Company, 1784–1822, the profits of industry during the Industrial Revolution," *Explorations in Entrepreneurial History*, vol. viii, no. 2, Dec. 1955.

2. See H. W. Dickinson, " Henry Cort's bicentenary," *Trans. Newcomen Society*, vol. xxi, 1940–41, pp. 31–48.

and his family," *Notes and Queries*, Feb. 16, 1952, pp. 77–82, contains the necessary genealogical foundation.

Other business histories of iron firms prominent in the late eighteenth and early nineteenth centuries are:

(a) P. Robinson, *The Smiths of Chesterfield: a history of the Griffin Foundry, Brampton, 1775–1833*, 1957.

(b) T. S. Ashton, *An Eighteenth-Century Industrialist: Peter Stubbs of Warrington, 1756–1806*, 1939, 2nd ed., 1961.

(c) R. H. Mottram and C. Cooke, *Through Five Generations: the History of the Butterley Company*, 1950—a disappointing compilation.

(d) R. Butler, *The History of Kirkstall Forge through seven centuries, 1200–1945 A.D.*, 1st edn. 1945, 2nd rev. edn. 1954.[1]

(e) A. Birch, "The Haigh Ironworks, [near Wigan], 1789–1856: a nobleman's enterprise during the Industrial Revolution," *Bulletin of the John Rylands Library*, vol. 35, no. 2, March 1953, pp. 316–33.

(f) W. K. V. Gale, *The Coneygre Story* (Coneygre Foundry, Tipton, Staffs.), 1954.

Rhys Jenkins elucidated the complex story of the introduction of the cementation process into this country in the early seventeenth century in his important article, "Notes on the early history of steelmaking in England," *Trans. Newcomen Society*, vol. iii, 1922–3, pp. 16–40, but the steel industry of the eighteenth and early nineteenth centuries has naturally not attracted attention on the scale of the iron industry. Alan Birch and M. W. Flinn have, however, published "The English steel industry before 1856, with special reference to the development of the Yorkshire steel industry," *Yorkshire Bulletin of Economic and Social Research*, vol. 6, no. 2, July 1954, pp. 163–77. Sidney Pollard has written a useful history of Marsh Bros. and Co. founded by John Marsh of Sheffield in 1631,

---

1. See also A. E., B. F., and H. M. Butler, *The Diary of Thomas Butler of Kirkstall Forge, Yorkshire, 1796–1799, with which are incorporated extracts from the memoirs of Elizabeth Beecroft, and an account of how Kirkstall Forge came into the possession of the Butler family*, privately printed, London, 1906, and two articles by Alan Birch in *Edgar Allen News*, Aug. 1952, pp. 209–10, and Sept. 1952, pp. 231–3, which contain extracts from Thomas Butler's MS. "Journal of a tour amongst the iron works of Staffordshire, 1815."

under the title of *Three Centuries of Sheffield Steel: the story of a family business* (1954). E. Wyndham Hulme's article, " The pedigree and career of Benjamin Huntsman, inventor in Europe of crucible steel," *Trans. Newcomen Society*, vol. xxiv, 1943–5, pp. 37–48, supplements Professor Ashton's account (*infra*, pp. 54–9). The fortunes of the British iron industry during the Napoleonic Wars are fully considered in F. Crouzet, *L'économie britannique et le blocus continental, 1806–1813*, 2 vols. 1958.

Illustrations of many of the ironworking processes and of the products of the industry may be consulted in:

(*a*) John Gloag and Derek Bridgwater: *A History of Cast Iron in Architecture* (1948).

(*b*) F. D. Klingender: *Art and the Industrial Revolution* (1947).

(*c*) Peter Mathias: *English Trade Tokens: the Industrial Revolution Illustrated* (1962).

(*d*) W. H. Chaloner and A. E. Musson: *Industry and Technology* (1963).

Finally, the accounts left by foreign observers of the English iron and steel industry have been increasingly recognized as valuable original sources. A beginning has been made in discovering and elucidating these sources, and particularly the Swedish ones, by Alan Birch and M. W. Flinn (A. Birch, " Foreign observers of the British iron industry during the eighteenth century," *Journal of Economic History*, vol. xv, 1955, pp. 23–33; M. W. Flinn, " The travel diaries of Swedish engineers of the eighteenth century as sources of technological history," *Trans. Newcomen Society*, vol. xxxi, 1957–9, pp. 95–109; M. W. Flinn, " Samuel Schröderstierna's ' Notes on the English iron industry ' (1749)," *Edgar Allen News*, August 1954; Jean Chevalier, " La mission de Gabriel Jars dans les mines et les usines britanniques en 1764," *Trans. Newcomen Society*, vol. xxvi, 1947–9, pp. 57–68; W. H. Chaloner, " Marchant de la Houlière's Report to the French Government on British methods of smelting ore with coke and casting naval cannon, 1775," *Edgar Allen News*, Dec. 1948 and Jan. 1949 (later reprinted as a separate pamphlet)).

University of Manchester   W. H. CHALONER
July 1962

CHAPTER I.

THE CHARCOAL-IRON INDUSTRY IN ENGLAND.

" . . . . . a land whose stones are iron, and out
of whose hills thou mayest dig brass."

Deuteronomy, viii, 9.

I.

A COMPARISON of any one of the textile industries today with
that of six hundred, two hundred, or even one hundred years
ago would abound in striking contrasts; and one of the most
fascinating pursuits of the economic historian has been to
trace the process by which these industries, formerly moulded
to a craft or domestic system, have assumed their modern
form. Researches in this field have been so fruitful and
convincing that there has been a tendency to generalise the
results, and to assume that gild, domestic, and factory systems
are categories applicable to the economic sphere as a whole—
inevitable stages in the march of all industries. It may not
be out of place, therefore, to begin a study of the development
of iron production by emphasising that in this industry no
such essential transformation has taken place : from the
earliest period of which we have exact information iron
making in this country has been conducted on capitalistic
lines—capitalistic not only in that the workers are dependent
upon an employer for their raw material and market, but
also in that they are brought together in a "works," are
paid wages, and perform their duties under conditions not
dissimilar to those of almost any large industry of modern
times. The scale of operations has increased enormously ; the
sapling has become an oak, deep-rooted and widespread ;
technique has been revolutionised. But in structure and
organisation there is no fundamental change.

The history of iron production is thus a record of the
growth of the business unit, the discovery of new sources

of raw material, the invention of mechanical and chemical processes, and the expansion of markets. In all these respects the greatest strides were taken during the eighteenth century, and it is with the events and personalities of this formative period that this volume is primarily concerned. But a brief account must first be given of conditions in earlier times.

In the Middle Ages the product of the industry consisted entirely of malleable iron; and though, no doubt, there were local variations in practice, the method of operation was generally as follows. The ore was first crushed into fragments and mixed with a small quantity of marl and lime which served to bind it together, and the mass was then divided into lumps which were placed on a forge and surrounded with charcoal. By means of a blast produced with leathern bellows, worked either by manual labour or by water power, the fire was maintained at a moderate temperature; and the metal was brought to a pasty, rather than a liquid form, the impurities being removed by repeated hammering, " even [says Sturtevant] as the whey is wrung out by the violence of the Presse, and so the cruds are made into a cheese." Several heatings and hammerings were necessary before the ore was finally transformed into a bloom of wrought iron, ready to be worked into implements by the smith. Though the quality of the finished metal was high, the quantity produced at any one forge was necessarily small, and a considerable weight of metallic iron was left behind in the cinders or slag.[1]

An informative account of an early ironworks in the North of England has been given by Mr. G. T. Lapsley.[2] In the fourteenth and fifteenth centuries the Bishops of Durham, as Earls Palatinate, were owners of the minerals within the county; and in 1408 Bishop Langley began to produce and work iron at his own forge in Weardale. The works consisted of a " bloomhearth," where the ore was reduced by repeated heatings, and of a " strynghearth," at

1. *Bristol and Gloucester Arch. Trans.*, xxix, 314; Sturtevant, *Metallica*, 113.
2. *Eng. Hist. Rev.*, xiv, 509. For details of an ironworks in Kent half a century earlier see M. S. Guiseppi, in *Archæologia*, lxiv, 145.

which it was further fined or forged. Nearly two tons of metal were produced each week, and as the work was carried on the year round, with but temporary stoppages for festivals, the forge must, in those days, have been one of considerable importance. The wage-earners included a colier, or charcoal-burner, a bloomsmith, who apparently first reduced the iron from the ore, and a smith who forged it into bars. A foreman was appointed to supervise the work of a number of labourers, some of whom had been brought to Weardale from as far as Rotherham and Wakefield; and the wife of the foreman, along with the wife of the smith, assisted in breaking the ore and attending to the bellows. All labour, with the possible exception of that of the women, was paid by the piece; in addition to the money wages the workers were provided with wooden dwellings, and an allowance of ale was made each week, with additions at certain seasons of the year.

How slowly the features of industry changed in the regions remote from the centre of trade may be seen by comparing this account with that recently supplied by Mr. Wigfall of a forge in South Yorkshire more than 160 years later.[1] Here also were employed a bloomer, a smith, and a "stringfellowe," each paid piece-wages, and each receiving some customary allowance for clothing; technique was apparently unchanged, and the structure of the industrial unit was the same as in the fifteenth century.

Elsewhere, however, changes of a momentous order had taken place : whereas formerly malleable iron had been produced directly from the ore, it was now prepared by first smelting in a blast-furnace and subsequently fining the cast metal at the forge. When and where the blast-furnace was first introduced is uncertain : it has generally been believed that the art of bringing iron to the melting point was unknown in this country prior to the late fifteenth century, and that it was then carried to England from Germany. Some years ago, however, Mr. Starkie Gardner showed that a grave-slab of *cast* iron in Sussex must have been produced at a much earlier period, and that though the primitive cannon of the fifteenth century were constructed of bars of wrought iron, bound into

1. *Hunter Arch. Trans.*, II, ii (1921), 194.

the form of barrels, they contained an inner chamber of cast iron.[1] It would thus appear possible that it was not Prussia—as has been claimed—but Sussex that saw the birth and early development of the art of casting, and that this took place before 1500, the approximate date usually assigned to it. The question will probably never be settled, for it appears likely that the blast-furnace was not the result of a sudden act of creation, but of a slow evolution, the stages of which can be inferred only by observation of processes in metallurgically backward areas at later periods. " The Catalan Hearth," it is said, developed into the " Osmund Furnace "—in which a bloom of malleable iron was made—and this in turn evolved into the " Stückofen," in which either the pasty malleable iron or the freely flowing cast iron, or both intermixed, could be produced at will. But such inferential reasoning is not historic fact : all that can be said with certainty is that in the days of Edward III most, if not all, of the iron used was the product of the bloomery or forge, while in the days of Henry VIII by far the greater part was smelted in the furnace and cast into finished articles, or into pigs that were subsequently fined into malleable bars at the forge.

Whether the art of casting was indigenous or not, its application to the production of ordnance was undoubtedly improved by the introduction of foreign skill in Tudor times. In 1523, for example, an expert founder of cannon shot was sent from Spain by Charles V ; Henry VIII employed as gun-founders a number of foreigners, of whom the most famous were Peter Baude, Arcanus de Cesena, and Van Cullen ; and evidence of immigration of both labour and enterprise on a fairly considerable scale is found in the parish registers of Sussex belonging to this period.[2]

Nevertheless the great majority of the ironmasters were Englishmen, and the capital engaged in the industry was drawn almost exclusively from native sources. It could hardly, indeed, be otherwise in view of the close association that had always existed between iron production and the ownership of land. Occasionally, it is true, miners and others

1. *Archæologia*, LVI, i, 134.
2. *Archæologia, loc. cit.* ; *Sussex Arch. Coll.*, ii, 186, xiv, 159.

of humble origin might conduct small works, like the *forgiae errantes* of the Forest of Dean; but even in early times the apparatus of an ironworks represented a volume of capital that few save landowners could command. Moreover the industry was intimately dependent on the land for its raw material in the form of ore, limestone, and charcoal; and it was the demand of the landed classes for the implements of agriculture and war that constituted the main reason for its existence. The Crown itself was proprietor of ironworks in several of the royal forests. Monastic bodies, like those of Flaxley, Wenlock, Kirkstead, Fountains, Rievaulx, and Conishead had long been active in the industry. And both before and after the suppression of the monasteries the Lords of Hallamshire, the Earls of Warwick, and other noblemen drew substantial revenues from the iron produced on their estates and sold to the metal workers of Sheffield, Bristol, and South Staffordshire. Nor were the landed proprietors merely passive factors in the industry : the Hon. Gilbert Talbot, for example, supervised the furnaces owned by his father, the sixth Earl of Shrewsbury, and the interest of the territorial magnates in iron making is attested by numerous references scattered throughout their personal correspondence.[1]

In sixteenth-century Sussex this connection was specially marked, for its abundant supplies of fuel and its proximity to the capital made the Weald the natural centre of cannon-founding in England. At least as early as 1546 Lord Seymour of Sudeley was casting guns and shot at Worth and Sheffield (Sussex) ; and during the succeeding decades an ever-increasing number of noblemen engaged in the business. In 1573 when the celebrated Ralph Hogge complained of the infringement of his patent for casting cannon, a list of Sussex ironmakers was drawn up which included, among others, Her Majesty the Queen, the Earls of Derby, Surrey, and Northumberland, the Lords Abergavenny, Montague, Buckhurst, and Dacre, Sir Thomas Gresham, Sir John Baker, Sir Richard Baker, Sir Alexander Culpepper, Sir John Pelham, Sir Robert Tirwett, and Sir Henry Sydneye.[2]

1. *Hist. MSS. Comm.*, 15th Rept., ii, 33.
2. *S. P. Dom. Eliz.*, xcv, 16, xcvi, 199; *V.C.H. Surrey*, ii, 272.

This list of 1573 is probably not comprehensive, and it is not always clear whether the person named is the owner of a furnace, or forge, or both; but particulars are registered in most cases, and it is possible to glean information as to the scale of the representative undertaking.

	Proprietors.	Furnaces.	Forges.
Furnaces only	17	18	—
Forges only	12	—	13
Furnaces and forges.	27	34	38
Total	56	52	51

The typical business was thus one in which furnace and forge were combined in single ownership, and specialisation of process was apparently confined to those who had not sufficient capital to engage in both branches of the industry. John Ashburnam held three furnaces and four forges, Sir Richard Baker three furnaces and two forges, and Anthony Morley three furnaces and one forge; but a single furnace associated with a single forge was clearly the predominant order. As to the numbers employed in the normal ironworks information is scanty. In 1549 there were 23 men working a furnace at Sheffield (Sussex) in addition to the two wainmen who tended the fourteen oxen;[1] and at a forge in the Forest of Worth 33 men were engaged. How many of these were full-time employees, and how many charcoal-burners or other workers who gave only part-time service, it is impossible to say. Richard Woodman, the martyr ironmaster of Lewis, when on trial for heresy in 1557, claimed to find employment for no fewer than a hundred men; but as he was also an agriculturist, and speaks of having been "at plough with my folks" when arrested, it is certain that not all these were permanent ironworkers.[2]

A surer index of the size of the industrial unit is the output of metal, and for this there exists more definite information. From the accounts of Sir Francis Willoughby's works at Duffield in 1591 it appears that 105 tons of metal were cast in 18 weeks, and that 75 tons of this pig iron were

1. *V.C.H. Sussex*, ii, 245.
2. Foxe, *Acts and Monuments of the Martyrs* (ed. Pratt), viii, 370.

required to make the 50 tons of bar iron which were produced at the forge in six months. Details of costs are also available. The founder, a highly skilled workman, received the astonishing wage of £1 a week, and the finer and hammerman were jointly paid 16s. for every ton of finished bar iron. At the Codnor Works, where 200 tons of bar iron could be produced annually, the weekly wages of founders, finers, and hammermen were estimated at £4-4s.; and much larger payments were involved in the hire of ironstone-miners, charcoal-burners, and labourers engaged in the carriage of materials to the works.[1] The circulating capital no less than that embodied in the plant was thus considerable, and the iron industry exhibits relatively large-scale industrial units long before these had appeared—apart from exceptional cases—in the textile and other trades.

The English cannon, which were the principal product of the industry, were of high quality, and their manufacture and exportation were subject to state supervision and control. In 1574, as the result of Ralph Hogge's complaint, the Privy Council obliged all makers of cannon to enter into bonds not to manufacture or sell without licence from the Queen. Every gun-founder was to deliver to the Master of Ordnance a statement of the number of pieces cast and to whom delivered; and at all ports inspection was made of guns put on board ships for defensive purposes. Two years later casting of ordnance in the Weald was entirely prohibited, on the ground that the supply in the country was adequate. Similar measures were again taken in 1579. In 1587 the number of cannon that might be cast at each foundry was fixed by the Master of Ordnance, and a list of London merchants was drawn up through whom alone they might be sold. Production was again suppressed in 1588 and 1589; two years later bonds were taken of all furnace-owners in the Weald in order to prevent exportation; and yet again in 1602 the Privy Council prohibited further casting.[2]

The very frequency of these attempts at regulation implies that they were ineffective. Sir Anthony Sherley is known to

1. *Hist. MSS. Comm., Middleton MSS.*, 496-7.
2. *V.C.H. Surrey*, ii, 265-6; *Sussex Arch. Coll.*, ii, 187.

have sent 100 pieces to the Spaniards; and that the surreptitious exportation was not confined to the Weald is indicated by instructions issued in 1602 which call special attention to the guns made by Edward Matthews of Radyr, near Cardiff, "because from that place very easilie they may be caried into Spayne . . . . and the officers of that Porte are very poore men, and such as dare not displease him." [1] There is, in fact, ample evidence that exportation took place both with and without licence from the Crown; [2] Kipling's story of the serpentines and demi-cannon that were carried to Rye under the wool-packs is no mere fantasy, and gun-running for the pirates of the Channel was almost a normal incident in the commercial life of Sussex at this time. [3]

It was not only in respect of the finished product that state supervision was exercised; the raw material of iron-making was also subjected to control. During the Middle Ages the woodlands had been regarded rather as an evil than as an asset; their destruction had been considered beneficial both to agriculture and to transport. But by the sixteenth century the enclosures and the demands of industry for fuel had brought about a shortage of timber trees that seemed likely to hamper shipbuilding and so to threaten national security. Among the causes of this dearth the voracity of the ironworks was regarded as the chief, and it was urged that the industry should be closely regulated if not entirely suppressed. At first tenderness was shown to the main centres of production : an Act of 1543 regulating the cutting of coppices was declared not to extend to the counties of Surrey, Sussex, and Kent. [4] When, five years later, a commission was appointed to inquire into the ironworks of the Weald, it was asserted that the shortage of wood was so great that soon Calais, Boulogne, Rye, Hastings, Dover, and other towns on both sides of the Channel would be without fuel, and that the fishermen would not be able to dry their clothes or warm their

1. *S. P. Dom. Eliz.*, cclxxxiii, 73 ; *Records of Cardiff*, i, 362-3.
2. Special licences were issued, *e.g.*, to Sir Thomas Leighton, in 1572 and to the Earl of Leicester in 1587. During the later years of the century the needs of the States General were met in this way. See *S. P. Dom. Eliz.*, cclxvi, 26, cclxxiv, 124.
3. Hal o' the Draft in *Puck of Pook's Hill*.
4. 35 Henry VIII, c. 17.

bodies when they came in from the sea.[1] In 1558 the ironworks were prohibited from using as fuel timber trees growing
within fourteen miles of the coast or any navigable river—a
restriction of area evidently dictated by the needs of the
shipbuilding industry and the domestic requirements of the
larger towns.[2] But again the Wealden area was exempted.
A generation later, however, this immunity was limited to
those ironmasters whose works were eighteen or more miles
from London and eight miles or more from the Thames;[3]
while an Act of 1585, forbidding the erection of new furnaces
and forges, also placed on the local industry the obligation of
maintaining the roads of the Weald, which had suffered
severely from the carriage of heavy materials to and from the
works.[4]

In the Crown forests special measures were taken to
conserve supplies of timber; in 1546, for example, the bloom-
smithies of Furness were abolished, though in 1564 tenants
were permitted to make iron for their own use, and five years
later other relaxations were introduced in the interest of the
Mines Royal. Similar action was taken in the Forest of Dean,
but here again policy fluctuated according as anxiety for the
navy or concern for a straitened exchequer was dominant in the
minds of rulers. On the whole the substantial revenues that
could be obtained from the grant of monopolistic rights to
projectors in the iron industry outweighed the desire for
conservation; and the end of the seventeenth century saw the
woodlands of this area seriously depleted.[5]

The growing shortage of fuel, and the restrictive legislation
to which it gave rise, turned attention to the possibility of
finding in peat or coal an alternative to charcoal. In brick-

---

1. Presentment of the jurors of Rye, Winchelsea and Hastings. *Sussex
Arch. Coll.*, xv, 21; *Hist. MSS. Comm.*, *Hatfield House*, xiii, 19-24.
2. 1 Eliz., c. 15.
3. 23 Eliz., c. 5.
4. 27 Eliz., c. 19.
5. Fell, *Iron Industry of Furness*, 101-111. For the history of ironmaking
in the Forest of Dean see *Brit. Arch. Journ.*, xvii; Rudder, *Gloucestershire*;
V.C.H. Gloucestershire; Scott, *Joint Stock Companies*, ii; and Nicholls,
Ironmaking in the Forest of Dean. It is worthy of notice that the Elizabethan
Statutes were themselves used as a means of revenue by the Stuarts. In 1636
Sir David Cunningham was granted a commission to compound with ironmasters for offences, and in the same year other offices were created in
connection with the iron industry. *V.C.H. Surrey*, ii, 265.

making, brewing, dyeing, and brass-casting this substitution had been effected during the sixteenth century, and Harrison points out that in many districts blacksmiths made use of coal in working iron into finished products. It was natural, then, that ironmasters should experiment with mineral fuel in the preliminary processes of smelting and fining. As early as 1589 a patent for the use of stone coal, pit coal, and sea coal was granted to Thomas Proctor and William Peterson; in 1595 Sir Robert Cecil held a similar licence; and in 1607 another was issued to Robert Chantrell. Although highly probable, it is not certain that these related to the production, as distinct from the manufacture, of iron; and the first patent that is definitely known to have covered smelting was that obtained by Simon Sturtevant in 1611—a patent in which shares were held by Prince Henry, Prince Charles, Rochester, and the King himself. The obligation of publishing an account of the process led to the verbose and almost meaningless *Treatise of Metallica,* but no practical result followed; within a few months the grant was withdrawn and another was issued in place of it to John Rovenzon, an assistant of Sturtevant's. He in turn was followed by others; and in 1621 Lord Dudley was granted a patent in respect of the process followed by his son Dud Dudley.

The claims of Sturtevant, Rovenzon, and other early projectors have received small credence; but the story of Dud Dudley has been accorded a more sympathetic ear, and most writers on the iron industry have seen in him the neglected inventor forced to pay to progress the tribute exacted of the pioneer. Such is the view taken, for example, by Mushet, Scrivenor, Percy, Smiles, Beck, and Mantoux; and, in face of it, it may be worth while to cast a glance at the career of this alleged discoverer.

Born in 1599, the son of Edward, Lord Dudley, and Elizabeth Tomlinson, "a base collier's daughter," Dud was brought down from Balliol—according to his own account—to supervise a furnace and two forges belonging to his father at Pensnet in Worcestershire. It is here that he claims to have made in the same year a small quantity of iron of good quality with pit coal, and, in the following year, many tons which were fined at Cradley Forges. The patent taken out by his father in 1621 covered a period of thirty-one years; and though the period was reduced by the Statute of Monopolies of 1624 to fourteen years, in other respects the grant was allowed to run. Thereafter, according to his own statement, Dud made " annually great store of Iron, good and merchantable, and sold it unto diverse men . . . at Twelve pounds per Tun." Only the ravages of floods, the antagonism of other ironmasters,[1] and his imprisonment for debt, he asserts, prevented his project from reaching full fruition. In 1638 a new patent was obtained; but the outbreak of the Civil War, in which Dud served as a royalist colonel, led to the loss of his estate and prevented the prosecution of the enterprise. In 1660 he begged for the restoration of his privilege, but without success; and it was in furtherance of his later petition that, in 1665, his *Metallum Martis* was printed. In this work the full catalogue of his misfortunes is set forth, and a claim is made that the iron produced by his method is actually superior in quality to that smelted and fined with charcoal.

This claim at least was exaggerated—unless indeed Dud Dudley had succeeded beyond the powers of all other iron-masters down to the present day. But there are reasons for doubting whether iron of even moderate quality was ever produced by him with mineral fuel. No mention is made in his treatise of any attempt to coke the coal, and with the blowing apparatus of the seventeenth century it would appear to have been impossible to produce sound iron with raw fuel. If, as he would have us believe, he was a high-minded patriot actuated only by a desire to save the timber vital to England's security, it is strange that he allowed his knowledge to die with him. But the few details of his life gathered from sources other than his own writings do not by any means indicate high-mindedness. That the memorial he erected to his dead wife should record his own rather than her virtues, is indicative of a boastful and assertive nature. His litigiousness is illustrated by the bill of complaint he brought against his

1. Patents for the same purpose were granted to William Astell in 1627, to Edward Ball in 1630, to Edward Jordan in 1632, to Sir Abraham Williams in 1633, and to Sir Phillibert Vernatt and Thomas Whitmore in 1636 and 1637.

father in 1631; and by his action against Richard Foley in the same year. Next he is found laying claim to the manor of Himley and evicting the sitting tenant. In 1637 he was engaged in litigation with the churchwardens and overseers of Dudley, respecting the sum of £50 which, according to their statement, had been bequeathed by his mother to the poor. And his mother herself stipulated in her will that Dud "should not see her writings," for " he might do somebody wrong." Later he was involved in long disputes with partners in his Bristol enterprise of 1651.[1] Dud's whole life, in fact, seems to have consisted of a series of lawsuits and assertions, some at least of which can hardly be described as other than preposterous.

Obviously these details of personal conduct do not in themselves dispose of Dud Dudley's claim to inventive genius. But they do decidedly modify the picture of the unrequited patriot that has so often been exhibited. And they disincline one from accepting without reservation a story the evidence for which is his own word unsupported by that of any less partial witness. That Dudley did produce some sort of iron with mineral fuel is probable enough, but that this was of sound merchantable quality is very unlikely; and there is no valid reason why this Balliol undergraduate, rather than any one of a dozen other projectors of the seventeenth century, should have been singled out for fame.

Of later patents mention may be made of those granted to Captain Buck and John Copley under the Commonwealth, to Sir Nicholas Stanning in 1673, to Frederick de Blewston in 1677, to Viscount Grandison in 1678, and to Thomas Addison in 1692. None of these, however, bore fruit, and it is small wonder that observers like Plot, looking back upon the hundred years of effort, should conclude that the problem was insoluble, and that Nature never intended the union of coal and iron to be fertile for the use of mankind.

---

1. *Salt Arch. Coll.*, v, 114-17. For further details see Rollason, *The Seamy Side of Dud Dudley* (reprinted from *The Dudley Herald*, 1921) and *Salt Arch. Coll.*, II, ii, 36-37.

II.

From the middle of the seventeenth century there are clear indications that the English iron industry had entered upon a period of decline. The Civil War, source of windfall profits as it was to some ironmasters, brought about the ruin of others. In 1643 Sir William Waller pulled down the royalist ironworks of the Weald, and similar destruction was wrought in the Forest of Dean and elsewhere.[1] In connection with a petition put forward by the Sussex ironmasters in 1664, a list of furnaces and forges was compiled, and the number still active was contrasted with that of 1653. In the earlier year, it appeared, there were 27 furnaces and 42 forges in operation in Sussex; in the later year only 11 furnaces and 18 forges. It is evident that a temporary trade depression was partially responsible, for at least ten additional furnaces were ready to be set in blast if conditions became favourable. The ironmasters themselves attributed the decay to external pressure rather than to chronic internal wasting; and their diagnosis produced reflections on the superior advantages of other countries, the low standard of life of the foreign workman, and the impossibility of keeping the breath of life in the English industry except it be state-nursed in the shuttered sick-room of a system of high protection.[2]

But, with or without protection, a contraction of iron-making in the Weald had become inevitable, for in spite of regulative measures the scarcity of fuel had become acute. Elsewhere there was the same story to tell, and, when the eighteenth century opened, the English iron industry in all parts afforded a striking illustration of what the modern economist knows as "decreasing returns." Although the statistics compiled by contemporaries are by no means free from error, it is probably safe to conclude that the national output about the year 1720 did not exceed 20,000 tons of bar iron; and that between this time and the middle of the century it diminished rather than increased.[3] The effects of this pressure in the ancient centres of Dean and Sussex are

---

1. *V.C.H. Surrey*, ii, 268; Nicholls, *Ironmaking in the Forest of Dean*, 41.
2. For other complaints to the same effect see Yarranton, *England's Improvement*, i, 62, and *Britannia Languens*, 418.
3. See Appendix B.

to be seen in the relatively small scale of the individual iron-works. Here and there some special quality in the local ironstone or process of manufacture might maintain a large undertaking—as at Tintern Abbey where the works produced peculiarly malleable and ductile metal, suitable for rolling into sheet-plate and drawing into wire. But generally in these districts the productive unit was minute: in Sussex, for example, the typical finery was one with an output of not more than fifty tons of bar iron in a year. As metallurgical processes developed in the Midlands and the North the forges of the Weald must have appeared to contemporaries as the Donegal weaver and the Honiton lacemaker appear to the present generation—as interesting survivals of an earlier economy maintaining but a precarious foothold on the steepening slope of industrial progress.

In the smelting branch of the industry activity was some-what less constrained, for a further effect of the shortage of fuel was the tendency to concentrate on this process, which required less charcoal per ton than the subsequent process of fining. The Weald actually possessed a larger number of furnaces than of forges, and from Defoe's reference to the production of kettles, firebacks, and ordnance here, it would seem that the founder was the mainstay of its dwindling prosperity. By short journeys by road the wares produced in Sussex reached the Medway and were thus readily carried by water to London. As in earlier times, the Office of Ordnance was the main pur-chaser ; and the conservatism of this body, during the long wars of the eighteenth century, helped to retain for Sussex an industry which would otherwise have passed elsewhere, strengthening that specialisation in smelting for which the shortage of fuel was primarily responsible.[1]

Similarly the capitalists of the Forest of Dean found it more profitable to use their limited supplies of fuel for smelting, and to convey the pig iron up the Severn to the newer forges of Salop, Worcester, Warwick, Stafford, and Chester. Yet even

---

1. Defoe, *Tour*, i, 106. Cited Mantoux, *Révolution Industrielle*, 273. The Lamberhurst furnace—at which were cast the balustrades that surround St. Paul's—still flourished in 1724 ; ordnance was cast by the Fullers at Heathfield, by Legas and Harrison, and by the Butlers of Fernhurst, at least as late as the year 1770. *Sussex Arch. Coll.* ii, 203 ; *V.C.H. Sussex*, 249.

the operations of the furnace were hampered by the shortage both of fuel and ore. Though supplies of the latter were brought to Flaxley and other works by sea from Whitehaven and Furness, as the century wore on ironmaking here steadily declined and finally became extinct.

The arrest of industrial progress in the older areas led to important results elsewhere. As the hunger for fuel increased ironmasters were forced to migrate into more remote lands; salvation could be found only in solitude, and the industry of smelting and refining was literally fleeing to the wilderness to escape destruction. Following upon the Elizabethan Acts against deforestation Anthony Morley left the Weald to set up works at Pontygwaith, near Merthyr Tydfil; and during the succeeding century the same centrifugal tendency led to the erection of furnaces and forges in South Yorkshire and Derbyshire, in Shropshire, Staffordshire, and other regions.

Ironmasters had for long ceased to rely on supplies of charcoal produced from virgin forest, or on the by-product of woods maintained primarily for other purposes : it had become the practice to preserve coppices specifically for the ironworks. As early as 1581 a southern ironmaster, Christopher Darrell, was exempted from the provisions of the Act regulating iron-mills in view of his having preserved the woods at Newdigate. And a hundred years later the practice was common everywhere. " It is now in all these parts " (wrote Andrew Yarranton of Gloucestershire and the Midland Counties[1]) " every day's experience, that Gentlemen and others do make it their business to inclose Land and sow them with Acorns, Nuts, and Ash Kayes, to rear Coppices Woods, they knowing by experience that the Copice Woods are ready money with the Iron Masters at all times." It was thus possible for Yarranton and other industrialists to argue that it was not the ironworks but the agrarian enclosures that were responsible for the deforestation of England ; arboriculture in fact had become a distinct industry, and the sale of charcoal to the ironmasters, coupled as it was with that of oak-bark to the

---

1. *England's Improvement*, Part II, 72. Yarranton admits, however, that some of the practices connected with the supply of charcoal led to the destruction of timber trees. *Ibid.*, 76.

C

tanners, proved a source of considerable revenue to land-owners.[1] This development was stimulated by the steady increase in the price of charcoal from the early years of the century until the general substitution of coke in the smelting process which came about during the 'sixties.[2]

In these circumstances it was naturally to those districts where a vigorous policy of conservation was possible that the iron industry gravitated. Such an area was that of the North-West of England. " A great Part of the Lands in Westmoreland and Cumberland, and some in Lancashire " (according to a writer[3] in 1750) " are customary Tenure, and divided into a great Number of distinct Manors, which belong to several Noblemen and Gentlemen as Lords thereof . . . . some Lords have sold the Woods growing, or that shall hereafter grow, upon the customary Tenements within their Manors, to the owners of such Tenements, which encourages the Tenant to take the same Care of improving their Woods as if it were on Freehold Land. I think all Lords of Manors should do the same ; for where the Lords claim a Right to the Wood upon their customary Tenants Ground, it occasions the Tenants discouraging, nay even destroying it as much as they can." Land was actually turned from the plough "tho' Arable Ground is scarce, nothing like sufficient to supply them with Bread."

At Clifton, between Cockermouth and Whitehaven, a pioneer furnace was erected to smelt the local supplies of kidney ore, and near by a forge was worked by James Spedding of Whitehaven; while about the middle of the century others were established in the neighbourhood of Workington.[4] In 1711 William Rawlinson and John Machell, the owners of

---

1. The fact that charcoal and bark were joint products led to alliances between ironmasters and tanners to defend their common interests. Thus in the long struggle relative to the encouraging of iron production in the plantations the tanners and leatherworkers gave active support to the iron-masters. *J.H.C.*, xxv, 1018. Bark from coppices was much preferred to that from timber trees. *Ibid.*, xxiii, 114.

2. According to Fell, *op. cit.*, 136, the price per dozen sacks was 28s. 6d. in 1715, and 40s. in 1765, after which it varied but little.

3. *Aris's Birmingham Gazette*, 21st November, 1750.

4. Jars, *Voyages*, 235, 250.

primitive bloomery forges in Furness, joined with others to form the Backbarrow Company, which, within a few months, had two furnaces in blast. The example set by these local capitalists was quickly followed by others : ironmasters from Cheshire became partners in the Cunsey Company ; and when, seven years later, William Rea of Monmouth and Edward Kendall of Stourbridge joined in the venture, the exploitation of Furness was assured. By 1748 there were no fewer than eight blast furnaces at work here in addition to numerous forges.

However energetic landowners and farmers might be in afforestation they could hardly hope to keep pace with this development : in Malthusian language, though the supply of charcoal might at best increase in arithmetical proportion, the needs of industry increased in geometrical proportion. Here and there attempts were made to smelt with peat instead of charcoal, but with small success. Costs of production began to rise and a further migration of ironmaking became inevitable. Hence in 1727 the partners in the Backbarrow Company joined with James Spedding of Whitehaven and others to set up a furnace at Invergarry in the wilds of the Highlands. There was here no local supply of ore, and this had to be carried by sea from Furness; masons to construct the furnace were brought from Edinburgh; charcoal burners from Ireland; and furnacemen from Yorkshire and South Wales : indeed the only advantage of the situation, apart from ease of communication by sea, lay in the density of the surrounding woods. Here, under the equivocal protection of Fort William, the furnace maintained a precarious existence, its staff subject to assault and robbery by Highlanders and soldiery alike, till 1736, when its operations came to an end. Again in 1752 the Newlands Company, shut out by its rivals from the woods of Furness, set up the Lorn Ironworks at Bonawe in Argyll; and as late as 1775 the Duddon Company lighted a furnace at Goatfield, near Inveraray.[1]

A similar movement of labour and capital was taking place further south. In Shropshire smelting had long been carried

1. Fell, *op. cit.*, 238, 260, 343-413.

on, first near the Wrekin, where furnaces were in operation
at Coalbrookdale, Leighton, and Willey; and, secondly, near
Ludlow, where the principal ironworks was the Bouldon
furnace, owned and worked by Edward Knight. From this
region there was a pronounced migration westward into
Wales. In the early years of the century John Hawkins and
Benjamin Harvey—relatives of the Darbys of Coalbrookdale—
in turn operated a furnace at Bersham near Wrexham.
Abraham Darby himself took a partnership in an ironworks
in Montgomery, and in 1715 is found smelting ironstone from
Cader Idris at Dolgan furnace, near Dolgelly, in which he was
followed by Samuel Milner of Bewdley and Henry Payton of
Dudley.[1] A second and later penetration took place into
South Wales: in the neighbourhood of Merthyr Tydfil the
furnace of Pontygwaith, originally put in blast by Anthony
Morley of Sussex, was still in existence, as were also works
at Llanelly and Kidwelly. But following 1755 a new influx
of English enterprise began, and the establishing of the large
undertakings associated with the names of Anthony Bacon of
Whitehaven and John Guest of Broseley, opened a new
industrial era in this region.

These illustrations of what has been spoken of as the
centrifugal tendency have been drawn almost exclusively
from the smelting branch of the industry. On first thoughts
one would expect this process to be concentrated near supplies
of ironstone or ore; and that geological formation did indeed
exercise a certain control over the location of works could be
shown by reference to Sussex, the Forest of Dean, Shropshire,
Furness, or South Wales. But though important in determining that some regions should have more ironworks than
others, the presence of mines had no great part in deciding the
exact location of particular works. In Nottingham, for
example, the furnaces were in many cases at a considerable
distance from the mines: and there were several instances of
the movement of ironstone or ore from mines in one part of
the country to works in another—from Furness to the Forest
of Dean, South Wales, the Midlands, and the Highlands;

1.   *V.C.H., Shropshire*, 461.

from Robin Hood's Bay to the interior of Durham; and from Cumberland to Cheshire and the Firth of Forth.[1]

More important than the distribution of iron ore was that of the coal supplies. The coalfields of South Staffordshire, South Yorkshire, and Durham had long been worked and had provided fuel which, though not yet used for smelting and fining, was entirely suited to the purposes of the smith; hence in each of these three areas there had sprung up the manufacture of such articles as nails, horseshoes, locks and bolts, chains, tools, and agricultural implements. Now it was obviously convenient, other things equal, for the forgemaster, who supplied the raw materials to the metal workers, to be situated near his market; and a centripetal pull was thus exercised on the fining branch of the iron industry which to some extent countered the tendency to dispersion resulting from dependence on charcoal.

The development of the metal trades was specially marked in the neighbourhood of Birmingham, Dudley, Wolverhampton, Walsall, and Stourbridge. According to a computation of 1737, within ten miles of Birmingham no less than 9,000 tons of bar iron were elaborated annually by workers employed under a domestic system of production.[2] Of these by far the greater number were engaged in nail-making, for which the grades of relatively soft iron known as "ordinary tough," "blend," and "cold-short" were required. Hence at least three-fourths of the bar iron produced in Staffordshire and Worcestershire was of this nature, and a single forgemaster, Edward Knight, supplied no less than a thousand tons a year to the nail-ironmongers of the district. For the purpose of cutting the iron into rods the slitting-mill was introduced, and large capitals were sunk locally in this branch of the

---

1. *V.C.H. Nottingham*, ii, 322; Fell, *op. cit.*, 92-98, 130-7; Jars, *op cit*, 250; Whitworth, *Advantages of Inland Navigation*, 44.

2. *J.H.C.*, xxii, 852; xxiii, 111, 114. In the previous century Dud Dudley had remarked on the sources of this development: ". . . . yet must I tell you of a supernumerary number of Smiths within ten miles of these Cole-Works near twenty thousand; yet God of his Infinite goodness . . . hath made this Country a very Granary for the supplying these men with Iron, Cole, and Lime made with Cole. . . ." *Metallum Martis*, 29.

industry.[1] Forges and slitting-mills, as distinct from furnaces, clustered along the tributaries of the Severn, and especially the Stour, which during the century was to develop into a veritable hive of industry. "The course of this river [says Nash[2]] is about twenty miles, and it has upon it upward of 30 works; slitting-mills, forges, a wire-mill, &c." Of the fineries the largest was Wildon Forge, owned by Lord Foley; and one of the best-known slitting-mills of this region was at Halesowen.

In the South Yorkshire coalfield forge operations to supply the smiths and toolmakers tended to concentrate in the vicinity of Sheffield, where the oak trees of Wharncliffe, of Rivelin, and of Loxley provided abundant supplies of charcoal, and the streams flowing into the Don could readily be turned to industrial purposes. At the beginning of the century both furnaces and forges in the immediate neighbour-hood of the town were owned by the Duke of Norfolk, as Lord of Hallamshire, while those to the North, near Barnsley, belonged to Lord Strafford. It was no longer the custom, however, for nobles to carry on industrial functions, and the Duke's forge at Attercliffe was rented to John Fell, passing in 1726 along with the forge at Wadsley to Edward Wortley.[3] A little earlier Samuel Shore had set up a competing forge near the town, and further South in the wooded district between Chesterfield and Worksop the Sitwell family conducted forge operations on a relatively large scale.

In the third main centre of the metal trades—that of the North-East—so strong was the specialisation to the later processes of ironmaking that no smelting whatsoever existed before 1745, when Isaac Cookson set up the Whitehill

1. Scrivenor attributes the slitting-mill to one, Box of Liège ; and Samuel Taylor Coleridge tells a romantic story of the first Foley, who, disguised as a poor fiddler, is said to have travelled through the ironmaking regions of Sweden, so obtaining the information which enabled him to establish the first slitting-mill in England. But Foley is known to have been a man of substance and the mayor of his native town of Dudley ; there is no evidence that he ever went through the adventures attributed to him ; and, if there is any truth in the story, the hero of it was more probably William Brindley. The fact that three of Brindley's daughters married three sons of Foley may account for the confusion. Shaw, *Staffordshire*, ii, 265.

2. *History of Worcestershire*, ii, 45.

3. Hunter-Gatty, *Hallamshire*, 167 ; *Surtees Society Trans.* lxv, 250 ; Diary of John Hobson of Dodworth Green.

Furnace near Chester-le-Street.[1] Moreover the association of the forges with the smithies was so close that, contrary to conditions in most other districts, both fining and the manufacture of ironware were controlled by a single capitalist, who built up an integrated business on a scale which was probably unique at this period. In 1682 Ambrose Crowley,[2] a smith or ironmonger of Greenwich, established works at Sunderland, in which at first about a hundred men were employed, and within a few years a much greater number. Many of his employees came from Liège, and the opposition which their foreign origin aroused was perhaps partly responsible for the removal of Crowley in 1690 to the less populous region of Swalwell and Winlaton near Newcastle. But a further reason was undoubtedly the greater supplies of coal and wood there available; and the fact that Newcastle was a centre of importation for Swedish iron perhaps also helped to determine the choice of site. In these works Crowley and his successors carried on all the processes, except that of smelting, in the production and manufacture of iron. At the finery forges pig iron from Sweden and America was worked into bars, which were turned into sheets at the large rolling-mills, or cut into rods at the slitting-mills. Swedish iron was converted into steel on a large scale, and iron castings were made by remelting pig iron in reverberatory furnaces. Finally, finished wares of varied types were manufactured : from Swalwell heavy forgings, such as anchors, chains, and pumps, were shipped direct to London, while at Winlaton nails, files, knives, saws, chisels, hammers, and agricultural implements were produced in quantity.

If, as these illustrations indicate, the tendency towards

1. Bell, On the Manufacture of Iron in connection with the Northumberland and Durham Coalfield. *Report of the British Association* (1863), 370, 734.

2. Ambrose Crowley was one of the most striking figures in the industrial life of the eighteenth century. Beginning obscurely, he raised himself to wealth and influence by the superior organisation of his concerns. In 1707 he was knighted ; the following year he became a member of the Master Drapers' Company, and in 1711 an alderman of London. In the same year he was appointed a director of the South Sea Company, and in 1712 became Deputy-Governor. At the time of his death in 1713 he was member of Parliament for Andover. Beaven, *Aldermen of London*, ii, 195. For further details see Jars, *Voyages Métallurgiques*, 217–235 ; Surtees, *History of Durham*, 168–170 ; and the *Law Book of the Crowley Iron Works* in the British Museum.

dispersion was less marked in the case of forges than in that of furnaces, it was entirely absent in the final stages of slitting, rolling, and the fabrication of hardware and tools. For here charcoal was of less moment and each process could be performed with the aid of coke. Rolling- and slitting-mills and manufactories tended therefore to settle in the larger towns like Sheffield and Birmingham; the fact that Swedish and Russian irons were imported through London, Hull, and Newcastle led to a development of steel production in these ports, as well as in the inland centres mentioned above; while foundries were relatively numerous in Bristol and Liverpool, through which American irons, as well as the surplus pig iron of other parts of Britain, were imported.

Nevertheless, the fundamental characteristic of the eighteenth-century iron industry was its scattered nature. Mills were rarely found in proximity to forges, and forges were commonly remote from furnaces. This geographical isolation was usually associated with severalty of ownership. A capitalist such as William Wood might concentrate in his own hands the control of a number of furnaces, forges, and foundries, but, speaking generally, the ironmaster was a specialist confined to one set of operations. Scarcity of charcoal was one factor in producing this condition, but of almost equal importance was the limitation of water power. Manual labour might serve in periods of drought or frost to keep the furnace active, and in a few cases, as at Adam's Forge and Sparrow's Forge near Wednesbury,[1] horse gins were employed to move the hammers; but such methods were too expensive for general adoption, and ironmasters were thus tied to sites on the banks of swiftly flowing streams. Attempts were made, it is true, to break down this tyranny of wood and water: in 1757 Isaac Wilkinson took out a patent for " a new machine or kind of bellows . . . for the blowing of furnaces or forges at any distance, to be wrought or put in motion by water or fire-engines . . . so that a furnace, forge, or any other works may be blowed from any waterfall or falls . . . to several miles distant . . . by means of a pipe." But there is no evidence that his methods were ever employed in practice,

1. Hackwood, *Olden Wednesbury*, 31.

and until late in the century ironworks continued to make use of direct water power. At any one point on a stream the fall of water was generally insufficient for more than one of these purposes : hence a further tendency to separation of the smelting and fining processes.

Finally to both furnace owner and forge master water carriage was important at this period of badly-constructed roads. To the former it was vital for the bringing of bulky raw materials to the works as well as for the movement of finished products; and thus the ideal situation for a furnace was at points like Coalbrookdale, or Upton, or Lidney, where rapid streams, which supplied the power, emptied themselves into navigable rivers or into the sea.

The reader who desires further details of the charcoal-iron industry—its processes, output, and markets—will find these in Appendices A, B, and C. The purpose of this chapter has been merely to sketch the geographical distribution of ironworks prior to 1776, to indicate their dependence on woods, on falling streams, and on the highways of river and sea. The cumulative effect of the technical improvements to be described below consisted not only of a vast increase in output, but also of a redistribution of the works themselves. The construction of canals was to lessen the dependence of ironworks on rivers; the steam-engine was to free them from bondage to falling water. And, while the century was still young, a furnace had been lighted in Shropshire, fire from which was carried to a hundred new and larger furnaces, springing up not in the silent woodlands, but in the busy haunts which the coalfields had already brought into being.

CHAPTER II.

THE DISCOVERIES OF ABRAHAM DARBY AND BENJAMIN HUNTSMAN.

> " . . . . . the dread things of Nature
>   Crouch low in his gaze :
> The fire doth his bidding ;
> The Iron obeys."
>   —*William Watson* : *The Blacksmith.*

I.

THE early attempts to find a substitute for the charcoal used as fuel in the blast-furnace have already been described; and it has been seen that the ironmasters of the seventeenth century had been uniformly unsuccessful in dealing with a problem that became increasingly urgent as time went on. Of the further efforts made by their successors of the eighteenth century brief mention must be made of those associated with the name of William Wood of Wednesbury, who achieved notoriety, not only as coiner of halfpence for Ireland, but also as the promoter of a pretentious scheme for the control of the English iron industry. Owner of woods at Wednesbury and of the forge at Upton-on-Tern, he obtained in 1720 a lease of all the mines on the Crown lands of England, and controlled " some of the best iron-works in the kingdom ; several forges for refining and drawing iron out into bars; also a slitting-mill for rolling, slitting, and preparing iron for its several uses in manufactures; furnaces for making pig-iron, pots, rails, and banisters, backs and hearths for chimnies, and all sorts of cast iron both with charcoal and pit-coal."[1] It is certain, however, that the process with pit-coal had not been brought to a successful issue, for in floating his bubble scheme of 1720 Wood suggested an extensive planting of coppices on waste ground in order to supply the required fuel. In 1726 he attempted to smelt with coke dust in a reverberatory furnace at Whitehaven, and patents for this process were taken out in 1727 and the following year.[2]

1. Macpherson, *Annals*, ii, 114.
2. Spec. of patents, No. 489—granted to his son Francis; assigned to William Wood, No. 502.

For the purpose of putting his " discovery " into practice and of extending it to the whole industry, Wood asked for a loan of no less than a million sterling, with which he proposed to purchase or erect a hundred blast-furnaces; and in 1728 he actually undertook to supply the Mines Royal with 3,000 tons of bar iron at a price of £11 or £12 a ton. His ambition, apparently, was to establish a gigantic monopoly of iron production such as an Elizabethan or Stuart projector might have dreamed of; and all the artifices of the company promoter—including a copious outpouring of pamphlets—were employed to further his scheme. In 1721 he and rival claimants were in vigorous dispute. Three weeks after the grant of the patent of 1727 William Fallowfield of Leek obtained a licence for smelting and refining with peat fuel;[1] and four years later Fallowfield explained the delay in putting his method into practice on the grounds of "the mighty Bustle made by Mr. Wood and his Party." Wood's claims were finally put to a test at Chelsea in 1731. In a first trial he claimed to have made iron " not brittle but tough and fit," at a cost of production that would allow of its sale in bars at less than £10 a ton. A Mr. Tomkyns, however, who also claimed to be able to make bar iron with pit coal, asserted that Wood's iron " in drawing out, took up an unusual time; that after its being shap'd into an Ankony, it requir'd 14 heats to draw it into a Bar, whereas it ought to have been drawn at three or four at least. That the ore used was tough; yet the Bar when broke, appear'd in some Places to be a cold short Iron." When a second trial, made a month later, gave no more satisfactory result, and the iron broke under the hammer, Wood tried to explain his failure by accusing the spectators of having " poisoned " the iron.[2] Whether or not Wood had overcome the first difficulty of smelting with mineral fuel, it is certain that he failed in his larger claim to transform the pit-coal pig into malleable iron; and even if it be granted that he had leapt the first obstacle, it can be shown that he was not the first in the race, and that mineral fuel had long been

1. Spec. Pat., No. 490.
2. *Gentleman's Magazine* (1731), 167, 215—referred to by Mantoux, *La Révolution Industrielle*, 292.

used in the furnaces—though not in the forges—of the Darbys
at Coalbrookdale.

It was the region of Shropshire lying to the north of
the Severn, directly before the river takes its great bend to
the south, that saw the most important developments in iron-
technique and output during the eighteenth century. At this
point the southern uplands of Shropshire push out into the
plains north of the Severn a wedge of high ground, culminating in the Wrekin, on the one hand, and Lilleshall Crag, on
the other. To the west of this peninsula the lower coal-
measures appear at the surface; and it was possible to obtain
ample supplies of both coal and ironstone from the same
shallow workings, while near at hand was the limestone of
Wenlock Edge. This "coalfield peninsula" was originally
part of the Wrekin Forest, and is still well-timbered, so that
wood for structural purposes and for charcoal-making was
readily procurable. Near the mouth of a small stream which
rapidly descends a steep-sided valley into the Severn stands
the village of Coalbrookdale; and it was obviously the
combination of abundant supplies of raw material with water-
power and water-transport that led to the establishing of ironworks here at an early date.

In the seventeenth century Coalbrookdale was part of the
estate of Sir Basil Brooke; and in 1696 two furnaces, together
with forges, were leased by the Brooke trustees to Shadrach
Fox, from whom by sub-leases they came into the hands of
Abraham Darby in 1708.[1] Darby was born in 1676 at
Sedgeley near Dudley. His father and grandfather, like so
many of their class, had apparently combined the making
of nails and locks with agriculture, and they have sometimes been spoken of as yeomen. After an apprenticeship
to Jonathan Freeth, a maker of malt-mills in Birmingham,
Abraham settled at Bristol in 1699, where, along with two or
three partners, he set up a brass and iron works at Baptist
Mills, and made experiments with a view to the substitution of
cast iron for brass in the manufacture of various small
commodities.

At this time the art of casting was far less advanced in

1. *V.C.H. Shropshire*, i, 461.

England than abroad; and the Dutch in particular, by reason, it was alleged, of superior skill, lower duties, and cheaper labour, were formidable competitors with the English founders in the home market, especially as regards the sale of iron pots and similar utensils.[1] It was to the Dutch, therefore, that English casters looked for improvement in their practice, and in 1704 Abraham Darby paid a visit to Holland and brought back skilled workmen to Bristol. Associated with him also was John Thomas,[2] who had previously been employed as a shepherd by Charles Lloyd at Dolobran; and the "New Invention of Casting Iron-bellied Pots and other Iron-bellied Ware in Sand only without Loam or Clay," which formed the subject of the patent taken out in April 1707, is said to have resulted from the joint researches of Darby and Thomas.[3]

That iron pots had been cast in England for generations past is well-known, and it is certain that Darby was by no means the first to adopt sand-casting here. It seems probable, however, that the shape of the bellied pots had hitherto presented an obstacle to the use of sand, and that the more tenacious loam had been employed for the purpose. But the exact nature of the discovery cannot now be determined: possibly it consisted of a special casting-box, or, more probably, of some new method of preparing the moulds.

Shortly after he had obtained the patent, having withdrawn from the partnership at Baptist Mills, Darby allied himself with James Peters of Bristol and Griffin Prankard of Somerton to set up an ironworks in Cheese Lane; and in 1708 he took over the lease of the furnaces at Coalbrookdale.[4] The earliest records preserved at the works are in a book the first pages of which are occupied with the accounts of a British merchant. The entries belong to the years 1679-82 and relate to the sale of "Italian silke," "Turkey Jammy," canvas, calico, and other textile fabrics; from which it seems probable that the

---

1. *J.H.C.*, xxii, 852. Evidence of John Bannister. See also *Records of Cardiff*, ii, 409-20. Among wares brought from Rotterdam were the following: 17 July, 1686, "three hundred and fforty Iron pots and Kettles." 17 Feb., 1698/9, "Seaven hundred and fifty Iron potts and Keetles."
2. For John Thomas see *Journal of the Friends' Historical Society*, xvii, 29.
3. The date is usually given as 1708, but the "docquet" of the patent in the British Museum is dated April 1707.
4. *V.C.H. Shropshire*, i, 461.

volume was a discarded day-book of one of Darby's partners—
perhaps James Peters. Later, in a different hand, and occupy-
ing some forty or fifty folios, is the Journal of Abraham Darby
for the years 1708 and 1709; and from this it appears that
during the first of these years the works at Coalbrookdale
were being prepared for operations which actually commenced
in 1709. For some time intimate relations existed between the
works at Bristol, which supplied tools and utensils, and those
at Coalbrookdale, which sent in return pig iron and castings.[1]
Within a short time, however, Peters and Prankard withdrew,
but business with Bristol was still carried on through Thomas
Goldney, a well-known merchant of the city, between whom
and the Darbys a warm friendship had grown up.

It is genrally agreed that it was in these works at Coalbrookdale that the process of smelting iron with mineral fuel
was first successfully accomplished; but how, when, and even
by which of the first two Darbys, have long been matters of
dispute. Thus Beck, following Scrivenor, set the date of the
discovery at 1713, and this was for long accepted. But in his
well-known work on Metallurgy Dr. Percy attributed the
discovery to the second Abraham Darby, and put the period
at 1730-5. Since the publication of his circumstantial
account of the discovery, most of the writers on the industry
have accepted his version, or at least have assigned to the

---

1. The following extracts are made by way of illustration :

1709.   *A. Darbye and Bristol Iron are Drs*

		£	s.	d.
11th mo : 4	To a parcell of Piggs 6 Tunn	36	10	—
	To a parcell of Backs, No. 11, 4.2.25, at 10d lb	2	7	3*
	To Bake Stones, No. 48, 9.2.2, at 10d	4	17	4*
	To 1 large Furnace	9	6	
	To 14 Square Pots for Coppᵉ	13	17	4
	Pots &c. } 117½ galls. at 10d Gall. Kettles }	7	16	8
		74	14	7

Sent by Ed. Owen with a parcell of Pipes.

11th mo : 9	By Sundry Boxes, Patterns and other Utensils as pr. Note from 4st mo/1708 to ye 9th mo 1709	337	5	5
	By 20 Iron Pots rcd from Th. Millner	4	5	
	By a Cask of Black Lead, Kettles, Boxes & 6 Ladles	7	1	
		348	11	5

* Evidently 120 lbs. went to the cwt., and 30 lbs. to the qr.

discovery a date later than that given by Scrivenor.[1] Despite this change of opinion there are good reasons for believing that it is to the father that the credit should be given, and that the innovation in smelting was made during the early years of the century, at a date prior even to the birth of the second Darby.[2]

The researches of the late Mr. W. G. Norris[3] have shown beyond all question that coal was coked and used in the blast-furnace at Coalbrookdale at least as early as September 1718 : the writer in the Victoria County History[4]—who appears to have obtained his information from an unpublished paper written by Mr. Norris—mentions that, in July of the same year, the stocks in the coal yard included large quantities of " coaks " and " brays "—small coke—and that there were turf and stacks of coke at both furnaces.

But it is now possible to go a step further. It is shown by the Journal, to which reference has just been made, that coal was purchased by Abraham Darby regularly, and in quantities by no means negligible, nine years earlier—in fact almost from the first days of the concern. This fuel was usually obtained from a master-collier, Richard Hartshorn, who also supplied ironstone from the same pits at Little Wenlock. A few typical entries relating to these transactions are set forth below.

1709		£	s.	d.
July 22	Richard Hartshorn & Co.			
	By Cash pd. E. Dorrell pr. theyer			
	order in part for Coles	8	04	06
Sept. 6	By Cash pd Edward Dorall for Coles	05	18	11

1. See Beck, *Geschichte des Eisens*, iii, 160-2 ; Scrivenor, *Iron Trade*, 55 ; Percy, *Metallurgy*, 888. Toynbee (*Industrial Revolution*, 70) speaks of the process as being brought into use between 1740 and 1750 ; Dr. Clapham (*Cambridge Modern History*, x, 733) says that it was finally accomplished about 1740 ; Cunningham (*Growth of English Industry and Commerce*, 523) and Mantoux (*Révolution Industrielle*) give 1735 ; Meade (*Coal and Iron Industries*) 1730-35.

2. Abraham Darby II was born 12 Mar., 1711.

3. Smiles, *Industrial Biography*, App. II.

4. *loc. cit.*, 461-2. The present writer is indebted to Mr. William Darby for the loan of Mr. Norris's paper.

1709			£	s.	d.
Oct. 14	R. Hortshorn		10	08	11½
	By Cash paid Dorrall for Getting Coles by theyer order		11	19	06
Oct. 18	Richard Hortshorn		20	0	0
Nov. 29	Pd. Richard Hortshorn & Co. pr.				
	William Garbit for Getting Coles		03	19	00
	Ditto pd. Ed^w Dorall		5	16	04

The fact that coal was purchased does not of itself prove that mineral fuel was used in smelting. But that the coal was not disposed of to others is shown by the absence of any records of such dealings. No finished wares of wrought iron were made, and hence the coal could not have been required for the work of a smith. There remains the possibility that the fuel was used—as it was elsewhere even at this early period—for a preliminary roasting of the ironstone before the latter was put into the furnace. That part of it was consumed in the raw state for this purpose is probable enough, but that another portion was coked, and used in the furnace itself, is proved by entries such as the following :

1709		£	s.	d.
Apr. 20th	By Cash p^d for Charcking Coles	00	01	03
Aug. 24	By cash pd. Edward Dorall for Coling [? Coking] Coles	01	12	4
July 2	Lawrence Woling			
	By cash pd him in part for Coles and Iron Wheal^d ye first blast .	30	00	00

Finally the paucity of entries relating to the purchase of charcoal implies that the bulk of the fuel used was of mineral origin ;[1] and since during this year, large quantities of pig iron, as well as pots, kettles, firebacks, mortars, pipes, and other wares were cast and sold, it must be assumed that Darby had already established coke-smelting of iron on a commercial scale as early as 1709.

Here again it is difficult to say exactly wherein the

---

1. For example :		£	s.	d.
Nov. 12	pd ye wood Coller for 17 days	0	13	0

discovery lay. The obstacles in the way of smelting with pit coal at an early date were many, for coal contains impurities absent from charcoal and is also less inflammable. To produce a satisfactory metal with mineral fuel it was therefore necessary first, to contrive methods of removing some of the impurities by coking; second, to construct a furnace of such a size that the ironstone could remain in contact with the fuel for a longer period than was the practice in charcoal smelting; and third, to increase the temperature by means of a more powerful blowing apparatus.

Darby was certainly by no means the first to produce coke : as early as 1627 a patent had been taken out for the process, and others followed during the century. The wording of that granted to Captain Buck in 1651 for making iron with stone-coal " without charcking " is itself evidence that some of the earlier attempts at smelting had been made with coke and not with raw coal.[2] Nor does it appear probable that Darby made any innovation in the matter of a flux, for lime or limestone was employed at Coalbrookdale, as it was in the charcoal-using furnaces of other districts.[3] Possibly Darby's furnace was larger than was customary, but it would seem most probable that his success was due to the introduction of a blast sufficiently strong and continuous to give complete fusion, produced by bellows superior in power to those in general use.

But whatever the nature of the new process, the written record leaves little room for doubt as to the date and author of its discovery; and in view of this, it is curious to note in passing the grounds on which the innovation has been attributed to a later generation. In the first place there is the account given to Dr. Percy in 1864 by the wife of a descendant of the ironmaster. According to this story it was the second

1. Mushet, *Papers on Iron and Steel*, 405.
2. Galloway, *History of Coalmining*, 46 ; Percy, *Metallurgy* : *Fuel*, 415.
3. This is proved by the following entries in the Journal :

			£	s.	d.
1709 June 4	By Cash pd. for 8 horsloads of lime		00	06	08
Aug. 24	By Cash pd. Mary Cope for Laying & drawing Lime		00	06	07
Oct. 18	Henry ffox for Getting Limestone		2	00	00

4. The following entry is of interest in this connection :—

11th mo 6 pd Ambrose Crowley for Bellow Boards	12	00	00

Darby who, for the first time, produced a suitable coke and employed it successfully in smelting : after six days and nights of sleepless vigilance on the bridge of the furnace—so the story runs—he was rewarded by seeing the metal flow out free and pure ; and, in a state of exhaustion and oblivion, the discoverer was afterwards carried away to bed by his workmen. The origin of this story ensured it a widespread acceptance ; and even so sound an historian as M. Mantoux has asked how, in face of it, can one attribute the discovery to the first Darby ; while another writer [1] has even suggested—albeit not without misgivings—that although the process was discovered by the first Abraham, it was discontinued after his death, and had to be rediscovered by the younger Darby at a later date. For this suggestion there is no evidence whatsoever. The records of the firm themselves disprove it. Associates and employers such as Thomas Goldney, Richard Ford, and John Thomas, who must have known what the first Darby was about, long continued active in the concern ; and it is almost impossible that the death of the discoverer should have meant complete oblivion of the process by which the business had been built up. Those who have inquired into the legends of their own families have learnt how easy it is for the events of one generation to be attributed to another, and they will know what measure of credence it is safe to put in the traditional word. If there is any truth in the account of the vigil at the furnace, it must almost certainly have been the first, and not the second Darby, who was the hero of the story. [2]

But, it may be objected, if coke-smelting were in operation as early as 1709, how comes it that, a quarter of a century later, other ironmasters were still experimenting in the same direction, and taking out one ineffective patent after another ? Why is there no printed record of the process till nearly the middle of the century ? Why no hint of it in the pamphlets relating to the industry, or in the evidence given before the Parliamentary committees of 1737 and 1738 ? Why, in 1709, was not the culmination of a century of effort proclaimed from the housetops, and the method put into practice throughout the country ?

1. *Dict. Nat. Biog.*   2. For conclusive evidence see Appendix E.

To begin with, it may be pointed out that, though the first printed account of the operations at Coalbrookdale was not made until 1747,[1] there are earlier references which, of themselves, prove that coke-smelting had developed at a date prior to that sometimes assigned to its discovery. Swedenborg, for example, wrote in 1734 of the use of coke for iron-smelting in certain districts, and though no direct mention is made of Abraham Darby, it was very probably Coalbrookdale that he had in mind.[2] Nevertheless the general absence of comment requires some explanation.

This is, perhaps, partly to be found in the character of the inventor himself. Like many other pioneers of technical progress in the eighteenth century, Abraham Darby was a Quaker: in temperament he was the antithesis of the Sturtevants, Rovenzons, and Dudleys of the seventeenth century, and of some of the figure-heads of the iron industry in the nineteenth century. Instinctively he shrank from anything in the nature of self-advertisement and, like Benjamin Huntsman, who refused the proffered fellowship of the Royal Society, he deliberately chose to remain obscure.

But there were other, more objective reasons : it seems very probable that the production of sound coke-iron was not a sudden creation but the result of many trials in which failure and success alternated. The inventory taken at Coalbrookdale in 1718 shows that there was an accumulation of "sculls," or defective iron, which were sold at a low price to a neighbouring forgemaster.[3] Such sculls may have been produced frequently in the early days of the process, and though it is beyond question that marketable iron was produced every year, it might have been difficult for Darby himself to say exactly when the problem had reached a final solution.

Further, it should be observed that not every grade of coal was fitted for smelting. Writing in 1741, the author of a little

1. The often-quoted, but inaccurate, account of Professor Mason, *Philosophical Trans.* (1747), 382 : " Mr. Ford from iron ore and coal, both gotten in the same dale, makes iron brittle or tough as he pleases, there being cannon thus cast so soft as to bear turning like wrought iron."

2. " Interdum vel aliquibus in locis usurpare volunt carbones fossiles, sed qui in cineres aut in cindres ut vocantur, primum combusti aut calcinati sint," *Regnum Subterraneum . . . de Ferro*, 153. Cited by Percy.

3. *V.C.H. Shropshire*, 462.

work on assaying distinguishes between the different types in this respect :

" Our Sea-coals or Newcastle Coals, or in general all the fossil Coals which cake in burning and run into Cinders, abound with Sulphur, and therefore are improper to be used about Iron, always making it brittle; but Pit-coals, Kennel-coals, and Scotch-coals, which burn to a White-ash like Wood, and abound in a Bitumen, may be used in the first fluxing of the Iron from the Ore, and if the Iron prove not so malleable as is required, this Property may be given to it by melting the Metal a second Time with Wood."[1]

At Coalbrookdale the sweet " clod " coal was found near the surface—a fact that had determined that it should be here and not elsewhere that coke-smelting began. But in many places suitable coal did not exist, or lay at too great a depth; in these districts it would, no doubt, be asserted that the use of mineral fuel was impossible; and in any case the uneven distribution of the clod coal would tend to limit the extension of the process.[2]

Finally, there is an elementary fact the significance of which has not been appreciated by most of those who have written on the early history of iron—that the industry consisted of two distinct branches, the one concerned with the making of malleable iron, the other with that of wares of cast iron. Of these branches the latter was by far the smaller, and but few commodities were produced by the founders of the early eighteenth century. The hardness and brittleness of cast iron limited the purposes for which it could be used; and since castings were made direct from the furnace, defects in the metal often presented difficulties and further narrowed the sphere of operations of the founder. It was to this branch of the industry that Abraham Darby belonged, and his second discovery, no less than his first, is to be regarded primarily as an advance in the art of ironfounding. Not only was it

1. Cramer, *Elements of Assaying*, 347 footnote.
2. As late as 1793, when Boulton and Watt were invited to become partners in the Neath Ironworks they wrote : " Qn. if you can obtain the right sort of Coal for making Iron, such as is called Clob (*sic*) Coal, for without that youl not make good Bar Iron."—B. and W. to Wilson, 11 Dec. 1793.

necessary that boxes and moulding materials should be improved, but also that a metal suitable for casting should be obtained. The chief drawback to the use of charcoal in the furnace is its liability to be crushed by the charge of iron-stone; and the height of the charcoal blast-furnace is thus strictly limited. Hence generally the metal is rendered less fluid than when coke is used; and it was this defect that in early times had confined the use of cast iron to massive articles such as fire-backs and grave-slabs. Once the technical difficulties had been overcome, smelting with coke in large furnaces produced a metal so fused that it could run freely into the smaller channels of the moulds; and founders could now obtain castings of lighter and more delicate design than had hitherto been possible.[1]

But, though superior for the uses of the foundry, coke pig-iron produced a bar inferior in tensility and ductility to that made from charcoal pig : it was " cold-short " and unsuitable for the production of wares of quality. For the cheaper kind of nails it would, no doubt, serve; but for ploughshares, or tools, or locks and bolts, the use of which demanded raw material capable of withstanding shocks, charcoal iron was required. Not only, therefore, did this remain the fuel used in the conversion of pig iron into bars, but the pig iron destined for conversion was itself almost invariably smelted with charcoal. That this was so even fairly late in the century we have M. Jars as witness. Writing in 1765 he asserts that the coke-smelted iron of the Clifton furnace was unfitted for working into wrought iron, and that charcoal pig had to be brought in for this purpose from abroad.[2] A small amount of coke pig-iron was undoubtedly refined in the forges at Coalbrookdale, but manufacturers would pay only a small price for it, and smiths refused to work it unless compensated by higher rates of pay. Not until about 1750 did the great

---

1. Moldenke, *Principles of Ironfounding*, 74; Jars, *Voyages Métallurgiques*, 337; Hawkes Smith, *Birmingham and its Vicinity*, 5.
2. " La compagnie ne fait point affiner la gueuse, ne pouvant en fabriquer un bon fer forgé, quoiqu'affiné au charbon de bois. On en a une preuve bien convainçante, en ce que partout où il y a des affineries, on fait venir des gueuses d'Amerique, qui proviennent des fontes au charbon de bois."—Jars, *op. cit.*, 237.

forgemasters of Worcestershire begin to make use of it, and probably by this time its quality was better and more uniform than in the early days.

Only in the relatively small province of casting, then, did the labours of Darby produce an early fruit. And even here the conservatism of the Office of Ordnance, combined with the fact that Sussex had long been the prime source of supply for cannon, meant that a large field was still under the control of the charcoal masters.

It is therefore not so surprising as might at first appear that so little was heard of the discovery ; the iron-smelter who wished to sell his product to forgemasters had no incentive to advertise the fact that it had been made with mineral fuel. The protagonists of the debates and committees were concerned with the charcoal iron, which alone was considered suitable for forge purposes ; and the patentees of the 'twenties and 'thirties also had in mind the production, with coke, of a material fit for conversion into malleable iron. There was, let it be repeated, a sharp line of demarcation in the industry—one might almost say there were two distinct iron industries—and many of the makers of bar iron might well be unaware of, or indifferent to, the transformation that was silently taking place in the seclusion of the Dale.

In the early years, knowledge of the process appears to have spread only within the circle of Darby's relatives and personal friends. In 1721 mineral fuel was substituted for charcoal at Bersham, near Wrexham, in the works leased by Charles Lloyd; but that the process was not efficiently conducted here is implied by the financial difficulties which forced Lloyd to relinquish the works in 1726. His successor was John Hawkins, a son-in-law of the first Darby, who is said to have received assistance in his operations from his relatives at the Dale; and he in turn was followed by Isaac Wilkinson, who had previously attempted to smelt iron, using peat as fuel, in Lancashire.[1] It has been asserted that the coke process was introduced at Pontypool in Monmouth about 1740,[2] but no evidence is given for the statement, and it is

1. Palmer, *John Wilkinson, App.* (contributed by W. G. Norris), 41-2.
2. Swank, *Iron and Steel in All Ages*, 41.

known that as late as 1790 the Pontypool furnace was making use of charcoal. It appears probable, indeed, that until about the middle of the century the process was confined to Shropshire and the adjoining district of Bersham. During the 'fifties new coke furnaces were put in blast in the Coalbrookdale district at Horsehay, Ketley, Madeley Wood, Lightmoor, and Willey;[1] and about the same time it was carried to Dowlais in South Wales. The setting up in 1760 of the great works at Carron, and of the large furnace at Seaton, near Workington, formed an outstanding advertisement for the new process, and after this time it was rapidly adopted at works in Staffordshire, South Yorkshire, Northumberland, and elsewhere.

During the 'sixties several minor improvements in technique were brought about. In 1763 the use of ovens superseded the old method of coking in open piles.[2] A year earlier James Knight of Bringewood had taken out a patent for a new type of blowing apparatus, in which cubical vessels of wood or iron with pistons were substituted for the simple wood and leather bellows;[3] and shortly afterwards Smeaton introduced his blowing cylinders, by the use of which a more complete combustion was made possible. Water-power, however, was still generally used for blowing purposes, and even where engines were employed these were of the atmospheric type: it was not until after the application of the double-acting blowing cylinder, actuated by the Watt steam-engine, that the victory of coke over charcoal became complete.

Even when the suitability of coke iron for general purposes was definitely established, it was still possible for the blast-furnace which specialised in foundry pigs to be used for the production with charcoal of pig iron for the forge: after the middle of the century either fuel was used according to the quality or type of metal desired. In 1766, for example, an advertisement,[4] offering for sale shares in the Bedlington Works in Northumberland, states that the furnace is " for

1. Scrivenor, *op. cit.*, App., 359.
2. Mushet, *op. cit.*, 69.
3. *Spec. of Patents*, No. 783.
4. *Aris's Birmingham Gazette*, 3 Nov., 1766.

smelting Iron from the Mine by Pitcoal or Charcoal," and
the information is added that it is at present making use of
pit coal, and is " Well-established in a Vend for Cast Ware,
&c."

All these facts help to explain why, sixty years and more
after Darby's discovery, the bulk of English pig iron continued to be smelted by means of charcoal, and laymen still
heard with surprise of the "new method " by which the
inroads on the woodlands might be brought to an end.
Humphrey Clinker was published in 1771, yet Smollett, who
was not ill-instructed or unobservant of industrial affairs,[1]
could make mention in it, as though of a novelty, of the use
of mineral fuel at Carron.[2]   Small wonder, therefore, if
modern students have been somewhat tardy in giving to the
first Abraham Darby the credit that is his due.[3]

II.

As already hinted, the use of coke in the blast-furnace led
to a great development of foundry products; and throughout
the eighteenth century there was a strong tendency for cast
iron to be substituted for wood, copper, lead, brass, and other
materials, but most of all for wrought iron.[4]   Cast iron wares
could usually be sold at a lower price than those made of
malleable iron, for not only was a cheaper fuel employed in
smelting, but there was the saving of the highly-skilled labour
of the forgeman, and of the smith who worked the bar or
rod iron into the finished commodity.

Whereas, then, the development of the textile industries

1. Scrivenor's passages on the controversy relating to American iron are
taken verbatim—and without acknowledgment—from Smollett's *History of
England.*
2. " In our way hither we visited a flourishing iron-work, where, instead
of burning wood, they use coal, which they have the art of clearing in such
a manner as frees it from the sulphur which would otherwise render the metal
too brittle for working." Letter from Matt. Bramble at Cameron to Dr. Lewis,
Aug. 28.
3. Development in coke-smelting was almost equally slow in France.
Mineral fuel was first used in 1782, but in 1819 only two furnaces were making
use of coke, out of a total of 350 furnaces. *Memoirs of the Geological Survey
of Great Britain* (1866), Vol. I, Pt. i, 506.
4. Thus M. Jars, writing of the Carron Works in 1765 : " Enfin on y
fabrique, en fer coulé, les mêmes ouvrages qu'on fait communément en fer
battu." *Voyages Métallurgiques,* 275.

in the eighteenth century has been represented as a race between two consecutive processes of spinning and weaving, that of the iron industry is to be regarded rather as a struggle between the two collateral and competing processes of the foundry and the forge : a struggle in which the tide of victory flowed slowly, but steadily, in favour of the former. It is obviously difficult to trace the successive lines of advance in a battle of this type, for the movement takes place silently and is hardly perceptible to contemporaries. But the capture of some positions is registered in the records of patents—though in reading them one has constantly to guard against the assumption that because a point has been claimed as won, it has also been consolidated.

A few examples will serve. In 1722 Richard Baddeley of Birmingham obtained a patent for making box smoothing-irons of cast, instead of wrought metal; and sixteen years later Isaac Wilkinson of Backbarrow took out another for the same purpose and carried the process to commercial success. In 1751 and 1761 patents were granted for making gun-carriages of cast iron, and others relating to cannon are referred to elsewhere. A small group of founders in Birmingham pushed out the frontiers in other directions : in 1769 Joseph Ashton introduced a process of making coffin-nails and tacks of pig iron, and in 1771 his methods were extended to the production of other kinds of nails. Four years later John Izon and Thomas Whitehurst patented a new method of casting iron hinges ready joined. In 1786 John Francis, formerly a partner of Joseph Ashton and now of Richard Dearman, took a patent for making cast-iron buttons. Dearman himself had a process of making hoes for the West Indian Plantations of cast iron ; and John Turton of Bristol made mancelas—armlets worn by negro slaves—of the same metal.[1]

Not always, however, were these incursions of the founder into the territory of the smith justified in their results. Richard Baddeley's attempts to make waggon tyres of cast iron were probably unsuccessful, for the material was too brittle for the purpose. And the confession in the specifi-

1. *Spec. of Patents*, Nos. 445, 683, 765, 938, 992, 979. See also Rushden, *Old Time Invention in the Four Shires*; and Prosser, *Birmingham Inventions*.

cation of Richard Dearman's "most impudent patent "[1] for hoes, that some of them "may be too weak and will require to be strengthened by a ferrule of malleable iron," is evidence of an attempt to extend the domain of cast iron beyond its natural frontiers. Even less legitimate was the substitution of cast iron for steel in the manufacture of cutlery and edge tools. Sheffield manufacturers complained bitterly of the "imposition and forgery " of using pig iron to produce forks, knives, scissors, and even razors; and Birmingham craftsmen pointed to the dangerous consequences of fashioning bits and stirrups of cast iron.[2] But in machine parts and material for the construction of steam-engines, in cannon and shot, in domestic stoves and fire-grates, in bridges, lock-gates, and rails, cast iron was to play an important part in the physical equipment of civilization.

The firms that were first established in this branch of the industry travelled with a momentum that carried several of them into the nineteenth, and one or two into the twentieth century. The new coke-smelting process led to a transformation of what had previously been relatively small-scale production into those forms of great industry, which, for want of a better phrase, are generically termed the "Factory System." This had existed in the metal trades even in the seventeenth century, as the examples of the Crowley and Sitwell undertakings clearly show. But the new processes of iron-making were to turn what had been exceptional and sporadic manifestations into a dominating tendency of industry. In this connection a brief account will be given of the four great typical concerns of the Darbys, the Wilkinsons, the Walkers, and the Carron Company.

Although the works at Coalbrookdale began on a relatively small scale there is evidence that even during the lifetime of the founder a considerable expansion was taking place; in the year 1715 the concern was worth something over £5,000,[3] and, in addition, Darby had an interest in ironworks at

---

1. The phrase is Prosser's.
2. Lloyd, *Cutlery Trades*, 331; Lardner, *Cyclopædia* (1833), Iron and Steel, 23, 25, 39.
3. In 1715 a share of one-sixteenth sold for £330. Percy, *Metallurgy*, 888.

Dolgan in Merioneth and Oulton in Cheshire. At this time the products of the firm were those commonly made of cast iron : mortars, boilers for soap-makers, fire-backs, bake-stones, garden-rollers, pipes, weights and so on. At the time of the death of the first Abraham in May 1717, his eldest son was a child of six years only, and a new partnership was formed between his widow, Thomas Goldney, and Richard Ford, who had formerly acted as clerk to the firm and had married Darby's eldest daughter. Ford at once became the leading spirit, and apparently sought to increase the scale of the business : an entry in the Day Book shows him in September 1718 at Chester Fair collecting money for the new company, and there are other indications of his activity. It was under his direction that the firm began to specialise in castings for the Newcomen fire-engines which, after the adoption of the hand-gear in 1718, were rapidly coming into use at collieries.

It will be recalled that Newcomen, who was a blacksmith or ironmonger, had been employed by Captain Savery, whose fire-engine patent was taken out in 1698. About the year 1705 substantial changes were made by Newcomen in the design, but it was apparently assumed that Savery's patent was sufficient to cover the improvements and no new powers were sought. In the early days Newcomen's engines had cylinders made of brass, pipes of lead, a beam of wood, and other parts of wrought iron. But in 1715 Newcomen visited the Midlands to erect an engine at Griff Colliery for Sir Richard Newdigate, and it was here probably that he made the acquaintance of Stanier Parrot of Coventry, who, in 1718, is found to be ordering castings and pipes for a fire-engine from Coalbrookdale. After 1724 sets of cast-iron cylinders and other parts were ordered on a large scale, and the reputation of the Dale Company for this kind of work was so high that practically all the fire-engine material, as well as the barrels and pipes for pumps, was in their hands. The firm indeed came to stand in respect to the Newcomen engine in much the same relation as John Wilkinson to that of James Watt at a later date. Savery's patent for fourteen years had been extended for a further period of twenty-one years and was due to expire in July, 1733. In March of that year

Richard Ford wrote to Thomas Goldney expressing his hope of a big expansion of fire-engine orders, and the following year he is found ordering a new wrought-iron spindle for boring cylinders, from an anchor-smith in Bristol.[1]

In 1743 the first engine at Coalbrookdale was erected by Abraham Darby II. for the purpose of pumping back the water to the reservoir, after it had passed over the wheels; and the advantage of having a continuous blast even in dry seasons was so great that a similar arrangement was afterwards made by many furnace owners throughout the country. Just as the Darby process of casting led to improvement and cheapening of the fire-engine, so the latter reacted in benefitting the iron industry—one of the earliest illustrations of that interdependence of technical discoveries that is the prime truism of " industrial revolution " studies.

The later history of the Coalbrookdale Company has been often told and need not be repeated here except in baldest outline; it may be pointed out that the specialisation in engine materials and other castings was maintained under the successive controls of Richard Ford (1717-45), Abraham Darby II. (1732-63), Richard Reynolds (1756-68), and Abraham Darby III. (1768-91). It was to Coalbrookdale that James Brindley came in 1756 to obtain the pipes and boiler plates for the engine he was erecting at Fenton Vivian, and again in 1763, for the ironwork of the engine he was building for the Walker Colliery near Newcastle; and, as will be shown later, the firm played an important part—though subsidiary to that of the Wilkinsons—in the provision of materials for the steam-engines of Boulton and Watt.

The growth of such business meant a steady increase in size : new furnaces were put in operation at Willey in 1732, Horsehay in 1755, and Ketley in 1756. In this year Richard Reynolds of Bristol became a partner in the concern; shortly afterwards he married the daughter of the second Darby, and after the death of his father-in-law took sole control during the minority of the sons. Later the Ketley and Horsehay works—which apparently were conducted by

1. *Proc. Inst. Mech. Engrs.*, Oct. 1903. Davey, The Newcomen Engine, 674-6, 701.

a separate company with the Darbys as partners—were in his hands; and until the early years of the nineteenth century the relations between Richard Reynolds and Coalbrookdale were very intimate. Waggon-ways were constructed to link the associated works, and to give access to the Severn; and in 1779 the river itself was spanned by the famous cast-iron bridge.

After 1750 the Company began to lease and work mines instead of purchasing coal and ironstone from outsiders. Though a forge had been leased at Coalbrookdale as early as 1720, and others were set up at Bridgnorth and elsewhere, throughout the century the firm was predominantly concerned with ironfounding. In 1776 the turnover of each of the furnaces at Coalbrookdale, Madeley Wood, Lightmoor, Horsehay, and Ketley was said to exceed £80,000 a year.[1] In a letter to Earl Gower, written in 1785, Richard Reynolds[2] speaks of " the many hundreds of poor people employed by us in working and carrying on mines, etc., for the supply of a large sale of coals by land and water, and of coals and mine for sixteen fire engines, eight blast furnaces and nine forges, besides the air furnaces, mills, etc., at the foundry at Coalbrook Dale, and which with the levels, roads, and more than twenty miles of iron railways, etc., still employs a capital of upwards of one hundred thousand pounds." In February, 1794, the Coalbrookdale Company was valued at £62,575, though the estimate was reduced on revaluation; three months earlier the concern of the Reynolds' had been estimated to be worth £138,067, and both William and Joseph Reynolds were also partners in the Coalbrookdale Co.[3]

Reference has already been made to the carrying of the coke process by Darby's relatives from Coalbrookdale to Bersham, and of the practice of it there by Isaac Wilkinson. Originally a workman at the Little Clifton Furnace near Workington, he had removed during the 'thirties to North Lancashire, where he was engaged as a pot-founder by the

---

1. Whitworth, *Inland Navigation*, 37.
2. Rathbone, *Memoir of Reynolds*, 283.
3. *Coalbrookdale MSS.*

Backbarrow Company. The conditions of his employment here have been described as an example of the domestic system in the metal-smelting industry : whether correctly or not must depend on our interpretation of that most ambiguous and elastic phrase. It appears that Wilkinson bought iron in a molten condition from the blast-furnace, and, carrying it in ladles across the road to his foundry, cast it into pots and other utensils, which were subsequently sold to the Company that had provided the raw material.[1]

Early in the 'forties, along with his son John, he initiated an independent concern at Wilson House near Lindale, where he had both a furnace and a refinery; and it was here that he attempted to smelt iron, using peat moss or turf as fuel. In the raw state peat is very inflammable : if subjected to a strong blast it becomes a source of danger to the furnace, while in a state of incomplete combustion its extreme friability renders it equally unsatisfactory.[2] It is improbable, therefore, that Wilkinson succeeded in smelting with peat alone, but it is not impossible that he used it without ill-effect along with charcoal.[3] In these experiments at Wilson House the restless imagination of John can be observed : a canal was cut in the turf, and a small *iron* boat was made for transporting the fuel to the works— both the forerunners of later enterprises of the younger Wilkinsons. Early in the 'fifties the family moved south and took over the lease of Bersham furnace. The advantages of this site for iron-production were manifold : coal was near at hand, charcoal was plentiful, and water-power was available for the creation of the blast; iron ore could be obtained from mines at Llwyn Enion, little more than a mile distant, from which the roads sloped gently downward to the furnace; and this itself was built against a cliff, so that it could be charged from the top and the smelted metal run out at a lower level.[4]

Here Isaac Wilkinson engaged in casting operations on

1. Dickinson, *John Wilkinson*, 10, 11 ; Palmer, *John Wilkinson*, 8.
2. Mushet, *Papers on Iron and Steel*, 408, 427.
3. " In Lancashire time out of Mind they have used Turf with Charcoal, and prefer it to Charcoal alone. They tried Pit Coal, but without Success." Campbell, *A Political Survey of Britain* (1774), 43.
4. Palmer, *op. cit.*, 14.

a large scale; and if the commodities enumerated in his
patents of 1753 and 1758 are an index of his own productions,
he was concerned with the manufacture of " Guns or Cannon,
Fire Engines, Cylinders, Pipes and Sugar Rolls." In this
he was assisted by his sons John and William, the former of
whom also acted as manager for the New Willey Company at
Broseley—near Coalbrookdale, but on the south side of the
Severn—an undertaking which in 1763 passed under his sole
control. Following upon the financial failure of Isaac, the
Bersham concern was reconstituted as a partnership between
the two sons under the name of the New Bersham Company.
A few years later, in 1770, John Wilkinson set up a furnace
at Bradley, near Bilston in Staffordshire, and by this time,
along with his brother, he had come into possession of three
important ironworks. Later the Wilkinsons were to engage
in refining, as well as in the working of mines of coal, ironstone, and lead ore; and their activities were to extend not
only to Furness, Cornwall, and other parts of England, but
also to France and Germany. But in the early 'seventies the
business of smelting and casting at Bersham, Broseley, and
Bradley afforded sufficient outlet for their activities. Like
their father and other ironmasters, they received a stimulus
from the demand for ordnance occasioned by the almost
continual wars which coincided with the sixty years of their
active life in the industry. From its first days the New
Bersham Company was busy with the casting of grenades,
shell, and cannon; a single entry culled by one of John
Wilkinson's biographers from an early account book relates
to the sale of 32 guns to the Office of Ordnance;[1] and, at a
later date, cannon in large quantity were supplied to the East
India Company. When in 1774 a new method of boring cast-
iron cannon was devised by John Wilkinson, the greater
accuracy of the guns produced at Bradley brought increased
business to the firm. In the following year the French
Government made application for permission to purchase

1. Palmer, *op. cit.*, 12.

sample cannon from the Wilkinson foundries,[1] and the order given at this time was followed by numerous others, some of them—according to tradition—executed during periods of war between Britain and France. The process was destined to be of some moment also to the development of peaceful civilization, since—as will be shown below—the apparatus was applied almost immediately to the solution of one of the main difficulties which confronted James Watt in the final stages of his invention.[2]

In South Yorkshire the practice of ironfounding was leading to equally striking developments in the scale of the industrial unit. In 1741 three brothers, Samuel, Aaron, and Jonathan Walker—described respectively as schoolmaster, mechanic, and farmer—set up a tiny foundry in a nailer's smithy at Grenoside, near Sheffield. After two years, during which Samuel continued to teach and Aaron to hammer nails, the brothers had acquired sufficient capital to build an air furnace; by 1746 the business had grown to a size sufficient to find full time employment for all three; and in this year John Crawshaw was taken into partnership and the joint-stock was raised to £600. At the same time a second furnace and a smithy were established at Masborough near Rotherham, which, by reason of its water-power, facilities for water

1. The following letter from the French Ambassador was transmitted by Lord Weymouth to the Lord President of the Council. *S.P.D.* Entry Bk. 143, page 143.

Whitehall le 23 Dec^re 1775.

Milord,
    Ma cour me charge de solliciter près de Votre Excellence la permission de faire venir à la consignation du Sr Garvay negociant a Rouen huit pièces de Canon de la Manufacture du Sr Wilkinson, Scavoir—2 de 32—2 de 24—2 de 18 et 2 de 12—. M. le Pde Masseru aiant il y a quelque temps, obtenu la même grace pour une fourniture très considerable, ma Cour a cru pouvoir faire sans indiscretion la même demande à Votre Excellence.
            J'ai l'honneur d'etre, &c.
                Le C. de Guines.

2. It has been asserted that about 1772 John Wilkinson began to smelt his ore with raw pit coal instead of coke (Randall, *The Wilkinsons*, 20), but it is improbable that this was ever accomplished prior to the introduction of the hot blast by Neilson at a much later date. Wilkinson is known to have experimented with a heated blast, but without success. The fact that he was one of the first to carry coke-smelting into Staffordshire has led some local historians into the error of supposing that he was the discoverer of the process. (See, *e.g.*, Lawley, *History of Bilston*, 245.) Further details respecting the Wilkinsons are given in the works already cited as well as by Hackwood, *Olden Wednesbury*, and Nicholson, *Proc. Manchester Lit. and Phil. Soc.*, xlix.

transport, and proximity to coal and ironstone, now became the centre of operations.

In addition to castings in iron and brass the Walkers made, and in fact specialised in, steel produced by the crucible process. This had recently been invented by Benjamin Huntsman and the knowledge of the process, it is said, had been gained by Samuel Walker through the meanest of imaginable ruses.[1] A steel furnace—evidently of the cementation type—was built in 1748; the first crucible furnace was set up in the following year; and several others of both kinds were added both at Rotherham and Grenoside. In 1754 a forge was built, and in May, 1759, the Walkers and Crawshaw obtained from the Earl of Effingham a lease of an old slitting-mill. A blast-furnace, a new slitting-mill, and works for grinding ironware were established—developments which made such demands on the limited supplies of water-power as to lead in 1762 to serious disputes with the proprietors of the Don navigation.[2] The precise details of the growth of the firm during the first eighteen years of operations are given by Guest, the chronicler of Rotherham, who reproduces them in facsimile, from the pocket-book of Samuel Walker.[3] The quantities of metal cast and the estimated values of the concern in successive years are set forth below:

Period. Nov. Nov.	Casting, tons.	Estimated value. £	Period. Nov. Nov.	Casting, tons.	Estimated value. £
1741—1742	5	—	1751—1752	256	3,600
1742—1743	10	—	1752—1753	283	4,200
1743—1744	31½	—	1753—1754	318	5,600
1744—1745	39	—	1754—1755	313¼	6,200
1745—1746	63½	600	1755—1756	308½	6,800
1746—1747	96	900	1756—1757	324¾	7,500
1747—1748	110	1,300	1757—1758	284¼	8,500
1748—1749	129	1,800	1758—1759	336½	9,500
1749—1750	181	2,400	1759—1760	432¾	11,000
1750—1751	206	3,000			

1. The story is told by Smiles, *Industrial Biography*, Ch. VI.
2. *J.H.C.*, xix, 159, 192.
3. Guest, *Rotherham*, 389-91.

In 1766 the castings amounted to 622 tons and the business was valued at £31,000. It will be observed that the rate of growth in capital is considerably greater than that in the weight of castings—obviously to be explained by the increased production of crucible steel and wrought-iron wares.

The market for these played no small part in the economy of the Walkers; but the greatest development came later when the good offices of the Marquis of Rockingham obtained for them lucrative contracts for the casting of ordnance. During both the American War and the later struggle with France, cannon were produced on a large scale : in 1781, for example, 1,221 tons—three-fifths of the total metal cast by the firm— were supplied to the Government. The practice of taking but a small part of the profits for their personal needs and leaving the remainder to accumulate in the business led to a rapid growth of capital : when the American War broke out the firm was valued at £87,500; and twenty years later the numerous undertakings of the Walkers were appraised at no less a sum than £213,393.

Yet another illustration of a large business structure built up round the coke-furnace and the foundry is that established at Carron, near Falkirk, in 1759. Those of the Darbys, the Wilkinsons, and the Walkers, from minute seeds of productive energy, planted in a soil previously prepared by the labour of others, had developed over a period of time into growths of girth with widespreading branches. But from the beginning the Carron Works were planned on a relatively large scale, in a district that had hitherto received little industrial development, and in which the principal partners were without any personal influence. They were the product of the capital and enterprise of two Birmingham industrialists, John Roebuck, who provided the technical knowledge and inventive ability, and Samuel Garbett, who supplied the shrewdness and capacity for affairs in which his partner was so deplorably deficient.

Born in 1718, the son of a Sheffield manufacturer and merchant, John Roebuck was trained in medicine at Edinburgh and Leyden, and in the 'forties was established as a physician in Birmingham. During the next few years, in which his leisure was occupied with chemical research, Roebuck discovered new methods of refining gold and silver and of recovering the minute particles previously lost in the process. His desire to put the methods into operation on a larger scale than was possible in his own laboratory led to his association with Samuel Garbett, already a business man of some standing and a figure in the political and social life of Birmingham. A larger laboratory and a refinery were set up in Steelhouse Lane, and it was here that Roebuck devised his process of manufacturing vitriol in vessels of lead instead of glass. In 1749 the partners set up a second establishment for this purpose at Prestonpans, near Edinburgh; and within ten years the enterprise had proved so profitable that its proprietors were able to launch out into the iron industry, with an equipment the size and efficiency of which attracted attention from all parts of the country.[1]

In 1759, in association with William Cadell, a local iron-master, Roebuck and Garbett set up their ironworks on the banks of the river Carron, and on 1 January, 1760, the first furnace was put in blast. The site of Carron had been carefully chosen : ironstone, limestone, and clod coal were all found locally, and there was direct transport by sea to European markets, while a short journey by land—and a few years later by canal—brought the products of the works to Glasgow, at that time a growing centre for the trade with America. By sea also were carried large quantities of hæmatite ore for use along with the local ironstone, and before the end of the century no less than 20,000 tons of this were brought annually to Carron from Cumberland.[2]

From the outset the capital was divided into 24 parts, of which Roebuck and Garbett held six each, the remainder being divided between Roebuck's three brothers and William Cadell and his son. In February, 1764, there appears to have been a division into 10 shares; at this time Roebuck and

---

1. Jardine. Account of John Roebuck, *Trans. Royal Soc. Edin.*, 4 Apr. 1796. Reprinted 1839 (Birmingham). *Information for Samuel Garbett, Defender, against the Carron Co.*, 3.

2. *V.C.H. Cumberland*, ii, 89

Garbett had as their partners the Cadells, Adam Fairholm,
John Adam, Ebenezer Roe, and Thomas Roebuck; while in
the following year a young man named Charles Gascoigne
was given one half-share. This Gascoigne had first met
Garbett while on a visit to Prestonpans. He was then a
youth under twenty years of age and without means, and
Garbett found him a situation, and ultimately a partnership,
with a friend in a London business. In 1759 Gascoigne
married the daughter of his benefactor; and four years later
his father-in-law helped him to set up an independent establishment at Carron wharf.[1]

Meanwhile Roebuck had become involved in other enterprises : in addition to his interests at Birmingham, Prestonpans, and Carron, he had acquired coal mines and soda works
at Borrowstoness; but this dissipation of energies combined
with the unfortunate flooding of his mines, led to financial
disaster. Having lost his own fortune, that of his wife, and
large amounts borrowed from his friends, as well as sums
belonging to the Carron Company, Roebuck was obliged to
withdraw from his partnerships. Though he was retained
by his creditors as manager at Borrowstoness, in 1766 his
active connection with the iron trade came to an end.[2] The
failure was a severe blow to the ironworks, and in common
with the rest of the business world Carron sustained further
losses in the commercial crisis of 1772. Immediately afterwards the Company was reconstituted, and a royal charter was
obtained to allow of its taking a joint-stock form with 600
shareholders.[3]

Up to this time Samuel Garbett had made the gun-
founding department his special charge, but in 1773 this was
handed over to Gascoigne, who now also became general
manager of the works.[4] It was as the result of this change
that a difference arose between the two men, for Gascoigne
resented what he considered as the interference of his father-in-
law in this department. Before long the quarrel led to a law-

---

1. *Information for Samuel Garbett, Defender*, etc., 10 Oct. 1778, p. 6.
2. *Ibid.*, 16 Nov. 1778, p. 7.
3. Wilkie, *Manufacture of Iron*, 6.
4. *Review of the State of Mr. Samuel Garbett's Affairs* (Edinburgh, 1778), 10.

suit in which Gascoigne accused Garbett of malversation of the Company's funds to the extent of £25,000. Into the tedious labyrinths of the financial dispute it is unnecessary to enter; but it is well to remember that it was this, rather than any weakness in the technique of production, that was responsible for the early difficulties of the firm.

On the technical side, in fact, extensive developments had taken place. From the first the works had been modelled on those of the Darbys: Robert Hawkins, a relative of theirs, had been appointed superintendent, and other skilled workmen had been imported from Coalbrookdale.[1] At the instance of Roebuck, James Watt had been brought to live near Carron; and when the blowing bellows, the magnitude of which had attracted the attention of M. Jars,[2] proved inadequate, John Smeaton was called in to solve the difficulty by his device of blowing-cylinders of cast iron, introduced about the year 1768. A mill for boring guns and cylinders was made to the engineer's designs and his advice was sought as to the damming of the Carron river, so as to make it a more effective source of power—a matter on which James Watt was also consulted in 1776.

Though forges were built and Roebuck made experiments in the conversion of iron with pit coal, it is clear that the principal products were those of the foundry. In the early days of the firm Carron acquired a reputation for its domestic stoves and grates—a specialty of the firm to this day—for iron pots, for fire-engine parts, and for castings of all kinds; but, again, the most profitable branch of the business was that concerned with ordnance and other materials of war. "Their great guns [says Macpherson,[3] writing of the year 1777], which were cast solid, and bored by a drill worked by the whole force of the River Carron, were exported to Russia, Denmark, Spain, etc.; and the quantities were so considerable that the Government was unwilling to let them be carried in ordinary ships, lest they should fall into the hands of the American cruisers. The company thereupon fitted out a

1. *V.C.H. Shropshire*, 464.
2. *Voyages Métallurgiques*, 273.
3. Macpherson, *Annals*, iii, 609.

stout ship of their own, properly armed and manned, for the purpose of carrying to Spain 300 iron guns from three to twenty-four pounders . . . . The war also greatly increased the demand for their iron ballast, which was universally used in the navy, and also in many merchant ships." In the year which saw the birth of the Carron Works, General Melville invented the small naval gun known as the " smasher "; but it was not until 1778, when Charles Gascoigne began to manufacture it on a large scale, that the Carronade, as it was now called, came into extensive use in the navy.[1] When Saint-Fond paid his visit to the works in 1784 " the place was covered with cannons, mortars, bombs, balls, and those large pieces which bear the name of carronades . . . . Under the sheds where the finished articles are deposited, we saw several rows of rampart cannon, battering guns, and field-pieces designed for Russia and the Emperor."[2]

Of the growth of the Company under this stimulus of war some indication is given by the share capital at various periods. According to the original articles of co-partnery this consisted in 1760 of £12,000 held in 24 shares; in February, 1764, of £50,000 divided into 10 shares; in 1771 of £130,000; and in 1773, after the reconstruction, of £150,000 in 600 shares, of which Samuel Garbett alone held 96.

The firms briefly described in the foregoing pages are outstanding examples of a process that was taking place throughout the industry. Everywhere the forgemen were falling back before the steady march of the founders : in every iron-producing area the production of war material was bringing large-scale armament firms into being. The rapid expansion of the works which Anthony Bacon set up in 1765 at Merthyr Tydfil is attributed to the contracts given by the Office of Ordnance during the American War; and even more striking examples of firms drawing nourishment from the same bounteous source existed later in the same district.[3]

---

1. Sir John Day. The Iron and Steel Industries of Scotland, *British Association Handbook* (1876), 32.
2. Saint-Fond, *Travels*, 182-3. Cited by Mantoux. M. Mantoux is in error in supposing the visit to have been made in 1796; the preface to the work makes it clear that St. Fond's travels were made before the Revolution.
3. Wilkins, *Iron, Steel and Tinplate Trades*, 36-47.

Coalbrookdale, Broseley, Masborough, Carron all became schools of instruction in the arts of smelting and refining, and each of them gave birth to a lusty progeny bearing a close likeness to the parent firm. In particular the corner of Shropshire which included Coalbrookdale and Broseley became the chief centre of dispersion for the new race of ironmasters. Thus, as already pointed out, ironworks at Horsehay, Madeley Wood, Ketley, and Lightmoor sprang directly out of Coalbrookdale, and from the same district labour was called to assist in the building up of Carron. In 1783 the Parkers, near relatives of the Darbys, moved from the Dale to Tipton in Staffordshire, where they set up the Coneygre furnace;[1] and establishments created by other connections of the same family are shown in the pedigree in Chapter IX. From Broseley John Guest went, in 1765, to begin his great enterprise at Dowlais ; while a little later the Homfrays moved from Staffordshire to Cyfarthfa.[2] From here also came the Thorneycrofts of Tipton, and the Bagnalls of Wednesbury and West Bromwich; Gilbert Gilpin, at one time clerk to John Wilkinson, also set up ironworks of his own at Coalport.[3] A quarrel between the Walkers and the Crawshaws led to the establishing of new works by the latter; it was at Masborough that Thomas Chambers, partner of George Newton in the large Thorncliffe Ironworks, received his early training ; and after the break-up of the enterprise of Samuel Walker, one of his sons moved with William Yates to the Gospel Oak Works in Staffordshire, out of which in turn proceeded several later smelting concerns.[4] Similarly within a few years the Carron Works became the model for the Clyde, Devon, Calder, Crammond, Cleugh, and Muirkirk Ironworks; and as late as 1819 the Falkirk Works began its operations with labour and capital drawn directly from the same source.[5]

1. See article on the Parker family, *Dudley Herald*, 19 July 1919.
2. Wilkins, *loc. cit.*
3. Palmer, *John Wilkinson*, 3.
4. *Guest, Rotherham*, 493. Samuel Clarke, one of Walker's assistants, carried on the smelting at Holmes.
5. Mayer. On the Rise and Progress of the Iron Manufacture in Scotland, *Journal of the Iron and Steel Inst.* (1872). See also Jardine, *Account of John Roebuck*.

The expansive force generated in these early enterprises could not be limited by national boundaries, and within a few years its effects were felt upon the Continent. During the 'seventies the new processes were carried to France by William Wilkinson, who directed the construction and working of blast-furnaces at Le Creusot between 1778 and 1781. In 1789 one of the Wilkinsons introduced the coke-smelting process into Upper Silesia; while six years earlier Charles Gascoigne had taken service under Catherine, and had carried skilled workmen from Carron to establish the new methods of gun-founding in Russia.[1]

III.

Parallel to these developments in the use of cast iron were those that resulted in the allied industry from the discovery by Benjamin Huntsman of the process of making cast steel.

In the early years of the century the raw material of the cutlers of Sheffield, London, and Newcastle, and the gun-smiths and sword-makers of Birmingham, was produced from Swedish bar iron by what is known as the cementation process. Bar iron of the best quality covered with fragments of charcoal was placed in a furnace and subjected for several days to great heat from a charcoal fire.[2] The effect of this

---

1. Dickinson, *op. cit.*, 49, 53; Mayer, *loc. cit.*
2. " . . . at the Tile-house at Bromley in the parish of Kings-Swinford, one John Heydon hardens whole barrs of Iron quite through, *i.e.*, makes them into Steel, which he does not out of English but Spanish or Swedish barrs, here called bullet-Iron; the manner thus. He has a round Oven built of brick, not unlike those used by Bakers at the top, having a grate in the bottom near the middle, about a foot and ½ or 2 foot wide, where he lays the coal; on each side whereof, and at the end beyond it, he lays his Iron inclosed in Coffins made of Amblecot-clay to keep it from melting, the coffins being proportioned to the barrs of Iron, which are broken into lengths of between 3 and 4 or 4 and 5 feet long; the longest being placed at the end of the Oven, and the shortest on each side; each Coffin containing about half a Tun of Iron. When a fire is put to it, it is constantly tended day and night till the operation is performed, which according to the goodness or badness of the coal is done in a longer or shorter time, sometimes in three days and 3 nights, other times in 4, and sometimes not under a weeks time, the critical-minute in which the operation is finisht being the great secret of the Art of making Iron into Steel. Which when done, they cut it into narrower barrs about half an inch over, and then break it into short pieces of an inch, or two inches long call'd Gadds, whereby the buyers may see whether it be good or bad (for there may be both in the same barr), otherwise they care not to buy it." Plot, *Natural History of Staffordshire*, 374. " Coal " here means charcoal and not mineral fuel.

was that the iron increased in carbon content and became what is known as blister steel, a metal suitable for many purposes though uncertain in its composition. To give the quality of toughness to the material it was then broken into small pieces, bound into faggots, covered with sand, and again treated in an air furnace, after which it was brought under a forge hammer. The product of this process, which is still carried on by substantially the same methods, is known as Newcastle or shear steel, and this is suitable for manufacture into cutlery, shears, and edge-tools, which are required to possess great tenacity but in which the maximum degree of hardness is not an essential quality.

Long before the eighteenth century opened, steel conversion was carried on in various parts of the country : in 1609 there were several steel furnaces at Robertsbridge in Sussex,[1] and Plot's account of the process is proof that it was not unknown in Staffordshire. But it was in the district around Newcastle —a centre of importation for Swedish iron—that the greatest development had taken place. The process is said to have been brought from Germany in the first instance; a German colony of steelworkers and swordmakers was established during the seventeenth century at Shotley Bridge, while near-by Ambrose Crowley, and, at a later date, Isaac Cookson were also engaged in steel-making. It was probably by way of Newcastle that the process was brought to Sheffield, where, in 1709, Samuel Shore is known to have owned several furnaces for steel converting.[2]

It was in Sheffield that the new steel, produced by what is known as the crucible process, was discovered by Benjamin Huntsman. Of German or Dutch parentage, Huntsman had established himself as a clockmaker in Doncaster, and it was here that he began his experiments with the object of finding a better material for the springs of clocks and pendulums. Between 1740 and 1742 he removed to Handsworth,[3] on the outskirts of Sheffield, where he perfected his process of

1. Swank, *Manufacture of Iron*, 54.
2. Bell, *British Association Handbook* (1863), 737 ; Leader, *Sheffield in the Eighteenth Century*, 71.
3. Smiles (*Industrial Biography*, 104) gives 1740 ; Leader (*op. cit.*, 71), 1742.

melting blister steel and scraps of shear steel in crucibles of clay heated by means of a coke furnace. According to the French metallurgist, M. Jars, who visited the works in 1765, the crucibles measured nine to eleven inches in height, and they were thus much smaller than those employed to-day; in these the iron was brought to the fluid state by continuous heating for five hours, and a special flux, the nature of which was jealously guarded, was added to the steel during the course of the operation.[1] The intense heat to which the crucibles were brought had the effect of freeing the metal from the small particles of silicate or slag which existed in even the best quality of iron and steel made by the older methods. When the refining process was considered complete the glowing crucibles were removed from the furnace with a long pair of tongs; the molten metal was " teemed " into moulds, and thereafter it was forged into bars and slit into rods of a size convenient for manufacture into articles of cutlery.[2]

The records of the firm during the lifetime of its founder have unfortunately been destroyed; but account books have been preserved from the year 1787, when William Huntsman, the son of Benjamin, was proprietor. From these it is possible to glean details of the commercial side of the business as well as a few stray facts relative to production. It appears that the chief aim of the long researches of Huntsman had been to secure a clay capable of being moulded into crucibles which could withstand great heat for several hours. This difficulty was overcome by mixing local earths with clay purchased from firms in Stourbridge and carried in barrels by waggon to Sheffield. In the early days of the enterprise, blister and bar (or shear) steel for refining were purchased from steel converters in the locality; and even in the 'eighties and 'nineties firms such as Young, Sharrow, and Whitelock were supplying bar steel in quantities by no means negligible, while scrap metal was sometimes accepted from working cutlers in part payment of their accounts. But by this time the bulk of the raw material used by the Huntsmans consisted of Swedish

1. Jars, *op. cit.*, 257-8.
2. An account of the process as practised in modern times is given by Lloyd, *Cutlery Trades*, 35.

iron purchased of Joseph Sykes, the well-known importer of Hull, and converted into steel by the refiners themselves.

The crucible steel was superior in hardness to that produced by the earlier processes : blister and shear steel continued to be used for files, saws, scissors, and many kinds of cutlery; but the harder and more uniform cast steel was more suited to the production of razors, pen-knives, and tools requiring a fine edge. Chains, watch springs, and files for the use of clockmakers are also among the commodities enumerated by Jars for which it had become customary to employ the new crucible steel.[1]

In spite of Huntsman's efforts to keep the process secret, knowledge of it passed to other manufacturers. It is said that Samuel Walker obtained the necessary information by disguising himself as a beggar and appealing to the charity of Huntsman's workmen, who gave him permission to warm himself by the furnaces at a time when operations were in process. Whether or not there is truth in the story, we have Walker's own note-book as witness that he constructed a crucible furnace during the twelve months preceding November, 1749, and it is probable that he was the first to tread upon the heels of the inventor.[2] In the Sheffield Directory of 1774 mention is made of three steel refiners—Huntsman, Bolsover, and Marshall; and in that of 1787, of twenty firms described as Steel Converters and Refiners, at least seven were engaged in the crucible process. Nevertheless the inventor appears to have preserved a part of his secret, for his steel was valued more highly than that of other makers. " We have now got a very good hand for making Cast steel from Mr. Huntsman whom he has made for about six year and he says he can make it as good as Huntsman," wrote a rival to Peter Stubs[3] in 1792. And even in the twentieth century craftsmen in certain Sheffield trades pay Messrs. Huntsman the high but embarrassing compliment of

1. Jars, *op. cit.*, 225, 228.
2. Cited by Guest, *op. cit.* Under date Nov. 1747 to Nov. 1748 occurs the note : " Mr. Booth and me bt. Steel Furnace," and the following year : " Built first Pot Furnace, Aaron Barn, Pot Warehouse . . ."
3. John Harrison to Peter Stubs, *Stubs MSS.*, Warrington.

demanding additional payment from their employers when put to work on Huntsman's metal.

Not only was steel sold by the Huntsmans in the form of rods—slit at their mills in the Wicker—but tools and cutlery were occasionally supplied to customers. Cast-steel wire was also an important product of the firm, and this was made for Huntsman by Robert Cocker, a wiredrawer of Hathersage. In the early days the working cutlers of Sheffield were prejudiced against the new steel, so that Huntsman was led to seek his principal market abroad. An attempt of the cutlers to obtain a prohibition of exportation to their foreign rivals failed, and under William Huntsman, who succeeded his father in 1776, the foreign business was further extended.

Large quantities of steel for use of Continental cutlers and watchmakers were sold through agents such as Philip Rivier, Dubois and Sons, and Jean Dukoveray of London; but the greater part of the foreign business was conducted without a middleman. Letters in possession of the firm show, for example, that J. Leroux, cutler of Paris, who had previously bought Huntsman's steel through Logette and Lepileur of Birmingham, began in 1792 to purchase supplies direct from Huntsman; both he and his successor Dolbeau subsequently gave large orders for rods suitable for manufacture into razors and pen-knives. During the year 1804 steel to the value of £3,729 0s. 4¼d. was sent to one Pierre Louis Sahler of Montbeliard; and the widespread nature of the trade with the Continent is indicated by the names of other foreigners with whom business was done on a large scale between 1787 and 1807 : among them J. C. Grill of Augsburg, Jacques Havelac of Berlin, Conrad Leichti of Winterthur, J. J. Larousi of Geneva, Stephano Guiseppe Loverato of Novi, Carl Wurs of Vienna, Charles Baird of Petersburg.

The home trade, however, was not neglected, and the new steel was of importance to other industries no less than to those of Sheffield : several needlemakers of Redditch bought supplies, usually in relatively small quantities, and after 1794 Jedediah Strutt had an account with the firm. It would be interesting to know whether the cutting tools used by Wilkinson for the boring of Watt's cylinders at Bradley were of

Huntsman's steel : certain it is that the Low Moor Ironworks were making purchases in small amounts between 1799 and 1803, probably for a similar purpose.   One of the longest accounts in the book is that of Matthew Boulton, who, after 1793, purchased cast steel, sometimes made up into blanks, for the dies used in his mint at Soho.   On more than one occasion partial payment was made in the coin struck at the mint, and on 14 August, 1798, no less than £100 was sent to Huntsman in the form of penny pieces.[1]

1. It is a testimony not only to the soundness of the foundation of the firm but also to the ability of successive generations of Huntsmans that most of the markets here indicated are still supplied by the firm : there are indeed businesses, accounts with which were opened in the eighteenth century, still making purchases from Messrs. Huntsman, and the reputation of their steel stands to-day as high as ever.

CHAPTER III.

The Relations between James Watt, Matthew Boulton, and the Wilkinsons.

" Partnerships ought to be founded on equitable principles and, like a pair of scales, be balanced, either with money, time, knowledge, abilities or possession of a market."

Matthew Boulton to David Rumsey, 14 Aug. 1788.

I.

REVIEWING the progress made since the beginning of the century, an observer of the English iron industry in 1775 would have found little cause for the use of superlatives. True, the art of casting had been developed and iron had taken the place of wood and brass in many articles of commerce; the use of mineral fuel had been adopted in the initial process of smelting, as well as in that of the foundry; and half-a-dozen large undertakings attested the economies made possible by the discoveries of Abraham Darby.

But these changes by no means constituted a revolution in the industry; and although all estimates of production for dates prior to 1788 must be regarded with caution, the statement that until 1775 the output of iron had increased by an average of not more than one per cent. per annum is probably not far from the truth.[1]   Within the next few years this rate of increase was to be multiplied many fold, as the result of the inventions associated with the names of James Watt and Henry Cort.   The year 1775, in fact, marks more clearly than most dates selected as boundary-stones the end of one economic period and the beginning of another.   For it was in this year that Watt pushed his invention from the experimental to the commercial stage, and began to supply steam-engines for the market under a patent which, by Act of Parliament, had been extended for a period of twenty-five years to Michaelmas, 1800.

1.   Eckel. *Coal, Iron, and War*, 9.

Watt's experiments with the fire-engine began, it will be recalled, in the year 1762, and by 1764 the all-important notion of the separate condenser had been conceived. " In three hours after the idea of condensing in a separate vessel had occurred to me," he wrote some years later,[1] " I had planned the whole Engine in my mind and in three days I had a model at work nearly as perfect . . . . as any which have been made since that time." To hit on new ideas and to construct models were for Watt matters of almost everyday occurrence : to perfect all the details of the complicated apparatus of boilers, pumps, beams, levers, and gearing was the work of many tedious years; and it was not until 1769 that the inventor considered a stage to have been reached at which a patent could be taken out. Even then there were enormous difficulties to be overcome, and yet another six years of effort were required before the steam engine was fit for industrial purposes.

During this long period of gestation of the idea the inventor was encouraged and financed by a number of friends, chief among whom were Dr. Roebuck of Carron, and Matthew Boulton of Birmingham. By the year 1767 Watt had contracted debts approximating to £1,000; and in return for the payment of these, and the provision of the capital necessary to complete the invention, Roebuck obtained the right to two-thirds of the prospective profits of the steam engine. In 1769 the first engine was erected for his use at Kinneil House, but defects in workmanship rendered it only partially successful. In the meantime Watt had come into contact with Boulton, who, along with his friend, Dr. Small, was anxious to become associated with the venture and tried to induce Watt to leave Scotland for Birmingham. Several attempts were made to devise a scheme by which Boulton, Small, Roebuck, and Watt should all be partners in the steam-engine, but the difficulties were insurmountable.[2] The death of Small and the total failure of Roebuck—tragic events as they were to their friends—opened up the way to a partnership between Watt and Boulton, the latter taking over Roebuck's interest in the

---

1. James Watt to the Chief Justice of Common Pleas, 1795.
2. Muirhead, *Mechanical Inventions*, i, 41, 82.

invention in consideration of the cancelling of debts amounting to £1,200 owed to him by Roebuck. Two years later, in
May, 1774, James Watt removed to Birmingham.

The Soho works, which had been erected for the production
of Birmingham " toys " and objects of art of various kinds,
had by this time reached considerable proportions as the result
of the enterprise and capital of Boulton and his partner,
Fothergill, a prosperous merchant who had come into the
concern in 1762. It was partly the need for reducing the
heavy cost of propelling the machinery by horses that drew
Boulton's attention to the project of Watt; though, as he
always insisted, it was the honour of being associated with
the new means of power, rather than a desire for gain, that
caused him to give to it his enthusiastic support. From the
first Boulton envisaged, perhaps more clearly than the
inventor himself, the possibilities of the steam-engine; but
Fothergill had less imagination and would have nothing to
do with it. The result of this divergence was the setting up
of an entirely new enterprise—Boulton and Watt—alongside
the existing business at Soho; and for this " new lottery," as
he called it, Boulton obtained the necessary capital not from
the old firm but from the sale to Lord Donegal of his own
estates at Packington.[1] " Money, time, knowledge, abilities,
possession of a market "—all of these he brought as his
counterweight to the ponderous inventive genius of Watt, in
the new partnership.

The long period of experiments with the steam-engine had
been necessitated not by any weakness in the original idea but
by the faulty material and poor workmanship with which the
inventor had had to contend in Scotland. As early as 1770,
long before Watt's personal association with Birmingham,
Small was endeavouring to obtain materials for the engine in
England, and it was naturally to the Coalbrookdale Company,
which had behind it the experience of over half a century in
fire-engine work, that he turned. The result, however, was
disappointing : " the people of Colebrook-dell sent us the
castings for the circular machine only a month ago " [wrote

1. Statement of Matthew Boulton in *Boulton v. Fothergill*.

Small[1] in September, 1770]. "They were unsound and totally useless, and done over with some stuff to conceal their defects. An eminent caster has settled during the summer at Bilston. We were obliged to have recourse to him, but he has not yet sent the things, though he says he will in a few days." The eminent caster was John Wilkinson, of whom some account has already been given. Though far from possessing the genius of Watt, he had a mind fertile in contrivance, and his practical inventiveness and mechanical acumen were for many years of great value to the Soho partners. It is true that he afterwards put forward an exaggerated estimate of the part he had taken in the perfecting of the steam-engine; and his subsequent treatment of Boulton and Watt was the source of much embarrassment and delay in their enterprise. But Wilkinson's neglect of the dictum as to the necessity of being irreproachable in claiming rights ought not to blind us to the real contribution he made to the greatest invention of his generation. The career of this remarkable man has been strangely overlooked by economic historians, and Samuel Smiles missed a golden opportunity of adding a portrait of character and originality to his gallery of men of invention and industry. This oversight must be the excuse—if excuse be needed—for a somewhat detailed survey of the relations between Boulton and Watt on the one hand, and John Wilkinson and his brother William, on the other. In breaking this new ground an extensive use will be made of the Letter Books of the Soho Works for the years between 1775 and 1800.

For some time John Wilkinson had given special attention to the production of ordnance, and in 1774 he obtained his first patent for a new method of boring cannon.[2] The gun was cast solid, and instead of making the boring rod revolve, as had been the previous practice, Wilkinson caused the casting to rotate about a fixed bar along which travelled a sliding cutter. By this method a more uniform bore was obtained than had hitherto been possible. One of the chief difficulties with which Watt had been beset was that of

1. Muirhead, *Mechanical Inventions*, ii, 5.
2. *Specification of Patents*, 1063.

F

procuring a cylinder sufficiently accurate in bore to prevent the leakage of steam; and the successful application of Wilkinson's cannon lathe at Bersham to the steam-engine cylinder marks the beginning of an industrial *entente* which lasted for more than twenty years and which brought considerable gains to both parties.

It is necessary at this point to emphasise the fact that Boulton and Watt did not manufacture steam-engines for sale: they acted simply as designers and erectors of engines, and as consultants to the firms making use of their invention. The individual business which required an engine was usually free to make its own arrangements with founders and smiths for the supply of materials, and the Soho firm provided the skilled labour as well as those parts of the mechanism which required special care in manufacture. But for many years Boulton and Watt insisted that all cylinders should be supplied by John Wilkinson from his works at Broseley or Bradley. Writing on 10 February, 1776, to Samuel Garbett at Carron, Boulton, who had offered to erect an engine on the usual terms, adds, " Wilkinson hath bored us several Cylinders almost without Error that of 50 Inches diam^r for Bentley & Co. doth not err the thickness of an old shilling in no part, so that you must improve in boring or we must furnish the Cylinder "; and again a week later: " I am a great lover of truth both moral and Geometrical—Bore your Cylinders as true as Wilkinson's and then say there is no truth in me if we are not good customers to Carron." Even as late as 27 July 1795, by which time some hundreds of engines had been erected, the younger Watt was able to write to a customer who wished to make his own arrangements for the cylinder, as follows : " It was only after many expensive Experiments that Mr. Wilkinson attained the degree of perfection in casting and boring which could satisfy us. We in consequence constantly recommended his castings, and in the course of twenty years we have not erected more than three or four Engines the cylinders of which were not of his manufacture."

The quasi-monopoly thus accorded to Wilkinson extended beyond the supply of cylinders : " Such parts of the foundry

as relate to the pumps we leave you at liberty to take where
you please, [wrote Boulton to a customer in December 1778],
but such parts as relate to the Engine end of the beam must
be had at Bersham in Wales as there is no other proper
apparatus in Britain for producing the parts with that truth
and exactness we require." In other cases where the purchasing firm left the provision of materials to the engineers, the
orders for most of the cast-iron parts, including pipes and
chains, as well as for brass work, were given to Wilkinson;
and whenever possible Boulton and Watt endeavoured to put
their friend in the way of lucrative trade.[1] Their efforts in this
direction were, indeed, sometimes a source of friction with their
customers. Wilkinson's prices were appreciably higher than
those current among other ironfounders; and, in contrast to
the long period of credit usually granted by these, Wilkinson
insisted on a quarterly settlement without discount. Customers
often complained to the Soho partners of these prices and
trade conditions; and ironmasters in particular resented the
obligation to purchase from Wilkinson the cylinders of the
engines they were erecting for their own use. James Spedding
of Whitehaven, for example, claimed to be able to supply
the same goods at 2s. per cwt. less; the clients of Boulton and
Watt, he declared, were wilfully made to suffer in order that
the connection between Soho and Bersham might be maintained.[2]

Such services, however, were reciprocal. From an early

1. See, for example, Boulton to Wilkinson, 12 Nov. 1779.
" Mr. Watt informs that many new engines will be wanted for Whl Virgin
and other mines and begs I would inform you that upwards of 100 fathom of
new pump will be wanted for Whl Virgin, but that you must apply yourself
to the mine for their order for that part as he can't do it without giving offense
to some of the quackers. We will back your application but its most proper
you should first apply." See also Boulton to Hornblower, 20 Jan. 1777, and
to John Wilkinson, 7 Nov. 1778.
2. Boulton to Meason, 26 Sept. 1778; Watt to Dudley, 18 July 1777; and to
Scott, 22 Oct. 1777; Spedding to B. & W., 7 Aug. 1785. In reply to John Scott
of Shrewsbury, on 22 Oct. 1777, Boulton wrote in vindication of Wilkinson:
" . . . we can only say that we have try'd other Founders, our experience hath
induced us to prefer Mr. W's Pumps at £18 pr. Ton to any others we have
had, or seen, at £14 per Ton . . . But as to the outside Cylinder and likewise
one part of the Steam Pipe . . . we do, with you, think £30 pr. Ton too
much and yet we have repeatedly battled that point with Mr. Wilkinson and
after all we have paid him (for some small engines for ourselves) after that
rate."

date Wilkinson was interested in enterprises abroad, and in 1770 he had, it is said, established a foundry in France.[1] At the time when Boulton and Watt began to erect steam engines commercially he was engaged in negotiations with the brothers Perrier, who were engineers for the Paris Water-works; and through his brother William, who spent many years in France, he obtained from them an order for some forty miles of cast-iron piping. One of the Perriers subse-quently visited Bersham with the object of purchasing a fire-engine for pumping purposes, but, seeing there an engine of the Watt construction, he tried to persuade Wilkinson to manufacture a similar one for him. His invitation was refused on grounds of both "honour and interest," and he was referred to the Soho firm.[2] But Boulton and Watt were already seeking a patent in France, and were not disposed to sell an engine outright to the Perriers. In a letter (11 May 1777) which indicates the intimacy which had already come to exist between the two firms, Watt delivered his opinion on the matter to Wilkinson :

> "Mr. B. is of the same sentiment as me upon Perrier's scheme that we should serve them cheaper if sole patentees in France than as we are. You will see your own interest connected with ours as sole Founder where we are sole Engineers. It is our common interest to lett them follow their own devices rather than sell our birth right for a mess of pottage—in time by bribery and experiment they may learn to make our engines, but without your assistance they cannot make the goods, so that amongst us we have them pretty safe, as I doubt not but their own interest if they see it will force them to agree to such terms as shall be fixed for them at a full meeting of the engine parliament to be held when Mr. B. returns."

Between 1777 and 1789 numerous orders flowed in to Soho through Bersham; according to his own statement Wilkinson often refused remunerative offers to execute the whole engine, contenting himself with the more honourable and, it may be

1. Dickinson, *John Wilkinson*, 49.
2. Watt to Boulton, 2 May 1777. Printed by Muirhead, *op. cit.*, ii, 104.

added, less hazardous, business of executing such parts of the work as were delegated to him by Boulton and Watt.[1]

The privileged position of Wilkinson did not, however, preclude other ironmasters from sharing in the new business which the invention of the steam-engine brought to the industry. The demand for piston-rods, for instance, was important; since the finest Swedish wrought iron was requisite for these, it was not to Bersham but to the charcoal-using anchor-smiths that the orders were given. In June, 1776, Watt ordered a trial piston-rod from James Spedding of Whitehaven, saying he selected the firm because the rods were made under the "great hammer"; and during the years that followed pistons were regularly supplied either by Spedding, Fisher & Co., of Whitehaven, or Spedding, Hicks, Senhouse & Co., of Seaton, near Workington. The rods were consistently charged at 7d. per lb., and other engine work at 4d.; and the goods were shipped first to Thomas Becket or Joseph Rathbone in Liverpool, and thence to the place at which the engine was to be erected. A single firm, however, could hardly supply the whole of the piston-rods required, especially as there was always the danger of stoppage owing to shortage of water or the freezing-up of the forge dam. In 1777, when the demand for engines for the mines of Cornwall first arose, iron for the same purpose was obtained from Blount[2] of Cleobury Forge in Worcestershire—though it was not fashioned there into the finished rod; and in the same year piston-rods were first supplied by Jukes Coulson, anchor-smith of London and Rotherhithe.

Castings for engines erecting in Scotland were sometimes, apparently, obtained from Carron. Geographical considerations also led to the giving of orders for iron required at Soho to firms outside the orbit of John Wilkinson. Pig and bar iron were purchased by Boulton and Watt from Isaac

1. At the time of the negotiations with Perrier, another Frenchman, Jary, who was interested in mines in Brittany, tried to convince Wilkinson that he would not be acting wrongfully if, as a founder, he executed any orders given to him and asked no questions. Like Perrier he was repelled, and the engine was subsequently obtained through the proper channels. John Wilkinson to Jary, Oct. 1777.

2. Watt to Boulton, 28 Feb. 1777. Printed by Dickinson, *Proc. Inst. Mech. Engrs.*, Oct. 1915, 496.

Spooner of Birmingham, or from Wright and Jesson of Wren's Nest; engine plates and rivet iron were supplied by Nicholas Ryder of Marston Forge, and also by Joab Parsons of Burton-on-Trent; while the proximity to Soho of the Eagle Foundry in Birmingham naturally led to the giving of extensive orders for castings—principally pumps and steam cases—to its proprietor, Richard Dearman.[1]   But it was the Coalbrookdale group of firms that became, after a few years, Wilkinson's chief rival in the supply of engine parts, other than cylinders : in 1778 Abraham Darby III. was supplying barrels for pumps, and in 1783 William Reynolds of Ketley was given orders for pipes for the engines which were in process of erection in Cornwall. [2]

Even in respect of cylinders Wilkinson could not expect to retain for long an exclusive market : in 1778 he was obliged to institute a suit in Chancery to restrain other ironmasters from using his methods of boring cannon;[3] and as the same process was applied to the boring of cylinders it was inevitable that the pirates should seek to produce these also.   Whether under licence from Wilkinson or not, the new boring apparatus was established by the Coalbrookdale Company in 1780, by the Walkers of Rotherham in 1781, and by Banks and Onions about the same time.[4]   Such cylinders as were cast and bored at these works must, however, have been for engines of the old type, for not until 1795 did the Soho partners place orders for cylinders with any but John Wilkinson.

1. Watt to Meason, 18 Mar. 1778; Spooner to B. and W., 7 Feb. 1792; Wright and Jesson to B. and W., 1775-85; Ryder to B. and W., 2 Feb. 1779; Watt to Ryder, 12 Feb., 5 Mar. 1779; Stuart to Parsons, 3 Apr. 1776; Parsons to B. and W. May and July 1785; Dearman to B. and W., 30 Sept. 1779
2. Boulton to Meason, 1 Oct. 1778; Wm. Reynolds to B. and W., 2 Sept. 1783.
3. *Aris's Birmingham Gazette*, 3 Aug. 1778.
4. William Reynolds to Watt, 19 May 1780, relating to the erection of a second engine at Ketley: " . . . we are now putting up a mill at the Dale to bore Cylinders in the manner J. Wilkinson bores his—and as we are in hopes we shall be able to do it as correctly as he does, we shall wish to give the order for the Cylinder, Hot water and Air pumps to the Dale Co.—and as some order might perhaps soon have been given to J. W. for them I thought it proper to apprize thee of our Intention." Samuel Walker to James Watt, 29 May 1781: " . . . . and tho' you are commenced Founders (for which there needs no apology) as we are preparing to Bore our own Cylinder as well as others hereafter upon the new plan) at a great expence, we must beg the favour of casting that with the Condenser ourselves."

As time went on, although the volume of work executed at Broseley, Bersham, and Bradley continued to be great, it probably came to comprise a smaller proportion of the total than in early days. This was partly the result of the increasing skill of other founders and of the growing cordiality between Soho and Coalbrookdale; but it was also partly due to the fact that, occasionally, reports were made of defective workmanship at the Wilkinson foundry. In 1786 complaints were raised by Rennie, then at the Albion Mills, of the fracture of an iron gudgeon made by Wilkinson. "I have totaly forbid the making any more Iron work at Bersham " [wrote Watt to Boulton, 20th March 1786]. "I have kept all the specimens of this Gudgeon for Mr. W.'s inspection and to stay his stomach in the meantime have treated him with a letter on that and on his Boiler plates but have yet said nothing of the accident which I believe broke the Gudgeon, as he is too ready to catch hold of any excuse." The cessation of orders was, however, only temporary, and good relations were maintained for some years longer.

II.

It was not only as producers of engine material that the ironmasters gained from the inventions of James Watt : the application of steam power was to have effects of almost incalculable magnitude in many industries, but in none were these more striking than in that with which we are concerned. An attempt will be made very briefly to trace the main stages in the introduction of the steam-engine to the production of iron.

It has been asserted by Smiles that the first completed engine supplied from Soho was erected for John Wilkinson at Broseley, and the statement has often been repeated by later writers. It is clear, however, from the records of the firm, that the Broseley engine was the third in order of completion. The first was that reconstructed from the old Kinneil engine : it had a cylinder of 18 inches, and was used by Boulton and Fothergill to throw back the water above the wheel that worked a grinding mill at Soho; and the second, with a 50 ins. cylinder, was a pumping engine for Bloomfield

Colliery. The engine designed for Wilkinson was, however, the first applied to purposes other than pumping; it had a 38 ins. cylinder, and was used to blow two blast-furnaces at Broseley, each of which produced about 20 tons of pig iron weekly. After this a small engine was erected at Stratford-le-Bow, and then, in 1777, the large pumping engine at Bedworth Colliery, the striking success of which brought a rush of enquiries and orders from all parts of the country.[1]

In the same year Wilkinson was furnished with drawings for the conversion of a common engine—known as Topsyturvy —to the new principles of Watt; and orders for two others were given by him, one for the blowing of his furnace at Wilson House in Lancashire, and the other for working pumps at his colliery at Snedshill in Staffordshire. From the first Wilkinson was a devout believer in the engine, and, being troubled by no false modesty as to his own share in its success, he applied to the Soho partners for permission to erect whatever engines he pleased for his own extensive undertakings. To this suggestion Boulton and Watt would not agree, but the concessions made to their friend could hardly be considered as lacking in generosity. All the engines already set up or in contemplation by him, with the exception of that to be erected at Snedshill, were to be exempt from the payment of premiums; and in the case of the Snedshill engine on which the usual premium—the equivalent of one-third of the coal saved—was required, the engineers declared themselves willing to accept payment in coal.[2] No such premium appears actually to have been received. In the two succeeding years furnace-blowing engines were also erected by Wilkinson at his Bradley and Snedshill works, and upon these annual premiums were payable of £34 and £57 respectively.

By 1780 Wilkinson had thus no fewer than four engines employed in producing a blast for the smelting of iron, and the success of Watt's invention in this sphere soon led to orders from other ironmasters. Many of these used the

---

1. Watt to Secretary of Chelsea Water Works, 22 Oct. 1775; to Le Camus de Limare, Feb. 22, 1779; and to William Chapman, 22 Feb. 1777.
2. B. and W. to Wilkinson, 17 July 1777.

engines only for pumping water in the dry season to turn the bellows' wheel; thus, early in 1776 Samuel Garbett proposed to erect a pumping engine for furnace purposes at Carron, but as coal was cheap here, and there could be little gain to either party, Watt suggested modifications in the existing engine plant rather than a new construction. At Ketley also the indirect method was at first employed : " As the present State of our Works does not admit of the immediate [*i.e.* direct] application of it to blow the Furnaces we are determined to erect an Engine . . . . at Ketley to work two Pumps," wrote Richard Reynolds in 1777. But later direct blowing without the intervention of a water-wheel was found possible; early in 1780 drawings for a second engine were ordered, and, in the following year, a larger one was under construction at Coalbrookdale, while an existing engine at Madeley Wood was converted and applied to the furnaces.[1]

As early as 1776 Watt offered an engine to George Matthews of Broseley, but whether this was accepted is uncertain; in 1779 an engine was set to work to raise water from the Severn at Wren's Nest for blowing the furnaces owned by Wright and Jesson; and in 1782 Samuel Walker was constructing to Watt's plans an engine to blow two furnaces at Rotherham.[2] As Walker complained that he had previously been limited in his operations by inadequate water supply, it appears that this was the first engine erected at Rotherham, and it was probably employed to actuate the bellows directly. Among other furnace engines of various dates may be mentioned those set up for James Stockdale of Cartmel (1786), John Booth of Sheffield (1788), Fox and Co. of Neath Abbey, Glamorgan (1792), Lewis, Tait and Co. of Dowlais (1797), Samuel Homfray of Penydarren (1798) and the Walkers of Rotherham (1798).

A further stage in the application of steam power to the iron industry was reached when the first forge hammer was moved by an engine. The idea of a rotative engine for this

1. Reynolds to B. and W., 12th mo. 1777, and 4th mo. 1778; William Reynolds to B. and W., 10th mo. 1780, and 24 Jan. 1781.
2. Watt to Boulton, 11 Nov. 1776; Wright and Jesson to B. and W., 1775-85; Letters to B. and W., 1775-85.

purpose and for the working of machinery in general had been present in the minds of Boulton and Watt from the first days of their partnership; but it was some years before the details were worked out. The first attempts in this direction were described by Watt in a letter to Kaller of Silesia, 10 Nov., 1776, as consisting of " a hollow wheel of Iron which is turned round by the powers of steam exerted within the wheel "; and in June, 1775, Boulton asserts that an engine on this principle had been erected at Soho to prove the practicability of the idea.[1] " We have completed several of our reciprocating Steam Engines " [wrote Watt[2] in 1776] " which are at work some in this neighbourhood and one in London. We have also made two different Rotative or Wheel Engines that are turned by the force of steam exerted within them, which species is directly applicable to the purpose you want." But there were, added the writer, " little difficulties to be cured before we offer them to the public."

In May, 1777, John Wilkinson announced his intention of " going to work in the forge way," and asked Watt to supply him with an engine capable of raising a hammer of 15 cwt. A week later the inventor replied describing a small engine of his construction which moved a hammer of 60 lbs. more than sixty strokes a minute, promised to begin a larger one of the same kind immediately, and added prophetically that " more may be done in this article than appeared at first sight." It soon became clear, however, that engines of the type described were not practicable, and Watt therefore turned his attention to devising apparatus for converting the to-and-fro action of the piston into rotary motion. Very soon he hit on the device of the crank; but the demand for the reciprocating engine was such as to occupy the whole of the inventor's time for some years and nothing was done with it. When at length he was able to return to his rotative engine he found himself debarred from the use of the crank—the idea of which

1. Boulton to Samuel Roe, 29 June 1775.
2. Watt to Proctor and Belby of Sheffield, 8 Nov. 1776

had been stolen from him by Pickard[1]—and was obliged to adopt the ingenious " sun and planet " action suggested by William Murdoch. Owing to these delays it was not until 1781 that Watt was able to take out his patent for the rotative engine, and in the following year the first forge engine was erected—again for John Wilkinson at Bradley.[2]

The report made by Watt on this development in November, 1782, was entirely favourable, and a few months later William Reynolds paid a tribute to its successful working.[3] The new application of steam at once attracted general attention, and among the first enquiries was one from Henry Cort at Fareham.[4] In February, 1784, William Reynolds ordered two forge engines, one of which was to replace the old waterwheel at Horsehay, and three years later Boulton and Watt permitted the Ketley Co. to erect a third engine for stamping purposes without the payment of any premium.[5] Among numerous ironmasters who sent orders for forge engines were Samuel Hallen of Bewdley (1783), Joseph Rathbone of Coalbrookdale (1785), James Spedding of Seaton (1785), Folliott Scott of Rotherhithe (1786), and Wright and Jesson of West

1. In his *Birmingham Inventions and Inventors*, 32, Prosser cast doubt on the received account, and suggested that Pickard was the original discoverer of the principle of the crank. But the crank is mentioned in a letter of Watt to Turnbull as early as 23 Feb. 1771, and the following extract from a letter written by James Watt, Junr., to Thomas Barnes, 31 Mar. 1795, may be accepted as a statement of what had actually happened : " The application of the Crank to the Steam Engine for mechanical purposes, was invented by Mr. Watt in the year 1780, and a model made by one of our workmen, who betrayed the secret (as he himself afterwards confessed) to a Mr. Pickard of Birmingham, and this Mr. Pickard took out a patent for it in the same year. Mr. Watt, instead of contesting the right of the above patentee, then invented the rotative wheels, which, being found to answer much better than a crank, have been constantly used by us ever since ; but Mr. Wilkinson and others of our friends who were acquainted with the above circumstances and thought a Crank preferable, have constantly made use of it without molestation, and we should have done the same without any scruple . . . . if we had had any occasion for so doing."

2. *Letter Book*, 1793-5, f. 279.

3. Muirhead, ii, 163 ; W. Reynolds to B. and W., 30 May 1783.

4. Cort to Boulton, 27 May 1783.

5. " As the engine you mention seems to be intended for experiment, and as we are well inclined to forward you in every thing in our power—We consent to your erecting a single Engine with a Cyl^r not more than 20 inches dia^r, not more than 6 feet long in the Strokes, without paying us any premium for the same, provided the same is applied only to cold stamping or cutting off the raw ends of the barrs drawn at the forges, and also provided the Dale Company make you a present of the Cylinder, &c., as you intimate." B. and W. to R. Reynolds and Co., 22 Feb. 1787.

Bromwich (1791). Rotative, as distinct from reciprocating, engines were entirely new to industry : it was thus obviously impossible to charge for them on the basis of fuel saved, and hence the users were required to pay a rent of £5 per horse-power per annum during the continuance of the patent. But it was also possible to buy out the premiums at a number of years' purchase : in 1786, for example, when the patent had still 14 years to run, ten times the amount of the annual premium sufficed to buy the engine outright.

To the third and final process in iron production—that of rolling and slitting—steam power was applied at a somewhat later date. Smiles,[1] it is true, declares that a steam rolling-mill was designed by Matthew Boulton and erected at Soho in 1781, but it is difficult to reconcile this statement with the fact, already mentioned, that rotative engines were not produced until the following year. In February 1784 William Reynolds informed James Watt that " the Coalbrookdale Co. will wish to have a fire Engine rolling and slitting mill and therefore hope your Ideas on that head are brot so near to perfection as to induce you to have one erected." It was, however, once more in the works of John Wilkinson that the application of steam to this purpose was brought about, and the initiative, it appears, was taken by the ironmaster himself. " We have never erected any Engine for Slitting and Rolling of Iron, but our friend Mr. Wilkinson has by licence from us annexed a Slitting and rolling mill to one of our Engines," wrote Boulton and Watt [2] in 1786; and from subsequent correspond-ence it appears that it was the engine which had first been used for forge purposes at Bradley that was now adapted to the rolling-mill.

Engines suitable for this purpose were of necessity expensive, and the demand for them was not immediately large; Green and Price of Birmingham made enquiries for one in 1787, but were deterred by the price; and in the following year, when Richard Crawshay ordered an engine for rolling, Watt's estimate for the erection was £3,000, over half of which, however, related to the mill as distinct from the engine.

1. Smiles, *Boulton and Watt*, 289.
2. B. and W. to Thompson, 8 June 1786.

Three other engines to run the great rolling- and slitting-mills at Bradley were constructed by Wilkinson [1] in 1789; and the Walkers of Rotherham also erected a Watt engine for rolling about the same time.

III.

Both as supplier of castings and as the first to make use of the new engines John Wilkinson was closely connected with the growth of the engineering business at Soho; while as a shareholder with Boulton and Watt in the Cornish Metal Co. he often conferred with them as to the policy to be adopted towards the mine owners of Cornwall and the rival Anglesey Copper Company. During the first dozen years or so of the undertaking the ironmaster was frequently in Birmingham, and often stayed for a week or more at a time as the guest of one or other of the partners. Friendship with John Wilkinson must always have been somewhat trying. His was a dominating, assertive nature, almost titanic in the force of its elemental passions, in its ambitions, its inflated egotism, and its capacity for hatred and revenge. When differences arose, whether with rivals, with customers, or with employees, he was relentless in his bitterness and blind to all consequences. " Peace is a most desirable thing," he once wrote to his friends,[2] " and the more so to one of my constitution who cannot be angry by halves. Resentment with me becomes a matter of business and stimulates to action beyond any Profit whatever."

With this masterful personality James Watt and Matthew Boulton succeeded, not without effort, in maintaining amicable relations for more than twenty years; and on at least one occasion they assisted him out of financial difficulty.[3] As

---

1. Statement of J. Watt, Junr., to Weston, *Letter Book*, 1795.
2. Wilkinson to B. and W., 9 Oct. 1784.
3.   Soho, June 21 1792.
 Mr. Jno Wilkinson,
  Dear Sir,
 In reply to yours we send you inclosed our draft on Mrs. Matthews value £1000, the receipt of which please acknowledge.
 B. and W. never were lower in cash than at present, for by our long absence in London our Customers were not craved, so that we have not received for castings this year the half of what we now send you. Mr. B. is gone

time went on, however, Wilkinson's visits grew less frequent, for he had been involved in disputes with Birmingham people and developed a distaste for the town.   As the control of affairs at Soho passed gradually from the hands of the senior partners to their sons, Wilkinson had to deal with younger men who had less understanding of his eccentricities and had no memories of former goodwill to help them to forbearance : the genial informalities slowly disappeared and business was carried on in a climate more rigorous than that of the 'seventies and 'eighties.   With the younger Watt, in particular, Wilkinson was rarely in agreement, and the creases in the relations between the two firms called with growing frequency for the smoothing hand of Matthew Boulton.   Moreover the warm friendship of the Soho partners and William Wilkinson—whose daughter afterwards married Boulton's son—was far from pleasing to John.   William, it will be remembered, was a partner with his brother in the Bersham Works, but, being in charge of the foreign business, he spent much of his time abroad.   When in 1787 he returned from France his brother's reception was not cordial, and it is clear from his correspondence with James Watt that the yoke of John Wilkinson sat far from easily on the shoulders of the younger man.   The exact point at issue between the two Wilkinsons is uncertain; but rightly or wrongly William conceived himself to be deprived of his fair share of the profits.   The purchase by John of the Brymbo estate, adjacent to Bersham, for the erection of an ironworks in which William would have no share, was probably also regarded by the latter as a menace.   By the middle of 1794 the rupture was public, and William was applying to Boulton and Watt for a statement

---

to Birmingham to procure you another £1000 on his own account and will write you. Wishing you happily over this crisis and that you may reap much profit and satisfaction from your new Estates,

I remain,

Dear Sir,

Yours sincerely,

JAMES WATT.

Mrs. Watt says that if you do not call at Heathfield and stay a day with us in your way down she will conclude you have quarrelled with her.

of their account with Bersham, which had been refused him by his brother.[1]

The Soho partners endeavoured to preserve a strict neutrality in the dispute between the Wilkinsons, which was carried to the Courts early in 1795. This was especially necessary in view of the legal disputation in which they were themselves engaged with the redoubtable Bull—a case involving the whole question of the validity of Watt's patent. But the fact that William Wilkinson employed Boulton and Watt's attorney, Weston, as his legal adviser, at once set up suspicion in the mind of John, whose resentment was quickly indicated by his selecting, for his own case, the counsel employed by Bull.

Boulton and Watt at once repudiated any conspiracy with William, and at the same time urged an understanding between the contending brothers : all they had done, they said, was to give, when requested by William, a testimonial to the abilities of their lawyer. But such protestations of innocence were unavailing : " I know his iron soul too well " [wrote the younger Watt to his attorney, Ambrose Weston, 30 March, 1795] " to suppose he will ever forgive us for having introduced his brother to your acquaintance." An offer of friendly mediation by James Watt was entirely ignored; and John Wilkinson's only reply to the letter in which it was made was a note by the hand of Cornelius Reynolds to inform the Soho partners that Bersham Works were now closed by injunction, and that existing contracts for cylinders could not be executed.[2]

To the engineers this was serious news, for without cylinders their business must come to an immediate end. Moreover, the tone of the letter, and an added accusation of their having attempted to seduce his workpeople, implied that Wilkinson intended to draw Boulton and Watt into the dispute; and the relations between Soho and Bersham had been so intimate that to do so would be a matter of no great difficulty. " I myself look upon all this as the forebodings of a storm which is to overwhelm us as well as you " [wrote

1. Watt to Wm. Wilkinson, 12 July 1787, and 7 May 1794.
2. Watt to Wm. Wilkinson, 8 Mar. 1795.

James Watt, Junr., to William Wilkinson in March, 1795],
"and I expect every day to see it break out in thunder and
lightning. However, until it does B. and W. having professed a system of neutrality will conscientiously adhere to it."

Not only had Wilkinson shut the works, dismissed
his employees, and carried away all the plant that could be
moved from Bersham, but he was now calling for the payment
of all outstanding debts. With Soho he had for many years
kept a running account, Bolton and Watt crediting him for
materials supplied, and debiting him with the premiums due
on engines in his various works. At the moment the adverse
balance against Soho was £1,700; but, on the other hand,
Wilkinson owed a considerable sum for premiums unpaid for
many years in respect of engines for the use of which no
written agreements had been made.[1]

Boulton and Watt were quick to meet their obligations,
and at once transferred their orders for cylinders to the Dale
Company. But the boring apparatus at Coalbrookdale,
though second only to that of Wilkinson, was inadequate, and
long delays occurred, so that orders for several engines had
to be refused.[2] It was clear that some other source of supply
must be found if the engine business were not to be brought
to a stop, and the Soho partners accordingly resolved themselves to undertake the casting and boring of engine parts.

This was not the first time such a project had been
considered; in September 1793 the engineers had been offered
by Edward Fox a share in the Neath Abbey Ironworks, and
the following year the Coalbrookdale partners had suggested
that they might purchase the furnaces and collieries at
Madeley Wood. Boulton and Watt had, however, no desire
to engage in smelting; hence an invitation of William
Wilkinson that they should unite with him to buy out
his brother from Bersham was also refused. It would be
sufficient if they could own a well-equipped foundry with
apparatus for boring and finishing engine parts.

1. J. Watt, Junr., to Weston, 21 Mar. 1795.
2. J. Watt, Junr., to Wilson, 22 Apr. 1795. A reference is made to the
"inconquerable vis inertia of the Dale Co." in a letter of J. Watt, Junr., to
Wm. Wilkinson, 30 Dec. 1795.

Accordingly a site was selected on the bank of the canal at Smethwick, and plans were quickly prepared for the building of extensive works—comprising a foundry, boring-mill, smiths' and carpenters' shops, quays, and dwelling-houses for workpeople—in the designing of which William Wilkinson rendered valuable assistance. Skilled labour was obtained from among those whom the "war" at Bersham had left unemployed, and attempts were made to secure Wilkinson's manager, Gilbert Gilpin, for the new works. By January 1796 all was complete, and the rearing feast of the Smethwick Foundry was held with all the ceremonial and speeches usual on such occasions.[1]

In the meantime arbitrators had been appointed to determine the dispute between the Wilkinsons, and on August 27 1795 an order was made for the sale of the entire works at Bersham. The auction took place early in November, and as John Wilkinson himself was the highest bidder, he became sole owner of Bersham as well as of the new Brymbo Works hard by.

To avenge his injuries, William Wilkinson now divulged to the engineers the startling information that his brother John was numbered among the pirates of their invention. Some years previously, in a weak moment, the partners had yielded to Wilkinson's repeated request to allow him to make the all-important nozzle as well as the other parts of an engine ordered for France. Drawings of the nozzles were sent to Bersham, and it now appeared that, since 1787, Wilkinson had not scrupled to erect for his own use whatever steam-engines he required, and that he had also supplied others to customers both at home and abroad. In September 1795, during the absence of John, William conducted the younger Watt on a tour of inspection through Brymbo and its surrounding mines, and the extent of the infringement was made manifest.

---

1. A full account of the proceedings is given in *Aris's Birmingham Gazette*, 1 Feb. 1796. In the early days there were difficulties : " We have got Abraham Storey from Bersham (J. Wilkinson's head man) and are going on humbly at the Foundry, where we have one furnace at work and are already able to cast— Grate Bars!"—J. Watt, Junr., to Lawson, 17 Mar. 1796.

G

" This terrific Antagonist " [wrote Watt's son [1]] " has lost with me all his terrors, and the crafty daring robber dwindles down to something unworthy of contempt. His conduct in the whole of this dispute with his brother has been truly despicable and many transactions have been brought to light which shew that he has dealt so with everybody."

From a statement drawn up for the attorney it appears that the engines erected in Wilkinson's various establishments, under licence from Boulton and Watt, numbered ten, including a blowing engine erected for Perrier at Montcenis (Creusot). In addition Wilkinson had constructed, without the consent or knowledge of the patentee, no fewer than nineteen engines for his own use, and there were two more in process of erection at Brymbo. For his Bradley works alone there had been built no fewer than twelve engines, the power from which was used not only for blowing furnaces and forges, but also for winding coal, lifting hammers, working rolling- and slitting-mills, and boring and turning ordnance; and of these twelve only the first two had been erected with the sanction of Boulton and Watt. Moreover, Wilkinson had built at least eight Watt engines for sale, including one sent to Cadiz, one for Perrier at Mons, and one for the lead mines of Count Reden in Prussia.

At the moment the engineers were busy with the tracking down and prosecution of other offenders—chiefly ironmasters. The younger Watt was not averse from using methods from which, no doubt, his more sensitive father would have shrunk, and his vigilance had brought to light the existence of numerous infringements of patent rights. It was revealed that, along with others, the Parkers of Oldbury, Sturges & Co. of Leeds, and Bateman and Sherratt of Salford, had not only made engines for their own uses but had supplied either whole engines, or parts covered by Watt's patent, to customers in the ordinary way of business. One by one the pirates were brought to heel, the mere threat of legal proceedings generally being sufficient to effect surrender; and by the end of the year

1. J. Watt, Junr., to Weston, 24 Sept. 1795.

the patentees were free to turn their attention once more to the arch-traitor.[1]

In December, 1795, direct application was made to John Wilkinson for compensation for the unpaid premiums, amounting, it was estimated, to between nine and ten thousand pounds. Wilkinson, who must have witnessed the discomfiture of the other pirates, wisely agreed to a settlement, and at a meeting with the younger Soho partners he agreed to make full reparation.[2] He was, however, in no haste to fulfil his promises, for there was still a chance that the patent might be overthrown in the courts; and six months later the claims of the engineers were still unsatisfied.

1. An example of the methods employed is given in a letter written by James Watt, Junior. to A. Weston, his attorney. Thackeray, of Manchester, was one of the most determined of pirates, and, in addition to the engine in his own works, had constructed another for James Stockdale, Wilkinson's brother-in-law, at Cark.

" I believe we have Mr. Thackeray fast also, but you must determine. Mr. Lawson, under the disguise of a Scotch Jockey, got acquainted with one of the Engine tenders (there are two as they work night and day), and obtained from him a compleat description of the Engine exactly conformable to Thorneycroft's which you have. He was proceeding under the direction of his instructor to sketch it down, when suspicions arising in the mind of the fellow, he charged Lawson with being employed by B. and W., which he, despairing of getting further information, confessed. The fellow appeared much frightened, wrung his hands, and said *he had done him*, and that he should be ruined for having told him all. Lawson told him he might easily get out of the Scrape and be no loser, if he would either procure him a sight of the Engine or make Afft. of what he had said. He preferred the former, and by his directions and taking Perrens with him for a guard, whom he left at the outer gate to be ready in case of need, about half-past ten he walked through the yard to the Engine house, the Watchman (who is paid a guinea a week for keeping people out of the Engine) being drunk, and the watch dog, good-tempered and friendly, although he met him, did not disturb his progress. When he got to the Engine door, which he says it would have been impossible to find without the previous description he had received, he looked in and seeing only the Night Engine tender, walked forwards and through another door saw the bottom part of the Cylinders and Valve Box, with the *Eduction* pipe going down into the *Water*, and the *Air pump rod* attached to the plug working at least 36 strokes per Minute. He then addressed himself to the Engine Man telling him that hearing the Engine work as he was passing that way, he had stepped in to look at it, supposing it to be something curious. Upon his speaking two women came out from about the Engine, and the Engine man, who I suppose was disagreably interrupted in his Amours, shut the door saying no one could be permitted to enter without leave from Mr. Bradley (Thackeray's Partner) and that he must go out immediately. Which intimation he complied with and joined his protector Perrins . . . . Theyton the Engine tender . . we will take into our Services."

2. J. Watt, Junr., to Weston, 10 Dec. 1795 : " I am persuaded that if the patent had fallen he would have exerted himself to the utmost to crush us to atoms."

One of the engines that Wilkinson had constructed under licence was that put up in 1784 for the Minera, or Maesyfynnon Wen, Lead Mines, which were situated on the outskirts of Wrexham, near Bersham. It had been agreed that the customary annual premiums, equal to one-third of the value of the coal saved, should be paid to Boulton and Watt; but the arrangement had been merely oral, and actually no premiums had been received. The other Minera adventurers, it appears, had allowed Wilkinson, who was the largest shareholder in the venture, to take considerable sums from the gross profits for the payment of the engineers. When, therefore, they were informed that the premiums had never been paid, they expressed their astonishment, and a meeting was called for 1 August, 1796, to deal with the matter.

Wilkinson now showed signs of an eleventh-hour repentance and wrote post haste to Soho for a statement of the Minera account, in order that it might be settled before the meeting took place. Matthew Boulton, who replied in a courteous and characteristic letter from a sick bed, assured Wilkinson that he would be glad to meet him at Soho for a settlement of *all* outstanding accounts, and at the same time announced his intention of being present at the Minera meeting. The attempt made by John to counter this move was feeble in the extreme and quite unworthy of his undoubted ability as a strategist. He replied that he had cancelled a proposed visit to the North and would be at Soho on August 1st, obviously hoping to keep Boulton away from Minera. This attempted diversion was easily dealt with by a division of forces : the younger Boulton was to travel to Minera, and the other partners would remain in Birmingham to meet the ironmaster.

Thus outgeneralled, there was no course open to Wilkinson except capitulation. Justice, however, was tempered with mercy : "We have not been immoderate in our demand, having conceded much to ancient friendship and former good offices, but still it amounted to more than I believe he ever expected," wrote one of the partners. In addition to payment of compensation, and an undertaking of good conduct in the future, Wilkinson gave his word that he would assist the patentees to secure payment for the engines he had erected for others.[1]

Following the agreement John Wilkinson spent several days as the guest of the Soho partners, and to all appearances the broken edifice of friendship was restored. In reality the treaty of peace had merely papered over the crack, and it was not long before this again became visible. Wilkinson indeed could never forget the humiliation he had suffered, and every little pin-prick became for him a serious grievance. It has already been mentioned that at the time of the civil war at Bersham some of Wilkinson's discharged employees—including his chief caster, Abraham Storey—had been found employment at Smethwick. As the works grew the proprietors began to look about for additional labour, and advertisements were inserted in the principal newspapers in different parts of the country. The extreme egotism and suspicion of Wilkinson is evidenced by the fact that the publication of one of these advertisements in a Chester paper was interpreted by him as an attempt to seduce his workpeople from Brymbo and Bersham to Birmingham.

Shortly afterwards he seemed to see an opening for revenge. In the famous case of Boulton and Watt *v.* Hornblower, the latter had invited the assistance of Wilkinson in his opposition to the patent; and, counting on the supposed restoration of amicable relations, Boulton and Watt applied to Wilkinson for a copy of Hornblower's letter for use in the trial. The request was the occasion of an outburst from John, filled with accusations of ingratitude, claims to a share in the invention of the steam-engine, and threats of future hostilities.

Bradley, 16 Jan[y] 1797.

Mess[rs] B. & W.

Gent[n],

From the Conduct that has been shewn towards me for some time back from your house or some of the partners in it—It appears that the length of time that has elapsed from the beginning of our acquaintance which is now above 22

1. James Watt, Junr., to Wm. Wilkinson, 8 Aug., and to Weston, 7 Aug. 1796.

years has effaced from your memory some of the circumstances that have occurred during that period—particularly
towards the former part of it—when if you carry your
recollections back so far—you must be well aware that a
piston I gave (to the very great detriment of my own Interest
which I have all along sacrificed to yours) was the means
of carrying you through many of the difficulties which
presented themselves in the bringing your Engine scheme to
perfection—particularly of pointing out to you the impossibility of condensing externally, according to the Condenser
you shewed me at Soho the necessity of adopting some other
method by internal Condensation—without which and the
effectual Aid I gave you on the occasion—you most probably
would have made no greater progress than in the five
preceding years—which must have been the case had you
gone on conformably to the Specification. You know it
has always been my advice to avoid if it was possible coming
to any trial—being well aware of the tender ground you
stood upon and I cannot account in any other way for your
not consulting me as formerly, or calling upon me or any of
my Agents or Engineers during the late Contests.

When I settled my Account with you at Soho it was
done entirely through Compulsion for fear of having my
work stopped and had you insisted upon a larger sum I
must at the time have submitted to it to prevent that evil,
which had been circulated, was to take place—and it was
my Intention when that settlement was made to open the
Account again, provided your Conduct towards me afterwards did not tend to close those wounds in our friendship
which had been opened. This has been very far from the
case—therefore I must be under the necessity of taking such
steps as I expect will do myself that justice which I think
I am entitled to—and which will at the same time put you
to the test of proving the validity of your claim upon me.

As I wish to do everything I undertake in an open and
not in an underhand manner—I now apprize you of what
my intentions are towards you and at the same time take
the liberty of annexing for your perusal the copy of an
advertisement I purpose putting into various newspapers in

different parts of the kingdom.—This I shall do immediately unless such steps are taken by you as will tend to a return of that friendship which formerly subsisted between you and
Your most ob^t hb^le Servt
John Wilkinson.

There was no need to treat too seriously the assertions made in this letter and the engineers had little difficulty in disposing of them. " You surely do not infer that either of us were ignorant of the method of condensing by injection " [wrote the partners on 28 January, 1797] " tho' we had reasons and very good ones too for doing it otherwise, that point has already been fully discussed in Courts of Law, and we are prepared to meet you should you continue to think we merit an attack of *that nature* from you." Wilkinson, however, thought better on reflection, and the threatened advertisements —offering to erect Watt steam-engines for all—were never inserted. For further disputes had arisen between him and his brother William in respect of the Minera Mines; and since the courts had assigned to Boulton and Watt the appointment and control of a temporary manager, their position was again too strong for Wilkinson to risk a fall with them. By April he was ready once more for peace, if not for friendship; and Matthew Boulton and James Watt, who had recently passed through so many storms, and who were both withdrawing from business life, were not disposed to continue the quarrel. " I agree with you " [wrote Watt, 11 April, 1797] " that the best disposal of old grievances is to let them sleep, and I know of no new ones." Henceforth, though never cordial, the relations of the Birmingham partners with the ironmaster were free from the strains and jolts of the past two years.

It may perhaps seem that undue attention has been paid to a somewhat sordid and melodramatic quarrel. Such disputes were common enough among the early industrialists; and if the economic record of the period consisted of nothing more, it would certainly possess as little value and significance as much of the old-fashioned writings on the political history of the eighteenth century. Some of the broader effects of the introduction of steam-power into the iron industry will be considered in the following chapter. But it has appeared worth while to give so much space to the personal affairs of those who first harnessed and directed that power. Even the quarrel between the engineers and the ironmaster was not without importance; for it hastened the evolution of the inventor and his partner from mere consultants to constructional engineers, and it led to the erection of the Smethwick Foundry, which, like Soho, was destined to become a nursery of men of invention and industry. From 1796 Boulton and Watt are to be counted among the ironmasters.

CHAPTER IV.

THE INVENTIONS OF HENRY CORT AND OTHER IMPROVEMENTS IN PRACTICE.

" That the wood of old England would fail did appear,
And tough iron was scarce, because charcoal was dear.
By puddling and stamping he prevented that evil,
So the Swedes and the Russians may go to the devil."
                    Song of John Wilkinson's workmen.

I.

IMPORTANT as had been the application of coke in the blast-furnace, its results were less momentous than those that were to follow the use of mineral fuel in the fining process, and that for two reasons. In the first place, as is pointed out elsewhere, Abraham Darby's process was for long applicable only to the production of castings and of forge pigs of low grade, so that for the making of bar iron of moderate and good quality it was still necessary to employ charcoal in the blast-furnace as well as at the forge.[1] In the second place, the fining process was far more prodigal of fuel than the smelting process: 16 cwts. of charcoal would be sufficient to produce a ton of pig iron; but to make a ton of bar iron about a ton and a half of pigs would be required, and 24 cwts. of charcoal would be consumed in the operation.[2]

In these circumstances ironmasters were persistent in their efforts to discover some means of applying mineral fuel to the later process, and a long list of patents attests the eagerness with which the secret was sought.[3] Most of these, however,

---

1. Even as late as 1787 the bar iron made from coke-pigs at Crawshay's Cyfarthfa works was said to be of very inferior quality. Smiles, *Industrial Biography*, 130.

2. Mushet, *Papers*, 407.

3. Specifications of Patents: No. 490 to William Fallowfield, Nos. 759 and 794 to John Wood, No. 780 to John Roebuck, No. 851 to Thomas Cranage, No. 988 to John Cockshutt, No. 1054 to John Wright and Richard Jesson, No. 1370 to Peter Onions, No. 1396 to Richard Jesson, Nos. 1351 and 1420 to Henry Cort.

must have been the expressions of aspiration rather than of achievement; and the specification of even so capable an investigator as Dr. Roebuck is so sparse and vague as to leave room to doubt whether any improvement whatsoever had been brought about.

It appears indeed likely that at a relatively early date some substitution of mineral fuel had taken place in the fining process. " In some Places upon the River Stower in Worcestershire " [said Lord Foley's agent before the Commons' Committee of 1737[1]] " they sometimes use Wood only to draw it into Coops and Anchonies, which takes up Four Cord only, and from thence they draw it into Bar with Stone Coal; but the greatest Part of Iron is drawn by Charcoal . . . .", Moreover, according to an ironmaster, in 1766 Upton forge consumed each week 8 tons of charcoal and 5 of pit-coal; Pitchford forge 4 of charcoal and 2 of pit-coal; and twelve forges in Shropshire and Cheshire, in producing 52 tons of bar iron, made use of 59 tons of charcoal and 37 of pit-coal.[2] In spite of the claims put forward by Roebuck that pit-coal was used throughout the process at Carron, it appears from the evidence of M. Jars that here also it was only after the iron had come from the finery and had received a first hammering that it was heated for a second time with a fire of coal.[3]

By the 'eighties, however, it is certain that a considerable proportion of the English output of malleable iron was produced solely by means of mineral fuel; and according to one estimate, in 1788, 15,600 tons of bars were already made with coke, and only 16,400 tons with charcoal. The stages in this transition during which over half the national output had come to consist of coke-made iron are difficult to trace; but it is certain that the result had been achieved by the introduction of a refinery furnace between the operations of the blast-furnace and those of the forge. " Some people in this country use no bellows in their Chaffery fire " [wrote James Watt[4] to a French correspondent in 1787], " but heat the

1. *J.H.C.*, xxiii, 854.
2. Whitworth, *Advantages of Inland Navigation*.
3. Jars, *Voyages*, 277.
4. Watt to Gaudin, Fils and Co., 6 Aug. 1787.

masses of Iron in a Reverberatory furnace, . . . which seems
to answer very well." The charcoal bar-iron made in 1788
was evidently produced at simple forges and, apparently, by
methods similar to those described in an earlier chapter. But
already there were 60 melting refineries in which coke was
used to convert grey into white iron, preparatory to the final
process of fining at the forge.[1]

In 1760 John Wood obtained a patent for converting iron
with raw pit-coal in a finery and air furnace into which it was
placed in moulds made of clay; and two years later a second
patent was taken out for another method in which the air
furnace was still employed. There is no evidence, however,
that these processes had any measure of success, and the first
substantial advance appears once more to have been made at
Coalbrookdale. In 1766 two brothers, Thomas and George
Cranage, the former of whom was in charge of the Company's
forge at Bridgnorth, and the latter a founder at the Dale
Works, devised their process of rendering iron malleable in
a reverberatory furnace. Though the wording of the patent
taken out in that year was purposely vague, it is known that
the hearth which held the pig iron was separated from the
grate which contained the pit-coal fire by a low bridge of
bricks, passing over which the flame was deflected so as to
play on the metal. In this way direct contact of iron and
fuel was avoided. From subsequent evidence it appears that
something very much like puddling was made use of during
the process.[2]

That a measure of immediate success was attained is
proved by the sales of iron " made in the new way " in 1767,[3]
and within the next twenty years the use of the reverberatory
furnace before fining at the forge was extensively adopted.
It appears that the iron produced by the Cranages was
not, however, suitable for all purposes, and this is perhaps
the explanation of the taking out of patents at a later date by
other ironmasters. From a letter of Richard Reynolds,[4]

1. Mushet, *op. cit.*, 44.
2. Spec. of Pat., 851. See the account given by Joseph Reynolds.
Percy, *Metallurgy*, 636.
3. Smiles, *Ind. Biog.*, 88 N.
4. Rathbone, *Memoir*, 280.

written in 1784, one gathers that the field which the Cranages had won from the charcoal industry was that which produced the raw material for the making of nails; and, as this branch of English industry was of great importance, the elimination from it of the use of charcoal must be considered a real advance, which later and more spectacular changes should not be allowed to obscure. " The nail trade " [he says] " would have been lost to this country had it not been found practicable to make nails with iron made with pit coal. We have now another process to attempt, and that is to make *bar iron* with pit coal; and it is for that purpose we have made, or rather are making, the alterations at Donnington Wood, Ketley, etc." This letter was written in July, two months after Henry Cort had taken out his second patent. In December Cort gave a demonstration of his methods at Ketley, and we have it on excellent authority that he then learnt that the puddling process had long been known and practised here, though probably only in the production of nail-iron.[1]

It was in 1783 and 1784, by two successive strokes, the result of many years of research, that Henry Cort broke down the final barrier which the " sulphurous and drossy " nature of pit-coal had presented to a wide extension of the new method.

The main facts of his life are well-known. Born at Lancaster in 1740, Cort was established as a Navy Agent in London at the age of twenty-five; and it was here that he began his experiments with the object of improving the quality of English wrought iron, so as to make it as sound for naval and ordnance purposes as that imported from the North of Europe. About 1775 he removed to Fontley, near Fareham, in Hampshire, where he erected a forge and slitting-mills. In 1779 he is found consulting Matthew Boulton as to the water supply of his mills, probably with a view to the erection of a steam-engine to pump back the water after it had passed over the weir.[2] A little later, on 14 December, 1782, Cort had an interview with Watt at Soho. " We had a visit to-day " [wrote the latter] " from a Mr. Cort of Gosport who says he

1. Percy, *loc. cit.*
2. Henry Cort to Matthew Boulton, 27 Nov. 1779.

has a forge there and has found out some grand secret in the making of Iron, by which he can make double the quantity at the same expense and in the same time as usual. He says he wants some kind of Engine but could not tell what, wants some of us to call on him, and says he has had some correspondence with you on the subject. He seems a simple good-natured man but not very knowing. He says he does most of the smith work for the King's yard and has a forge and rolling and slitting mill. I think him a brother projector—and have therefore put him off until some of us can view the ground, which he readily agreed to as he has water for most of the year. . . . . ."

Whether the steam-engine was ever used in the works at Fontley is uncertain : a letter of Cort's written in 1783 implies that he had been waiting until the rotative engine was perfected ;[1] and though steam was applied to the forge hammer in 1782, there is no record of any engine construction at Fontley.

In describing the processes of Henry Cort it is best to begin with those which formed the subject of his second patent.[2] Like the Cranages, Cort first heated a reverberatory furnace with raw pit-coal and either melted pig iron in this or carried the molten metal to it from the blast-furnace in ladles. Apertures in the door of the furnace enabled the workman to stir the iron from time to time. "After the metal has been for some time in a dissolved state, an ebullition, effervescence, or such like intestine motion takes place, during the con-

---

1. Sir,
    When I did myself the pleasure to call on You at Soho—We had some Conversation on the Subject of Iron—I intimated I had sollicited a Patent for my invention of Manufactg. Iron—on an improved method—wᶜʰ have obtained and You were kind enough to say You would mention me to Mr. Wilkinson. I have therefore taken the liberty of enclosing a Lʳᵉ to that Gent and I will be obledged to You to forward him—amongst other things I profess to make Ordʸ Iron—Tough—by a short and simple process.
    When you can say anything of the forge to be worked with Steam—I will thank you to communicate the same to me—excuse this trouble—I will do as much or more for You.

                        I am
                            Sir
                                Y most Hble St
Iron Mills   Henry Cort.
    Near Fareham, Hants,
    27 May '83.
2. No. 1420.

tinuance of which a blueish flame or vapour is emitted; and during the remainder of the process the operation is continued (as occasion may require) of raking, separating, stirring, and spreading the whole about in the furnace till it loses its fusibility, and is flourished or brought into nature. As soon as the iron is sufficiently in nature, it is to be collected together in lumps, called loops, of sizes suited to the intended uses." At this stage in fining it had previously been the practice to remove the iron and stamp it into plates; but Cort allowed his to remain in the furnace, brought it to a welding heat, and then shingled it into half-blooms under the forge hammer. The process of forming an anchony was thus avoided.

Next the main feature of the first patent came into operation.[1] Instead of being further heated and hammered the half-blooms were passed at a welding heat through rollers similar to those which had long been in use for rolling and slitting finished iron. The effect of the successive operations of puddling and rolling were well described by one of Cort's friends in a homely analogy[2] : " As the stirring of cream, instead of mixing and uniting the whole together, separates like particles to like, so it is with the Iron : what was at first melted comes out of the furnace in clotted lumps, about as soft as welding heat, with metallic parts and dross mixed together but not incorporated." These " great cinders of iron " were first brought under the forge hammer and afterwards passed through the rollers, " and by this simple process all the earthy particles are pressed out." The iron made by Cort's process was spoken of as peculiar in its grain, but it was pronounced to be superior in quality to Swedish oregrund iron.

The claim to innovation put forward by Cort and his successors was strenuously contested at a later date, and it is impossible for a layman to determine what part of the method was new, and what had been taken over from predecessors. That Cort was not—as has sometimes been supposed—the first to make use of coal in fining iron is clear from what has already been said; and indeed, no one who reads with care

1. No. 1351.
2. See *A Brief State of the Facts.*

the specification of his patents would imagine that he had any pretensions to have originated either the use of the reverberatory furnace or the application of mineral fuel : in both, it would appear, he had been forestalled by the Cranages. Moreover a few months before Cort took out his second patent, Peter Onions, an ironfounder of Merthyr Tydfil, had devised a process of puddling strikingly similar to that employed at Fontley. And, as early as 1728, a grant had been made to one, John Payne, of a patent for the use of iron rollers in the fining process. None of these facts, however, can invalidate Cort's title to rank among the inventors. The similarity of his process and that of Onions does not prove that either was indebted to the other : the coincidence is not unique in the history of discovery. John Payne apparently never put his process into practice, and the memory of his patent was only revived when interested ironmasters wished to repudiate their obligation to Henry Cort. Whatever success these may have had in showing that isolated operations in the methods of puddling and rolling had been practised before 1784, the fact remains that Cort was the first to combine and co-ordinate these fragmentary improvements into a single and new process. The effects of his labours were immediate. Whereas a tilt hammer had been able with difficulty to produce a ton of bars in twelve hours, no fewer than fifteen tons of metal could be passed through the rollers in the same time; and the iron, produced as it was throughout with pit coal, was of a quality which enabled it to be substituted for charcoal iron in all uses except that of making steel.

Of the later history of this " Samuel Crompton of the Iron Industry," it is unnecessary to treat except in barest outline.[1] Before taking out his patents Cort had entered into partnership with Samuel Jellicoe, and had set up works at Gosport. Adam Jellicoe, the father of his partner, not only induced the Navy Board to state publicly that no iron other than that made by the Cort process would be accepted by them, but, in addition, advanced, during a period of years, no less than

---

1. The story has been told with more than wonted thoroughness by Smiles and also by Percy.

£50,000 to the iron enterprise. During the inquiry made in 1789 it was brought to light that a large portion of this had come, not from Jellicoe's own estate, but from public funds which had passed to him as Deputy-Paymaster of Seamen's Wages. As security for these advances, the origin of which was probably unknown to him, Cort had handed over to Jellicoe his patent rights; and the discovery of the defalcations thus spelt ruin to Cort in only less measure than to Jellicoe. Even before these unhappy disclosures, however, the iron-masters had managed to adopt the main principles of the process without the payment of royalties; and even if Cort's rights had continued there is no guarantee that he would have been successful in combating a piracy conducted by so many and powerful industrial interests. As it was, the patent was confiscated and no attempt was made to collect the royalties. Henry Cort was obliged to leave the industry, and had hence-forth to subsist and maintain a large family on the meagre pension of £200 a year which, after many appeals, was granted him by the State from 1794 to the time of his death in 1800. In the latter year Lord Melville, Treasurer of the Navy, was granted a release of £25,000 to cover part of the deficiency due to Jellicoe's default. To what extent Melville himself was responsible is uncertain; but it is beyond doubt that a wise administration of the patent might have brought to the State at least some portion of the large profits that went into the pockets of the ironmasters who first adopted the puddling process.

The story of the appeal of Cort's widow for assistance from the Government is not edifying reading. In 1802 she was given an annual pension of £125 only; and when later Cort's eldest surviving son petitioned for a further grant, the Commons' Committee reported against it, overinfluenced, it is said, by the evidence of William Crawshay and Samuel Homfray. The fact that these men had brought about slight improve-ments in the process is no justification of their opposition, and, on the face of it, their conduct savours of something worse than ingratitude. In 1811, at a general meeting in Gloucester, the ironmasters agreed to raise a subscription for Cort's dependents, while the Yorkshire meeting instructed

Joseph Butler to apply to the iron trade at large for donations.[1] The response to these appeals was meagre in the extreme, and only £871 10s. was received in all.

II.

From the first days the puddled and rolled iron was used for anchors, and during 1787 and the following year some 300 tons were supplied to the Navy Board. But it was quickly applied also to other uses, and in South Wales, in particular, it found such immediate acceptance that for a time the puddling process was spoken of as the Welsh method. It may be as well at this point, therefore, to cast a glance at the expansion that was taking place in the industry in this region.

Although iron had long been produced on a small scale in the counties of Monmouth and Glamorgan, the modern industry of South Wales owes its birth to the initiative of a small group of Englishmen who migrated thither during the second half of the eighteenth century. Of these the earliest were John Guest of Broseley in Shropshire, and Anthony Bacon of Whitehaven and London. It was in 1767 that John Guest entered into partnership with Lewis, who had obtained a sub-lease of mining properties in the neighbourhood of Merthyr Tydfil ; and with this partnership the Dowlais Ironworks took the first step in its progress to a gigantic prosperity. In the year 1765 Bacon, who had previously engaged in the exportation of iron ore from Cumberland, took a lease of some 4,000 acres and set up a furnace and forge at Cyfarthfa. Additional furnaces were worked at Hirwain and Plymouth, and a considerable fortune was acquired by the ironmaster. But it was not until the 'eighties that the period of rapid development began. In 1782, Samuel, Jeremiah, and Thomas Homfray—like Guest, natives of Broseley—entered into relations with Bacon and began forge operations at Cyfarthfa. The agreement lasted, however, for two years only, at the end of which Bacon leased his properties and retired from the industry. The way was now open for the rise of new

1. *Minute Book of the Ironmasters*—Jackson Collection, Sheffield.

H

men : Richard Hill took over Plymouth furnace, the Homfrays obtained Penydarren, and Lewis and Tate controlled Dowlais. More important still was the ascent of Richard Crawshay. The son of a farmer of Normanton in Yorkshire, his early life had, apparently, included all the essential elements in the career of romantic tradition—he had run away from home, apprenticed himself, married his master's daughter, and obtained his initial capital by good fortune in a State lottery— and he now entered into partnership with James Cockshutt of Sheffield, in the ironworks at Cyfarthfa.

All these ironmasters were responsible for important advances in the industry. In addition to Penydarren, the Homfrays built furnaces at Ebbw Vale, Abernant, and Trede-gar ; and by 1803 Richard Crawshay owned no fewer than six furnaces, and employed over 2,000 men at Cyfarthfa alone, while his activities, or those of his successors, extended also to ironworks at Blenavon and Nantyglo.[1]

It was no accident that the great expansion of ironmaking in Wales occurred during the 'eighties, for it was closely associated with the new methods of production. It is known that in 1787 Cockshutt and Crawshay visited Cort at Fontley and took back with them not only plans of the puddling and rolling plant but also trained workmen. No doubt practical details had to be worked out, and modifications, such as Homfray's substitution of a metal plate for the sand floor which Cort had used in his furnace, added greatly to the efficiency of the process. " Rapid improvements are daily making by spirited and ingenious proprietors of iron works in the *quality* of that useful metal," wrote Richard Crawshay and William Gibbons in February, 1798, and they added that this was being brought about by a more thorough refining.[2] Such improvements enabled the less scrupulous among the ironmasters to claim for themselves some of the merit, as well as the profit, of the new process; and the want of moderation in the claims for public recognition made by Cort's successors

1. See Wilkins, *Iron, Steel and Tinplate Trades*, 35-66 ; Baring-Gould, *A Book of South Wales*, 113—121 ; Malkin, *Antiquities of South Wales*, cited Scrivenor, *op. cit.*, 122-3.
2. Printed in full in Dr. Macnab's *Letter on the Supply of Coal to the Metropolis*, 54.

probably retarded the formation of a just appreciation of the inventor's work.[1] The fact that Cort's patent was suspended and that after 1789 no royalties were payable on the process accelerated its introduction. In 1788 the make of bar iron in Great Britain was about 33,000 tons, but three years later that of puddled and rolled iron alone is said to have reached 50,000 tons—a growth largely concentrated in South Wales at this period.[2] In 1787 Crawshay was with difficulty producing 500 tons of bar iron; by 1812 his output was over 10,000 tons; and a parallel development was taking place at the works of the other ironmasters. The rapidity of the change is indeed registered on the face of the country-side; and the sudden disorganisation of a simple community produced a rank crop of social evils which has not yet been cut down.

Large-scale conduct of the new process required the use of considerable power, and though the description of the rolling-mill as " one of the elder-born offspring of Watt's steam-engine,"[3] is hardly accurate, it is clear that its potentialities could only be developed in association with the new and cheap form of power. As early as March, 1787, Folliot, Scott & Co., of Rotherhithe, were offering to demonstrate to friends the effectiveness of the combined inventions;[4] and in the early months of the following year James Cockshutt paid a visit to Soho, and placed an order for an engine to work the rollers at Cyfarthfa.[5]

The coincidence in time of the final victory of mineral fuel in ironmaking with the application of steam power to the furnace, forge, and mill had, indeed, remarkable results. Statistics of the output of bar iron are difficult to obtain, but the increased output of bars is reflected in the prosperity of the smelting branch of the industry indicated in the following table.

1. See R. Cort, *Observations*, in which Henry Cort is described as " the greatest benefactor of the human race."
2. It was not until 1790 that the process was adopted in Yorkshire, and almost the end of the century before it reached Northumberland and Durham. *V.C.H. York*, ii, 395; Bell, *op. cit.*, 761.
3. Hawkes Smith, *Birmingham and its Vicinity*, Pt. III, 10.
4. Letter of Folliot, Scott and Co., printed in *A Brief State of Facts*.
5. *Letter Book*, 1788-90, f. 8, B. and W. Coll.

NUMBER OF FURNACES AND OUTPUT OF PIG IRON IN GREAT BRITAIN.

District.		1788.[1]			1796.[2]			1806.[3]		
	Furnaces	Output	%	Furn.	Output	%	Furn.	Output	%
		tons			tons			tons	
South East	2	300	0.4	... 1	200	0.2	... —	—	—
South West	7	4,700	7.0	... 8	3,100	2.5	... 6	4,100	1.6
Midlands	33	31,800	46.8	... 37	46,200	36.9	... 84	104,400	41.8
Chester & N. Wales	2	1,000	1.5	... 4	3,300	2.6	... 4	2,100	0.8
S. Wales	13	10,800	15.7	... 25	34,400	27.4	... 47	75,600	30.2
York & Derby ...	15	9,600	14.2	... 25	20,100	16.0	... 45	37,000	14.8
North West	5	2,800	4.2	... 4	2,000	1.6	... 8	4,000	1.6
Scotland	8	7,000	10.2	... 17	16,100	12.8	... 27	23,200	9.2
Total ...	85	68,000	100.0	...121	125,400	100.0	...221	250,400	100.0

The results of the industrial revolution exhibited in these figures were manifold. In the first place the new powers of production freed the British workers from a dependence on Swedish and Russian iron that might have had serious consequences during the great war. Iron produced by puddling and rolling was considerably cheaper : in 1812 it was estimated by a partner of Richard Crawshay that whereas the price of oregrund iron had varied during the preceding ten years between £35 and £40 a ton, that of English puddled iron had been £20—£28 a ton.[4] Though the higher grades of Swedish iron were still imported for use of the steelmakers, many attempts—reflected in the records of patents—were made to improve the quality of the steel produced from English iron, and these were not without a measure of success. At the beginning of the nineteenth century Sweden was still responsible for about ten per cent. of the iron output of the world; but the check to exports occasioned by the war led to a fall in production of about one-third; and after 1815 English puddled iron was increasingly applied to purposes for which

1. Mushet, *Papers*.
2. Estimate drawn up at the time of the proposed excise on coal and pig iron.
3. Estimate drawn up for use in excise controversy. The figures for this year relate to the production of coke iron only. There were in addition 11 charcoal furnaces with a joint output of 7,800 tons.
4. Statement of William Routh. R. Cort, *Observations*, 35.

Swedish bar had previously been used.[1] In 1797 Britain became for the first time an exporter of bar iron on an appreciable scale; by 1812 the exports of British bar already exceeded the imports of foreign iron retained for home consumption; and by the later 'twenties they exceeded the gross imports fourfold.

A second result was to hasten the decline that had begun as early as 1750 in the production of charcoal iron. Already in 1788 there were 59 coke furnaces in blast, as against 26 charcoal furnaces, but by 1806 the coke furnaces numbered 162, and only 11 charcoal furnaces were to be found in the whole of Great Britain.

The application of coke to the series of processes and the widespread use of the steam-engine brought other momentous changes. Better pumping apparatus made possible the working of deeper seams of coal and ironstone; and the increased supply and lower cost of raw materials removed some of the causes that had hitherto kept the industrial units small and scattered. The adaptation of the steam-engine to the crushing of ores had also useful results.[2] And more important still, Watt's invention freed the ironmasters from their dependence on constant supplies of running water for their bellows, hammers, and mills. Before its introduction it was estimated that the average period of working was about forty weeks in a year, but a season of drought might curtail this considerably, and result in financial loss to the masters and distress to the workers.[3] Attempts at economy of water had been made by various devices : at Coalbrookdale the water which had passed over the wheel had been raised above it again by means of a Newcomen engine, and in Furness hand-

1. Drachmann, *Industrial Development of the Three Scandinavian Countries*, 35.

2. See letter of J. Watt, Junr., to Seaton, 27 Mar. 1795.

3. " I know that you Iron-miners, and your Masters, many times stand in need of, and want great sums of monies to pay for Wood, and Workmens Wages; and the Reason thereof is, That when the waters are plentiful, and in the winter-time, then you make great quantities of Iron, and lay it up in the store Houses, but cannot carry it out into the Country to sell, because of the unseasonableness of the time, and badness of the wayes; and thereby you contract many debts, and your Credits sink, and your Trade lessens . . . " Yarranton, *England's Improvement*, ii, 167.

pumps had been used for the same purpose.[1] But such measures were obviously of limited efficiency : in a hot summer many of the works were brought to a complete stop. Again and again James Watt himself had suffered from delays in the delivery of materials owing to this cause,[2] and the relief which the new form of power brought with it was felt in every industry in which heavy machinery was employed. Henceforward ironworks were no longer bound to localities where a head of water could be obtained; now that the whole process could be carried on with cheap mineral fuel there was no longer any reason for that separation of furnace, forge, and mill that had characterised the iron industry in the early years of the century. The typical concern of the new era was integrated in its structure : it mined the ore and coal, smelted, refined, rolled, and slit the iron into its finished form of plates and rods. From this time onward, therefore, very large capitals began to be sunk in the industry; and, in 1812, to give an example of one locality, there were in the neighbourhood of Birmingham no fewer than ten ironworks, each of which had cost over £50,000 to establish. It was by no means uncommon to find 300 or 500 men employed in a single works, apart from the colliers and others connected with the supply of raw material.

Hence also the geographical dispersion described in Chapter I gave place to industrial concentration. Drawn by a powerful magnet, the iron industry became localised on the coalfields of the Midlands, Yorkshire and Derbyshire, and South Wales. According to the defective estimate of 1720, about 59 per cent. of the national output already belonged to these districts; but in 1788 the proportion had grown to 77 per cent., in 1796 to 80 per cent., in 1806 to 87 per cent., and in 1820 to 90 per cent. During the ten years following 1796 the furnaces of Shropshire increased from 23 to 42 in number, and this at a time when the local industry was sending both labour and enterprise to other parts of the country. In Staffordshire

---

1. *V.C.H. Shropshire*, 462 ; and Fell, *op. cit.*, 235.
2. See, *e.g.*, Watt to Boulton, 8 June 1786. " I know not where to get plates. Parsons forge will have no water at present and we may be long enough before we can get them from him." See also Watt to Spedding, Hicks, Senhouse & Co., 15 July 1786.

the increase was even more marked—from 14 to 42 furnaces—
and a similar development was taking place in Yorkshire,
Derbyshire, and Glamorgan. So rapid indeed was the growth
of ironmaking towards the end of the eighteenth century, and
the early days of the nineteenth, that the collieries could
hardly keep pace with the increased demand for fuel. In 1793
it was said that the Carron and Clyde works alone consumed
as much coal as the whole of the inhabitants of Edinburgh;
and in 1800 William Reynolds and John Wilkinson complained that the number of men engaged in coal-mining was
insufficient to keep the industry fully supplied.[1]

For the first time for many generations there was no feeling
of shortage of supplies of raw materials in the iron-manufac-
turing trades. " I can remember our giving £20 a ton for
iron " [said a nail manufacturer[2] in 1812]; " we now can buy
it at £12 per ton . . . ; in consequence of those immense
erections in Staffordshire of steam engines for the manufacture
of iron, and the reduced price of the articles of nails . . . we
are not afraid of being undersold, or of a competition from
any market whatever."

It might have been expected that the cheapening of
malleable iron thus effected would have reversed the tendency,
in operation since the first days of coke-smelting, for castings
to take the place of wrought iron in articles of common use.
But though it is true that the malleable iron trades underwent
a remarkable expansion, for at least half a century the founder
continued to hold his own and more. The introduction of the
steam-engine itself led to a great demand for foundry products;
and this was especially marked after 1800 when Watt's patent
expired and it became possible for other firms to manufacture
the engines for sale. Further, after Rennie's successful use
of cast-iron wheels and other parts of machinery at the Albion
Mills, the metal was extensively substituted for wood and
other materials. " Moulders are still a desideratum with us "
[wrote James Watt[3] in 1796] " and there appears to be a
general want of them throughout the country, owing to the

1. Macnab, *Letter on the Supply of Coal to the Metropolis*, (1801), 27, 36.
2. *Minutes of Evidence against Orders in Council*, Whitehouse, 24.
3. Watt to Barnes, 17 May 1796.

vast increases of the consumption of Cast Iron articles.'' In almost every district new works were coming into being and many of them specialised in this branch of the industry. The Low Moor Company, established near Bradford in 1789, was one outstanding example,[1] and another was Messrs. Newton, Chambers, of the Thorncliffe Ironworks, set up in 1792, near Chapeltown. The application of steam power to the textile trades not only provided orders for iron-smelting and casting firms of this type,[2] but it also brought specialised foundries into existence in the main cotton and woollen centres. Small establishments had for long existed in Liverpool and other large towns, but these had worked for a narrower market than the new type of foundry, which undertook also many of the functions of the modern engineering firm. Thus Bateman and Sherratt of Salford not only made steam-engines—they were among the most persistent of the pirates with whom Watt battled—but also cast-iron machinery for the cotton mills; and no fewer than five other foundries existed in Manchester at the time. Since about 1785 the firm of Hannah Lees and Sons of Park Bridge, near Ashton-under-Lyne, have combined the production of finished iron with the manufacture of iron rollers and other parts of textile machinery. About 1790 Dobson and Barlow, of Bolton, and Samuel Lees, of Oldham, were engaged in the same kind of work; and of the corresponding development that was taking place in the woollen and hosiery centres, Prince Smith & Son, of Keighley, Fenton, Murray, Wood & Co., of Leeds, and the Ashwell Foundry in Nottingham, may serve as examples.[3]

This growth of machine-making necessitated a higher quality of work than had hitherto been attained, and it was to meet this that William Wilkinson devised the cupola—an obvious extension of the principle of the blast-furnace to the re-melting of pig iron. The reverberatory or air-furnace produced a hard but somewhat brittle casting; but the cupola,

---

1. It was not until 1803 that the puddling process was adopted here; evidently ironfounding provided a sufficient outlet for the abounding energies of the partners until this time.

2. Newton Chambers supplied castings for cotton mills in large quantities to Wells, Heathfield and Co., and other customers. *Thorncliffe MSS.*

3. *V.C.H. Lancs.*, ii, 367-9; *Yorks.*, 403-4; *Notts.*, 366.

heated by engine blast, afforded a more fluid metal, which, when cast, was less liable to break, and was peculiarly suited to the production of machine parts as well as hollow-ware.

Similarly, at the Smethwick Foundry, at Brymbo,[1] at Thorncliffe, and elsewhere, the demands for munitions, and—after 1812—for water pipes and gas apparatus led to many minor improvements in foundry practice; and the accumulated effect of these was almost as great as that which had resulted from the more spectacular development at the forge and rolling-mill. Not indeed until nearly the middle of the nineteenth century were the processes of stamping, pressing, and cutting so far practised, and the machine-tool so perfected as to enable malleable iron to replace castings to any appreciable extent.[2]

1. In 1795 John Wilkinson devised a new mill for boring cannon and similar castings.
2. See Rushden, *Old Time Invention.*

CHAPTER V.

OVERSEAS COMPETITION AND COMMERCIAL POLICY BEFORE 1776.

" Produces, not Manufactures, are the Business of a Colony.'
—*The Interest of Great Britain*, 2.

AT the beginning of the eighteenth century no observer could
fail to be struck by the contrast between the lusty vitality of
the cutlery, nail, and other iron-working trades and the
arrested development of the iron industry in the narrow sense
of the term. This contrast was entirely due to the fact that,
whereas mineral fuel could not yet be used for furnace and
forge purposes, it had long been successfully applied in the
smithy : on the coalfields lying within a radius of ten miles
of Birmingham, no fewer than 45,000 metal workers, it was
said, drew subsistence from the manufacture of iron wares.[1]
It is clear, however, that the shrivelled seed of English iron
could not of itself have yielded a harvest so rich and varied ;
and over two-thirds of the bar iron used in the British metal
industries was brought in from abroad, principally from
Sweden.

English iron was thus sold in the home market in rivalry
with a foreign product. The competition was felt the more
keenly in that the demand for iron was—if we may express
the opinion of an eighteenth-century merchant[2] in the
terminology of modern economics—highly inelastic : it was
such that a relatively small increase in the quantity put upon
the market produced a more than proportional fall in price.
Small wonder, therefore, that the harassed English ironmaster
was highly protectionist, and that the storm centre of

---

1. Estimate of Abraham Spooner. *J.H.C.*, xxii, 854.
2. *J.H.C.* Evidence of Abraham Spooner : " A Little Mullars and Tuley
Iron brought from Russia recently so reduced the Price that many Forges
ceased to work : This is a strong Proof, how small a Quantity of Iron
more than is wanted, will affect the Price of it."

industrial politics should have been the terms on which overseas supplies of iron were to be admitted to this country. Speaking generally, the interests of the ironmasters had not been overlooked by the State : in the later years of the seventeenth century large concessions had been obtained by the industry at the expense of the consumers of iron and the community in general. The prohibition on the exportation of iron imposed as early as the fourteenth century (28 Ed. III, *c.* 5),—with the object, presumably, of reducing the price in the home market—was given up in 1694 (5 W. and M., *c.* 17); and the English ironmaster was henceforth free to sell where he could obtain the maximum gain. Four years earlier the duties on the importation of foreign iron—imposed since 1679—had been raised substantially (2 W. and M., *c.* 4); and in 1692 the special privilege accorded to iron and iron wares imported from Ireland was abolished (4 and 5 W. and M., *c* 5), though the shortage of iron occasioned by the demands of war led to renewal of the preference in 1695 (7 and 8 W. and M., *c.* 17). At the period with which we are now concerned the duties on all kinds of bar iron imported in British ships from foreign countries amounted to £2 1s. 6d. per ton, and from Ireland to 19s. 11d. per ton.

Since only the smaller portion of the iron used in Britain came from home sources, the consumer of pig and bar iron found himself heavily taxed by this protective legislation; and from the beginning of the century suggestions were put forward for the opening up of a new source of supply in the British Colonies of the New World. The advantage of these areas for iron production had been recognised from an early date; and, indeed, the possibility of utilising the apparently limitless forests of America to relieve the strain on the woods of the Mother Country had been one of the prime motives in the colonisation of Virginia. The early experience with ironworks in this plantation had not, it is true, been encouraging, but the failure had been due not to lack of skill or of natural advantages, but to the ravages of the Indians and other misfortunes.[1] It did not therefore appear unreasonable to hope that, as further settlement took place, the rich

1. Bruce, *Virginia in the Seventeenth Century*, ii, 445-449.

supplies of ore known to exist at points within easy reach of the Atlantic coast might be smelted and forged for the use of the craftsmen in England; and that the metal industries might thus be drawn from the fatal slope down which, it was asserted, they were slipping in accelerated progress.

The proposal for the encouragement of iron production in America, and the subordinate question as to the appropriate form of stimulus to be applied, formed one of the chief topics of industrial politics during the first half of the century. In Parliament and Press the matter was debated with wearisome iteration for over forty years; and it was not until 1750 that a decision was finally taken. Any politico-economic movement of this nature—the Free Trade movement of the nineteenth century at once springs to the mind—may be described from at least three points of view: it may be regarded as a fight between opposed economic classes culminating in the victory of one set of vested interests over another; it may be treated as a struggle of doctrine in which one theory of national well-being triumphs over a rival theory; or it may be looked at from the point of view of State politics, in which case the determining cause of action is found in the exigencies of the political or diplomatic cockpit, rather than in the arguments of the theorists or the blind forces of class-war. Earlier writers have occupied themselves mainly with the first and second of these aspects; it is therefore proposed to deal lightly with these, and to lay stress on the political forces which, whether they were or were not the ultimate determinants, at least decided the time, and therefore, to some extent, the effects, of the measures taken.

Whatever differences there might be on other issues, on one point all Englishmen were agreed—that the American market was a British preserve in which the paths that might be trodden by the settlers, no less than by the foreigner, were to be strictly circumscribed. By the Statute of 1663 all importations to the Plantations must pass through the Mother Country, and it was customary, on the exportation from England to America of goods of foreign origin, to allow a drawback equal to the duties paid on importation into this country. In justification of these drawbacks the mercantilist urged that without them the price of such wares in America would be raised inordinately, and the consequent fall in the amount demanded would cause loss to the British carrying trade. But such drawbacks were keenly resented by the English manufacturers, who felt the competition of the foreign goods in the overseas market. Hence early in 1704, the iron manufacturers of London complained that the wares of their chief rivals, the Dutch, were passing to the colonies by way of this country : the high import duties on bar iron from Ireland and Sweden, it was explained, raised the costs of production for the English smith, while the drawback on the exportation of wrought-iron wares encouraged merchants to bring in nails and other manufactured goods from Holland for re-exportation to America.[1] The complaint obtained a sympathetic hearing in Parliament, and the drawback on the export of wrought or manufactured iron and iron wares was abolished (2 Ann, *c.* 9). Again in 1709 attention was directed to the competition of the colonists themselves : the drawback on *unwrought* iron and steel re-exported from England stimulated, it was said, the growth of manufactures in America. Since the duties levied by the colonists themselves were small, the American manufacturer obtained his raw material at a lower price than that paid by the English manufacturer; hence mercantilist equity demanded the removal of this offending drawback also.[2] Again Parliament acquiesced, and (by 9 Ann, *c.* 6) yet another gain was vouchsafed to the British manufacturer at the expense of the British shipper and the American manufacturer. Henceforth the latter, obliged as he was to buy only through England, had to pay for the Spanish bar iron he imported a price raised by the full amount of the British duties.

These measures registered the growing power of the English iron manufacturers; but they were also in accord with the prevailing sentiment as to the place of the colonies in the imperial economy. It was theirs to supply the more mature industries of the Mother Country with crude materials, and to afford also a market for the finished goods of English indus-

1. *J.H.C.*, xiv, 362.
2. *J.H.C.*, xvi, 179 and 502.

trialists. In this view ironmasters no less than manufacturers concurred; for to both it appeared that industrial development in America would mean the loss of markets. It was not sufficient to trust to "natural forces," or even to the operations of a carefully devised tariff system to prevent such development. Legislation must be called in to make manufacture impossible; and it was an ironmaster—Joshua Gee—who in 1729 devised the Procrustean bed on which, a generation later, British legislators attempted to mutilate the infant iron industries of the New World.[1] The question at issue was simply whether pig and bar iron were to be regarded as "produces" to be encouraged or, like nails, tools, and agricultural implements, as manufactures to be suppressed. The answer to this question was given neither on grounds of abstract principle nor on those of purely economic expediency. The producers and manufacturers might have pelted each other with pamphlets and letters in the press—as indeed they did for half-a-century—without disturbing the peace of the politicians : it was only when force was exerted from outside that a decision was reached in Parliament; and the springs of action are to be found in the diplomatic relations of England with the North of Europe, rather than in the theorisings of mercantilists, or in the pressure of interested classes.

When the century opened, political relations between Britain and Sweden were relatively cordial; in 1700 a treaty of mutual defence had been concluded, and William III had joined with the Dutch in sending a fleet to the Baltic, and in forcing Denmark to sign the Treaty of Travendal. This attitude towards Sweden was dictated partly by political considerations, but partly also by others of an economic nature. In addition to iron, Englishmen brought from Sweden all those commodities described as naval stores—including timber,

1. Gee proposed that the colonists "shall for time to come never erect the manufacturing of any [nails] under the size of a Two-Shilling Nail, Horse-shoe Nails excepted. That all Slitting-mills, and Engines for Drawing Wire or weaving Stockings be put down ; and that every Smith who keeps a common Forge or Shop shall register his Name and Place of Abode, and the Name of every Servant which he shall employ ; which Licence shall be renewed once every Year, and pay for the Liberty of working at such Trade." *Trade and Navigation of Great Britain*, 81.

hemp, flax, tar, pitch, and turpentine—essential to the existence of a maritime community. But the value of the manufactured wares of wool and iron, together with the West Indian produce sent by Britishers to Sweden, fell far short of that of the imports received; so that an adverse balance of trade existed against this country; and, according to the doctrine of the time, bullion must flow out to Sweden.[1]

Possibly one cause of the " unfavourable " state of trade is to be found in the high import duties imposed on English goods in the interests of the Swedish manufacturers. In a report of the newly appointed Commissioners of Trade, in 1697, complaint is made that the King of Sweden " did about the year 1680 lay a duty of above 50 per cent upon our woollen goods imported there, and encouraged woollen manufactures in his own dominions carried on by the help of wool from England (as we are informed) but exported thither by way of Scotland, and encouraged the expense of such by the example of the court."[2] In addition to the usual mercantilist devices of customs and navigation laws, heavy disabilities were placed upon English merchants living in Sweden, and the period of their residence in the Kingdom was sometimes strictly limited. Moreover, export duties were imposed by the Swedes, and that on iron, which had recently been raised 25 per cent., now stood at £3 12s. 6d. per ton.[3] As the demand for Swedish iron in England was intense, the incidence of this duty, like that of the British import duty, probably fell more heavily upon the English consumer than upon the Swedish producer of bar iron.

While, therefore, considerations of national security appeared to dictate a policy of friendship with Sweden, any

1. For the year ended Michaelmas 1697 the imports of goods of all kinds from Sweden were valued at £150,313, while the exports to Sweden totalled only £40,767. The value of iron imported into London alone was £68,000 out of total imports into London worth £105,672. C. P. Dixon,, " Notes on the Records of the Customs House, London," *Eng. Hist. Review*, xxxiv, 78-79.

For the imports and exports of later years see Sir Charles Whitworth's *State of the Trade of Great Britain* (1777), xxxvi, and Table, p. 35. Estimates of the proportion which these imports bore to the value of iron produced at home are impossible ; for the value of the latter is a matter of conjecture, and some of the Swedish iron was re-exported, in particular to Africa.

2. Quoted by J. F. Chance, "England and Sweden in the Time of William III and Anne," *English Hist. Rev.*, xvi, 679.

3. Macpherson, iii, 72.

plan for reducing the unfavourable trade balance was eagerly discussed by economic writers and the advisers of the Government. The Commissioners of 1697, for example, urged the stimulation of the production of naval stores in America; and six years later the refusal of the Tar Company of Stockholm to sell its products to any foreign merchant—except under conditions felt to be onerous in the extreme—led to the adoption of their recommendation in the well-known Act of 1703.[1] A subordinate, but probably important, consideration in the minds of those responsible for the measure was that it might serve to deflect American energies into channels in which they could not compete with English industries.[2]

The undue dependence on Sweden for supplies of iron meant that with the outbreak of war, or even the rising of a diplomatic storm in the Baltic, chilling winds might blow to Britain, freezing up the normal channels of employment in Sheffield and the iron-working centres of the Midlands. Nevertheless iron was not included among the " naval stores " enumerated in the Act of 1703, and the omission was the subject of protests from the manufacturers and others, especially at periods of strained relations with the Northern Powers.

With the accession of George I a change of orientation occurred in foreign relations. At this time Charles XII was engaged in the great struggle with the coalition which aimed at driving him from the territories held by Sweden along the southern and eastern shores of the Baltic. As Elector of Hanover, George was a member of the Anti-Swedish League, by entering which he hoped to add the provinces of Bremen and Verden to his electorate. To this end an agreement was made with Denmark in November, 1714, and with Prussia in April, 1715, and thus Britain became indirectly concerned with the war in the North.

It appears very improbable that George I could have persuaded Parliament to take action simply in order to further his own dynastic ambitions in Europe; but when it became

1. 3 and 4 Ann, c. 10.
2. Ashley, *Surveys*, 321.

possible to show that economic interests were threatened, the case for some measure of intervention was greatly strengthened.　After his expulsion from the ports of the East, Charles XII had forbidden all trade with them; and this prohibition—followed as it was by the Ordinance of Privateers, and the seizure by the Swedes of British and Dutch vessels—resulted in the sending by Britain and the United Provinces of a joint fleet to the Baltic, with the ostensible object of protecting trade.　Such a fleet, however, might easily combine the function of guarding commerce with the fulfilment of the obligation implied in the agreement by which Bremen and Verden had been assigned to George I.; and in 1715 it was, in fact, engaged in preventing aid from reaching Charles XII who was at that time besieged by the coalition in Stralsund. In 1716 Admiral Norris was again sent to the Baltic.　To this menace Charles XII retorted by giving countenance to the scheme of Baron Görtz for an alliance with the English Jacobites and a Swedish landing in Scotland in aid of a new rebellion against the dynasty.

While still in an early stage the plot was betrayed to British ministers: in January, 1717, Count Gyllenborg, the Swedish envoy to Britain, was arrested; an Act was speedily passed giving powers to prohibit all trade between Sweden and this country,[1] and a proclamation to this effect was issued on March 13th.

The cessation of importation at once reacted upon the iron manufacturers, for the supplies of foreign iron were reduced to between one-half and one-third those of a normal year.[2]　In 1717 stocks of imported bars were quickly exhausted, and the consequent rise in prices brought an unexpected harvest of

---

1.　*J.H.C.*, xviii, 473-477.

2.　The imports for a number of years are shown in the following table abridged from Scrivenor, App., Table I, 25-7.

	Sweden. Tons.	Holland. Tons.	E. Country. Tons.	All other countries. Tons.	Total Tons.
1714 ...	19,754	62	286	1,797	21,899
1715 ...	14,545	523	156	2,428	17,652
1716 ...	11,889	245	73	2,621	14,828
1717 ...	1,428	1,927	43	4,140	7,540
1718 ...	75	7,931	4,334	4,896	17,236

I

profit to the English ironmaster. "The King of Sweden seizes all our ships he meets with in the Baltic Seas," wrote William Stout[1] of Lancaster, " and all commerce with Sweden being interrupted, has caused this iron to advance here from 16£ to 24£ a ton." In 1718, it is true, some Swedish iron was imported via Holland and the " East Country "—the region between the Oder and the Gulf of Finland—but this method of evading the prohibition was expensive, for the Dutch charged a premium of no less than £4 a ton for their services.[2]

The gains of the English ironmasters were reflected in the losses of the importing merchants, no less than in those of the domestic manufacturers; and early in 1718 some four hundred London merchants petitioned for the reopening of commercial intercourse.[3] This petition was probably not a spontaneous production : it was, apparently, formulated by Jacobites—including Lord Oxford—by whom the merchants were dexterously used as an instrument for embarrassing the Government. But the distress was real enough and Jacobite instigation is not in itself sufficient explanation of the petitions which poured into Parliament from all sides. Merchants and ironmongers, anchor-smiths, nail-makers, and cutlers were all affected, and even the woollen workers of Leeds protested at the loss of the export trade to Sweden. Shippers complained that the expectation that the Dutch would follow the same policy as the British had not been realised, and that England was losing, and Holland gaining, a valuable branch of international trade. This claim is borne out by the " Memoir " on the state of trade sent by the " King's friends " to the Pretender in May, 1718: "The English had formerly a beneficial trade with Sweden, or at least they sent enough of their manufactures, corn, leather, salt, etc., to answer the commodities of the growth and produce of Sweden, which they brought from thence, and which they cannot possibly be without, such as iron, etc. Now they have prohibited commerce with Sweden and take Swedish commodities from the

---

1. Fell, *Iron Industries of Furness*, 207.
2. Chance, *George I and the Northern War*, 253.
3. *J.H.C.*, xviii, 691-753.

Dutch and from Hamburg, with this remarkable difference that the prime cost is above a third more, and must be answered with silver or gold."[1]

It was in these circumstances that the demand for encouragement to colonial iron was first brought to the notice of Parliament, from so many quarters that it could no longer be ignored. That the colonists themselves were not oblivious to the opportunity offered by the crisis is evidenced by the scheme brought forward in July, 1718, by the Council of the Assembly of Massachusetts Bay for a bounty on the production not only of bar and rod iron but also of scythes, nails, and hollow-ware ; while in New York proposals were made for the issue of paper money, out of the profits of which loans at 5 per cent. might be made to ironmasters, repayment to be accepted in the form of the iron produced.[2] In England, however, no action was taken this year; but in the following session, when a Bill was introduced to encourage the production of naval stores in the Plantations, it was at first proposed to include pig and bar iron in the measure.

Immediately factions arose within and without the House : most of the forge-masters were willing enough to make use of colonial pig, but objected strongly to the encouragement of colonial forges; and it was only by a majority of one that the original wording was retained in the Bill as it left the Commons.[3] In the Lords, the protectionist forge-owners were more successful : the colonists were to be prohibited from converting pig into bar iron, and were thus to be limited to the production of crude material. The making of rod iron and of all cast or hammered wares, whether of native or imported iron, was, by common agreement, to be declared illegal—a proposal which, as the colonists urged, meant that not so much as a single bolt or nail might be made in the Plantations.

The Bill, however, never became an Act. The failure was due not to the opposition aroused among the furnace-owners; certainly not to any realisation of the futility of attempting to secure British trade by thwarting the aspirations of English-

---

1. *Hist. MSS. Com. Calendar of Stuart Papers*, Vol. 6, 84—107, 444.
2. *J.H.C.*, xxiii, 115.
3. *Ibid.*, xix, 82, 113.

men overseas; but simply to the passing of the international crisis which had called the proposal into being. Before the end of 1719 the political landscape had, in fact, suffered an entire change : the death of Charles XII in the trenches at Frederikshald, followed as it was by a revolution in Sweden, quickly put an end to hostilities on the part of Britain, and meant, incidentally, that Swedish iron could again pass to England directly, instead of through the tortuous channels followed in 1718.

Under Ulrica Eleanora and her husband, Frederick I, Sweden was ruled by the opponents of Görtz and Gyllenborg, and British mediation was employed to bring about treaties of peace, in 1720, with Hanover, Prussia, Poland, and Denmark. There remained only the arch-enemy Peter the Great, and against him Sweden had not only the moral, but also the material support of Britain. Between 1718 and 1720 Englishmen had, indeed, been engaged in the process of "changing their enemies." As early as 1716 the presence of Russian troops in Mecklenburg had appeared to threaten the security of Hanover; George I and Peter had a personal dislike of one another; and it was known that Görtz and Gyllenborg had entered into relations with Russia at the Aland Conference in 1718. Finally, British opinion was hostile to the possible growth of Russian naval power in the Baltic, and until the Treaty of Nystad (1721) the British fleet was used to prevent Russia from domination in the northern seas.

Here again economic antagonism reinforced political animosity. At this time Peter was busy with his schemes for the industrial development of Russia; in 1719 Colonel Henning, the director of mines at Olonetz, had visited several countries to study metallurgical methods, and in the same year a college of mines was set up in Russia.[1] These developments did not pass unnoticed in England, and attempts made by Russians to obtain knowledge of British trade processes and to transport ironworkers and cutlers abroad, led to

1. Scrivenor, *op. cit.*, 161-2.

vigorous protests.[1] In this matter Parliament was quick to respond, and the Act to prevent the seducing of artisans in British industry was passed.[2] Though in its original form the Bill related only to the manufacture of iron and steel, the spirit of national exclusiveness on the part of other trades also led to its conversion into a measure of general application.

Nevertheless Russia had awakened from her sleep, and the attempt by such methods to prevent her arising was as futile as that which aimed at imprisoning the procreant energies of American industry within the narrow walls of the Colonial System. With or without the aid of British workmen, forges were set up in Russia—stimulated, no doubt, by the demand for munitions of war—and in Siberia, in particular, where the Demedoffs held ironworks under a grant from the Crown, extensive developments were beginning. Before long the animosity towards Russia died down, and England began to import bar iron in quantities no longer negligible. In 1714 only 13 tons of bar had been brought from Russia, and in 1718—an exceptionally favourable year owing to the absence of imports from Sweden—only 334 tons. But in 1728 the imports had increased to 1,085, by 1732 to 4,456 tons, and for certain grades Russia had become a serious alternative source of supply to Sweden. [3]

This development of trade with their old enemies perhaps served to intensify the mercantilism of the Swedes—represented in the Schedule of Products or Navigation Act of 1724—though during the eighteen years in which Arvid Horn and the " Caps " held power political relations with England remained friendly. In December, 1734, a commercial treaty was concluded between England and Russia, whereby, *inter alia*, the British Government promised a welcome to Russians

1. *J.H.C.*, xix, 78 and 83. The Birmingham petition asserted " That there hath been several foreigners . . . Muscovites, lately put Apprentice in this Place, to learn the Art of making several of our Iron Manufactures, for which they have given large and unusual Sums of Money . . . and do intend . . . to return to his Czarish Majesty's Dominions, to instruct others."

2. 5 Geo. I, c. 27. Vide *infra*.

3. By the middle of the century the industry was, according to the standards of the day, an example of large-scale production. " It is not forty years since the Russians began to open iron mines, and yet in the year 1750 they exported 20,000 tons; the ordinary annual export may now be called 12 or 15,000 tons." Hanway, *Travels*, 57, 97.

who should come to study trade processes in this country. Whether as a retort to this, or simply as a step in a continuous policy of high protection, in the same month the King of Sweden issued an edict increasing the tariff on imports in such measure as entirely to prohibit many classes of English goods. The question of imports of iron into England was, in the minds of politicians, closely bound up with that of the exportation of manufactured goods; and a Parliament that would look with complacency on the bringing in of foreign iron in exchange for English woollen wares, at once became critical when this means of payment was refused. Moreover, the Swedes, contrary to treaty—so it was alleged before the Committee of 1738—imposed a differential duty on iron exported by Britishers, and doubled the duties on iron carried in British ships, so that some Englishmen were forced " to abjure their native Country " if they were to trade at all.[1]

Such measures brought new strength to the movement in favour of colonial iron; and by this time advocates of the policy were able to point to the steady development of the production of pigs and bars not only in Virginia and the Carolinas but also in the northern Plantations. In 1732 the Commissioners of Trade had reported the existence in Massachusetts Bay of several forges and furnaces; and in New England the Surveyor of Woods found six furnaces and nineteen forges at work. Two years later the Commissioners expressed the opinion—surely born of the wish—that the remission of the existing duty on pig iron imported into England would of itself be sufficient to induce the colonists to meet in full the requirements of the Mother Country for iron. Further, the trial of samples brought over by the Crowley undertaking in 1735 had shown the colonial bar iron to be of high grade, and, with the exception of that from Maryland and Philadelphia, it was certified by the officers of the royal dockyards to be equal in quality to the best imported from Sweden.[2]

When, therefore, early in 1737 a body of merchants and

1. *J.H.C.*, xxii, 862, 828; xxiii, 114.
2. Macpherson, iii, 851; *J.H.C.*, xxii, 851; reports printed in Scrivenor, App. B.

ironmongers petitioned for the free importation of pig and
bar iron from America, political considerations again obtained
for them sympathetic hearing, and a Committee of the House
was appointed to consider the matter. Petitions and counter
petitions were sent in from all parts of the country, and
evidence was given by merchants, shippers, ironmasters,
manufacturers, and other interested parties. The arguments
arrayed on both sides were those that had seen long service
since the question of colonial iron had first been raised, and
the conflict of opinion was such that no conclusion was
reached. In 1738, however, the depressed state of trade led
to a fresh crop of petitions and the appointment of another
committee to consider the whole question of colonial production and manufacture of iron.

That the cleavage of opinions would run along the lines
of economic differentiation is obvious enough : on the one
side were ranged the employers and domestic workers in the
secondary iron trades—nailworkers, smiths, cutlers, and so
on—eager for fresh and cheaper supplies of raw material; on
the other, the ironmasters in both furnace and forge branches
of the industry, anxious to shield their product from the rude
breath of American competition. The former group was
supported by the merchants of London and the outports
engaged in the American trade. The latter was aided by the
tanners and leather-workers—who feared for their supplies of
oak-bark if the ironworks should cease to maintain the
coppices[1]—and still more powerfully by the landlords and
owners of woodlands themselves. Finally, in the political
sphere the cleavage was darkly mirrored in the opposition
between Whigs and Tories, the one party with its leanings
towards trade and the " moneyed " men, the other with its
tenderness for the susceptibilities of the landed interest.[2]

In April, 1738, the Committee finally reported, and the
Commons agreed to resolutions in favour of restraining the
output of existing forges and bloomeries in America, while
slitting-mills and steel-furnaces were to be entirely prohibited.
A Bill subsequently introduced to encourage the production

1. *J.H.C.*, xxiii, 114.
2. Cunningham, *Growth*, 526, footnote.

and manufacture of bar iron in England, and to prevent their increase in the Plantations, failed, however, to get beyond the first reading; and the whole question, so far as Parliament was concerned, was allowed to sleep for yet another decade. The close of the Parliamentary battle found the champions of colonial iron, who had been the first to take the offensive, in a strictly defensive attitude; and it was only with difficulty that they managed to preserve the *status quo* with respect to importations from America.

After 1738 the relations between Britain and Sweden became steadily worse. In that year Arvid Horn was finally overcome by the Francophile Hats under Gyllenborg, and henceforth Sweden became a pensionary of the French. In 1741 the British representative was withdrawn from Stockholm, and after 1748, when this occurred a second time, the clouds of war in the North-East again appeared ready to burst.[1] Whether with or without cause, the Russians declared that the Hats were planning a *coup d'état*, and that the contemplated change in the Swedish constitution would be hostile to Russian interests. Thus at a time when the ink was hardly dry on the Treaty of Aix-la-Chapelle, Russian and Swedish troops were facing each other along the frontiers of Finland, and Europe was in danger of a new war. Prussia and France were pledged to Sweden, while Britain was bound by a treaty of 1742 in certain contingencies to send men-of-war to the support of Russia. Indignation at the treatment of the British representative, dislike of a treaty recently concluded between Sweden and Denmark, and apprehension lest Britain should be involved in another struggle, are all reflected in the parliamentary debates and newspapers of these months.[2] It was in such an atmosphere that, in February, 1750, a Committee of the whole House, set up to consider the trade with Sweden, reported in favour of removing the duties on pig and bar iron imported from the American colonies. The protests of the landowners, ironmasters, and tanners,

---

1. Firth and Chance, *Diplomatic Relations with the North of Europe*, 3.
2. *Parliamentary History*, xiv. Speech of Horace Walpole, 494, and Sir John Hynde Cotton, 822. See also *Adams's Weekly Courant* (Chester), 6 March 1750.

expressed though they were in numerous petitions, were unavailing, and the well-known measure of 1750 was speedily introduced and passed.[1]

If further proof is needed of the view here expressed that political rather than economic forces were the determining factor in the struggle, it may be supplied by the pen of a contemporary.

" I could not forbear wishing " [said an anonymous writer[2] a few weeks after the passing of the Act] " while our Fishery Bill hung so long suspended, that some minister had happily drawn us into a Quarrel with our *good Friends* and Allies; since it might have forwarded that Bill, as our *Northern* Broil had occasioned this for the Importation of Pig and Bar Iron from our American Plantations : For it is plain we owe to M——l Enmity, what the joint Interest and Intreaties of the Mother Nation and her Children Colonies could never obtain . . . . As Sweden has long been under the Direction of France, heedless of the commercial Interest, she could be no Friend to us, but an Enemy : Our wiser Engagement with Russia gives us a more useful as well as a more formidable Ally.

" And as it incumbent on us to maintain the Independence of, and a freer Navigation in, the Baltick, Russia becomes of course our natural Ally, more especially as our Commerce with her is considerable; and to keep Sweden in a State of Depression, is our natural Interest, as she is inevitably engaged in Alliance against it . . . .; for now we seem to have given her our last Farewell, and that we shall probably never have further Occasion of any Intercourse in Trade of any consequence with her."

This frank exponent of economic nationalism was, however, unduly optimistic. The Act of 1750 did not by any means put an end to the trade with Sweden : it merely provided encouragement to colonial production by giving exemption from the payment of import duties to colonial pig

1. 23 Geo. II. c. 29.
2. A citation from the *Old England Journal* in *Aris's Birmingham Gazette,* May 14th 1750.

and bar iron. As the duty on the former—by far the most
important form of iron imported from the colonies—had
previously been only 3s. 9½d. a ton, the stimulus afforded by
the Act cannot have been great. Moreover in the case of bar
iron the exemption from the payment of duties was confined
to the single port of London; and in practice relatively small
quantities of bar iron came from America, either before or for
many years after the Act. The special privilege granted to
London appears to have resulted from its remoteness from
the chief producing areas of this country. Unable as they
were to obtain adequate supplies of English iron at a reason-
able price, the London craftsmen had relied on those brought
in from Sweden; and it was hoped that the limitation of free
importation to London would suffice to deliver a severe blow
to the Swedes without causing much injury to the English
ironmasters.[1] The same aim dictated the clause that no
American iron should be exported, carried coastwise, or moved
more than ten miles by land, from London unless for the use
of the royal dockyards.

Though welcome to the English ironmasters, this restriction to the port of London was naturally resented by the
manufacturers of iron wares in the provinces, as well as by
the merchants of the outports. Not for long, however, was
London to enjoy this exclusive privilege. In 1753 the Swedish
Crown took measures—including the granting of special
privileges to workmen and restrictions on the exportation of
iron[2]—to stimulate the development of manufactures in
Sweden. These measures were largely ineffective, for the
exports to England actually increased in the following year.
Nevertheless feeling in this country ran high. When, finally,
the Seven Years War broke out, Sweden, true to her traditional allegiance, followed at the heels of France, and Russia
also was now numbered among the enemies of Britain. In
these circumstances, and in face of the great rise in the price

---

1. *Cf.* the assertion of the Earl of Lonsdale, that " no English iron or very
little is brought " into London. "By this limitation our own ironworks will not
be immediately affected, but if this attempt has the success that is expected, in
all probability they will suffer by it in time." *Hist. MSS. Comm., Le Fleming
MSS.*, 357.
2. *Aris's Birmingham Gazette,* 17th Sept. 1753.

of English bar iron which resulted from the war, Parliament could not turn a deaf ear to the petitions of the Merchant Adventurers of Bristol, and of numerous others,[1] for equal rights with their fellows in London. In 1757, therefore, the limitation as to the port to which bar iron might be brought, and the prohibition against moving it from London by land carriage, were abolished. In view of the large profits that the war was bringing to the ironmasters and woodowners, their opposition was of no avail. When it became clear that the Bill was about to pass, the woodowners of Yorkshire concentrated their energies on securing the repeal of 35 Henry VIII, *c.* 17, which had prohibited under penalties the grubbing up of coppices—an interesting confirmation of the view that the early Acts against deforestation were not entirely a dead letter, even in the middle years of the eighteenth century.

The measures of 1750 and 1757 were thus passed at periods of special need, and were directed towards increasing the supplies of iron available for use in England. A further step was taken in 1764, when iron was added to the list of "enumerated" commodities, so that henceforth all iron exported from the Plantations to European countries must pass through the hands of merchants in Great Britain.[2] The following year, however, a small breach was made in the system when the colonists were given liberty to send iron of all kinds direct to Ireland;[3] and at the same time the prohibition of the re-exportation and coastwise transhipment of iron from London, imposed in 1750, was given up.

There has been some discussion as to the incidence between Britain and the Colonies of the gains and losses involved in these measures of 1750, 1757, and 1764. That the removal of the low duty on pig iron would tend somewhat to increase importation from the Colonies and so stimulate production there is obvious enough; but the extent of the benefit to the

---

1. For the petitions, *vide J.H.C.*, xxvii, 686-849. Meetings of iron manufacturers were held with the object of obtaining free colonial imports; a reference is made to one of these held at the Swan Inn, Birmingham by S. Lloyd, *The Lloyds of Birmingham*, 28.

2. 4 Geo. III, c. 15. Direct exportation was allowed to other parts of America, Asia, and Africa.

3. 5 Geo. III, c. 45.

planters must not be overestimated. Exemption from the payment of a mere 3s. 9½d. on each ton of pig iron cannot have appeared a great matter to the colonial exporter; and when, after 1764, American producers of iron found themselves practically confined to the single market of Great Britain, they may well have felt that they were paying something for the privilege. Perhaps, however, there is little reason to quarrel with the verdict of Adam Smith[1] that the exemption from the duties more than counterbalanced the limitation of sales to the British market—" the one part of the regulation contributes more to encourage the erection of furnaces in America than the other to discourage it." Reference to the table of imports shows, in fact, a moderate but steady increase in the quantities of pig iron imported, though it is impossible to say how much of this resulted from the policy of encouragement, and how much was the inevitable consequence of the growth of population and a more settled life in the regions of the south and middle states. In the case of bar iron the exemption from duty, which amounted to over £2, appeared a matter of greater moment. After the adoption of the policy of enumeration in 1764, the imports of bars certainly increased from a previous annual average of between two and three hundred tons to over a thousand tons; and between this year and the Revolution it remained about the same figure, rising only in 1771 to more than two thousand tons.[2] From this it would appear that the colonists had previously secured other outlets for their small surplus of bar iron, and that the Act of 1764 did to some extent succeed in its object of deflecting supplies to this country.

There is, however, little reason for accepting the view that American iron played a truly important part in the economy of Great Britain during the eighteenth century. A recent writer[3] has indeed attempted to show that even before 1750

1.   *Wealth of Nations*, Bk. IV, Ch. VII, Pt. II.

2.   Practically no bar iron came in from America before 1731; in 1735, about 55 tons were imported by the Crowley firm—apparently for experimental purposes; not until 1745 did the imports exceed 100 tons, and not till 1764, 1,000 tons. The maximum was in 1771 when 2222 tons were brought in. *Vide* Scrivenor, App., Table XIII.

3.   Eckel, *Coal, Iron, and War.*

the American exports to Britain were equivalent to no less
than one-fifth of the output of this country.   But this conclusion is reached by accepting what was certainly a faulty
estimate of the home production of *bar* iron,[1] and comparing
with it the imports of *pig* iron from America in a year when
these were exceptionally high.   Even so, it becomes clear that
colonial iron was of far less significance than would appear
from Mr. Eckel's statement, when one reflects on the magnitude of the supplies of Swedish and Russian iron consumed,
along with those of native origin, by the English smith.   The
following figures of imports into England, representing
annual averages, give a truer impression of the part played
by America in this respect.[2]

	From the Colonies. Tons.	From Foreign Countries. Tons.
1731-5	2,361	24,539
1741-5	2,555	—
1751-5	3,335	27,954
1761-5	3,107	40,919
1771-5	4,798	44,263

When, further, it is remembered that the foreign iron was
all in the form of bars, while by far the greater part of that
from the colonies consisted of the less valuable unrefined pig,
the real insignificance of the latter becomes evident.   The
truth is that neither before nor after the passing of the Acts
of 1750, 1757 and 1764 were American supplies of any great
moment to Englishmen.   The writer already criticised has
further declared that the encouragement given to the colonial
shipments of pig iron and bar iron was " very effective," and
that in the years immediately preceding the Revolution the
export of crude iron from the American colonies " was perhaps a third as much as Great Britain was producing at
that time "—a statement which again can only have been
arrived at as the result of an under-estimate of the British

1. *Infra* Appendix B.
2. The figures for each year are given in the appendix of Scrivenor's work.

output, and a gross over-estimate of the supplies received annually from America.[1] As a matter of fact, the latter at this time totalled little more than the output of a single one of the new works growing up at Carron, Bradley, and Rotherham.

So far attention has been directed only to what may be termed the developmental clauses of the Act of 1750 : nothing has been said of the clauses prohibiting slitting- and rolling-mills, plating-forges, and steel-furnaces in the colonies. The object of these was, of course, to prevent the Americans from competing in their own or other markets with the iron and steel manufactures of the Mother Country ; and they have been defended on the grounds that the colonists might not unreasonably be asked to make some return for the preference given them in the matter of crude and refined iron. Writing of such prohibitions in general, Adam Smith urges that, at the stage of development reached, it was probably more profitable to the colonists to import finished wares from England than to manufacture for themselves, and that self-interest alone would have prevented the growth of such industries. The prohibitions were therefore merely " impertinent badges of slavery imposed upon them, without any sufficient reason by the groundless jealousy of the merchants and manufacturers of the Mother Country." This view has been further developed by Sir William Ashley in the course of his persuasive apologia for the old colonial system, though it is frankly admitted that the legislation respecting iron forms the weakest point in the defence. It is clear, indeed, that no injustice was done to the southern plantations, whence came the bulk of the pig iron exported to England, for no manufactures had been attempted in this region. But it is equally clear that a number of slitting-mills, plating-forges, and steel-furnaces in the northern colonies were actually

1. The writer appears to have taken the imports of the exceptional years 1770 and 1771 as typical. Between this time and 1776 the exports fell considerably. There is an apparent discrepancy between the figures of exportation from America and those of importations into England. In 1770, 5,747 tons of pig iron, and 2,102 tons of bar iron were exported to Great Britain (Macpherson, 572); but only 4,232 tons of pig, and 1,716 of bar were imported into England (Scrivenor, Table XIII). The balance apparently went to "that part of Great Britain called Scotland."

suppressed[1]; and new enterprises were prevented from coming into existence. In 1773 Edmund Quincey claimed to have found on his estates in New England ore of superior quality, suitable for making steel; but though he proposed to enter into partnership with men resident in Great Britain, the steel interests of Bristol were strong enough to induce Parliament to prohibit his setting up a steel-furnace and tilt-hammer.[2] To men in his position it was small consolation to reflect on the new prosperity that had come to the iron furnaces in Virginia and Maryland.

Further the fact that it was part of the policy of the British Government to stimulate the production of bar iron, as well as pig, cuts the ground from beneath the feet of those who contend that the Act of 1750 was passed with the beneficent, if misguided, object of keeping the Americans to the less skilled processes. The permission and, in fact, the encouragement given to the fining of iron constituted a recognition of the capacity of the Americans for skilled employments. Indeed, the later processes of manufacture were such as could have been performed, and had already been performed, by unskilled slave labour; and the nails and horseshoes which it was intended the colonists should purchase from England might, in part at least, have been made by the village smiths, or even by the wives and children of the northern settlers.[3] Finally, that the resentment of the colonists at the measures was not merely the product of an ignorant impatience of interference from England, is evident from the testimony of Samuel Garbett, himself a British ironmaster and a keen economic nationalist. Writing in December, 1765, to the Earl of Dartmouth of the poor quality of the iron used for nail-making in Birmingham, he asserts that there are " nearly 2,000 tons of bad iron now on hand : America, the principal market for sale has long complained of the quality of our nails and will most unquestionably, if the imposition con-

---

1. References to slitting-mills in America are made by Weeden (*Economic and Social History of New England*, ii, 499-500, 734), who shows that they existed as early as 1650.

2. *J.H.C.*, xxxiv, 93, 147, 149.

3. The making of nails by farmers in their spare time is mentioned by Weeden, *op. cit.*, 499.

tinues, endeavour to raise works of their own as other countries have done.''[1]

The colonists did not indeed submit quietly : slitting-mills were still used in America in 1765, and a reference is made to *new* mills erected at Dorchester in 1769 and 1771.[2] Moreover it was still possible for the colonists to cut their bars by manual labour instead of by wheels; and thus manufactures of iron, although hampered, were not rendered impossible. The boycott of British goods which arose out of opposition to the Stamp Act gave a further incentive to colonial manufacture, and the production of scythes, spades, axes, and other iron wares was stimulated during the 'sixties.[3]

Controversy has raged, and differences will continue, as to the motives underlying the trade and colonial legislation in general. By some it has been urged that the regulative and restrictive Acts were based on a clearly conceived ideal of a self-sufficing Empire in which a wise division of labour between Englishman and Colonist would result in economic gain to both. " Up to 1763 " (writes Mr. Beer[4]) " England acted consistently on a false, but historically justifiable economic principle. She had developed a rounded colonial system, based on economic principles, and but slightly influenced by political considerations.'' No attempt is here made to pass judgment on this verdict as to the Colonial System as a whole. But a study of the laws which related specifically to the iron trade lends support rather to the older theory put forward by Weeden that economic principles had little to do with legislation, and that colonial policy was " controlled by the exigencies of English contests with continental powers.''

But whatever the ground for dispute as to motives and " causes,'' there can be little, among those who look closely at the facts, as to the results. This plan to call in the New World to redress the trade balance of the Old, was hardly, in the event, one of the outstanding successes of mercantilism.

1. *Dartmouth MSS.*, xv, Pt. 1, Vol. iii, 180.
2. Weeden, *op. cit.*, 734.
3. Macpherson, iii, 421.
4. Beer, *Commercial Policy of England towards the American Colonies*, 89.

In spite of the fact that the restrictions were, to some extent, evaded, they probably caused real loss to certain sections of the colonists, and they certainly supplied many with a grievance. The alleged benefits to the Mother Country, on the other hand, were never large; and for many years to follow British manufacturers remained dependent on foreigners for the larger part of their supplies of bar iron. When at length this dependence was brought to an end, it was not from mercantilist subtlety, or the prescience of politicians, but from the practical genius cf James Watt and Henry Cort that deliverance came.

K

CHAPTER VI.

The Iron Industry in Peace and War.

"Those who cannot remember the past are condemned to repeat it."
—George Santayana.

I.

It is now becoming a matter of agreement that many of the more catastrophic processes associated with the industrial changes of the eighteenth century were the result not of economic but of political forces. "The social retrogression and evils which mark the Industrial Revolution period are only in a very secondary sense to be attributed to the economic movement: the primary cause is to be found in the war in which the country was engaged," writes Professor Daniels; and in his work on the English Cotton Industry abundant evidence is presented in support of the thesis. Heavy taxation, shortage of foodstuffs, the drying up of the channels of international trade produced, during the war periods, poverty and unemployment; and the restraints on individual liberty—justified by politicians on grounds of national security—led to disturbance of social relations and an increasingly sharp cleavage of economic classes. In trades like cotton spinning and manufacture, depending largely on foreign markets, the connection between cause and dismal effect is too patent to escape observation: to them war must always appear a disaster of the first order. But in the industry with which we are here concerned the outbreak of hostilities meant not a diminished but an increased demand for iron in the form of cannon, gun-carriages, shot and fire-arms, and for steel in the shape of swords and bayonets. Contracts from the Office of Ordnance operated as a Food of the Gods, and the industry grew in proportion as the need for munitions of war increased. This effect has already been observed in the outstanding cases of the Wilkinsons, the Walkers, and the Carron partners, and other illustrations are given below. It has even been argued that technical progress and discovery were the direct result of war: " gun-casting " it has been said,[1] " was the great stimulant of improved technique in the foundry "; and the claim of Henry Cort to the gratitude of his fellow-countrymen was based primarily on the contribution he had made to military security. Moreover the quantity of English iron and steel exported was negligible compared with that brought into this country from abroad: so far, therefore, from cutting off his customers, the restrictions of war gave to the British iron producer a firmer hold on the market and operated as a measure of protection against the foreign competitor.

It is true that during the commercial crisis that invariably followed the declaration of hostilities the industry suffered along with others; but its recovery was always swift, and in each of the wars a trade boom was generated. This does not mean—let us hasten to add—that the iron industry escaped the inevitable ill-consequences of war, but simply that these were deferred: under the influence of the political storm the normal wave of the trade cycle became a billow on the crest of which the iron trade was carried high for a period, only to be dashed later on the rocks with a force proportioned to the height from which it had been hurled. After each war came trade depression—more intense and prolonged than that experienced by other industries—during which the ironmasters painfully adapted their works to the products of peace; and sometimes the process was still incomplete when the outbreak of a fresh struggle brought the call for a reconversion of ploughshares into swords. In such circumstances stable industry was difficult: big profits were wiped out by big losses, and temporary high earnings were consumed during succeeding periods of unemployment. It is but a shallow view, therefore, to suppose that the interests of the ironmaster diverged from those of other industrialists, and that causes impoverishing the nation as a whole brought any but a transient prosperity to the workers engaged in producing the materials of war.

These elementary generalisations could probably be

---

1. Sombart, quoted by Dr. Clapham, *Economic Journal*, xxiii, 401.

justified by reference to each of the wars of the eighteenth century : information respecting the effects of the earlier struggles is difficult to come at, and here stray wisps must suffice to indicate the direction of the wind; but for the later wars—and especially those of 1793 to 1815—the accumulation of evidence is unmistakable in its bearing.[1]

Of the effects of the trouble with Sweden during the years 1715-19 some account has already been given.[2] In this minor war no great stimulus came to the ironmasters from the demand for munitions, but the shutting off of imports from the Baltic meant that English furnaces and forges were kept in constant work and that new enterprises were brought into existence. Proof of this access of prosperity is afforded by the records of the Backbarrow Company, which, in the year 1716, made a profit of £3,850 on a capital not exceeding £6,000.[3] It was this opportunity of exceptional gain that, in the same year, led Shore and Cotton to break into the local monopoly of the lessees of the Duke of Norfolk, by setting up their ironworks in Sheffield; and the more grandiose schemes of William Wood in 1718 no doubt owed their conception to the same prospect of windfall profits. With the resumption of trade with the North came depression in iron production. Of the 130 forges in the enumeration of 1720, no fewer than thirty-three were lying idle owing to lack of orders; the price of iron was low, and gloom had settled upon the whole industry. It should, however, be remarked that this condition of trade was not merely the anæmia resulting from war, but was due in part to the bursting of the financial bubbles in 1720; and even had the war not come to a sudden end the ambitious schemes for refloating the industry, generated between 1718 and 1720, must inevitably have come to grief.[4]

1. Even in the seventeenth century the process can be observed : a list of Sussex ironwork existing in 1653 was compiled eleven years later, and of the 27 furnaces enumerated the greater number are described as having been engaged in making " guns or shotte in the late warrs for supply of his mai'es stores." But the peace that followed the Restoration had thrown many of these out of use, and in 1664 only eleven remained, while of 42 forges carrying on operations in 1653, only 18 were still at work. *S.A.C.*, xviii, 15.

2. *Supra*, 111—113.

3. Fell, *op. cit.*

4. Macpherson, ii, 97, 114.

After 1720 the price of iron remained low, and it was not until 1725 that it rose to its old level. Thereafter trade was good, for not until 1738 did complaints of depression again make themselves heard. This appears to have been quite a temporary matter, and the Sussex ironmasters, who at this time were the principal beneficiaries of the Office of Ordnance, found in the wars that broke out in 1739 a new incentive to activity. In this and the following year the foundry at Heathfield completed no fewer than 217 guns of various sizes for the King's service[1]; and John Legas, who died in 1756, is said to have made a fortune of some £30,000 from gun-casting in the same district. Cannon were also cast at Coalbrookdale, and probably at Bersham, during this period.[2]

It is not, however, until the Seven Years' War that information becomes sufficiently detailed for the full reaction of war on the industry to be adequately observed. On the outbreak of hostilities in 1756 the price of iron moved suddenly upward : and the Furness ironmasters agreed in the following year that " no bar iron at home be sold under £19, at Liverpool £17 per ton."[3] As we have seen, the special difficulty of obtaining bar iron was the occasion for the relaxation of the regulations governing importation from America; but the colonies were not yet in a position to send supplies in sufficient volume materially to affect the market, and the British forge masters were able to take full advantage of the shortage. Similarly with the founders : not only were firms like those at Heathfield and Lamberhurst in the old munition centres very active, but even works which had refused orders for cannon were kept busy : in December the newly-established Horsehay furnace was described as being " at a top pinnacle of prosperity, twenty and twenty-two tons per week, and sold off as fast as made, at profit enough." Such conditions naturally brought new works into being. In addition to that at Horsehay, the Hirwain furnace in Glamorgan, and the Halton furnace near Lancaster, were first in blast in 1756, and

1. Delany, *The Wealden Iron Industry*, 44.
2. *V.C.H. Sussex*; *V.C.H. Shropshire*, 462.
3. Fell, *op. cit.*, 254.

the following year new furnaces were built at Ketley, Light-moor, Madeley Wood, and, it is said, at Bradley. In 1757 also the Willey Company was formed at Broseley, and in 1759 the Dowlais furnace was erected by Lewis and Company. In 1759 the Carron Ironworks, afterwards to become the greatest arsenal in the country, was projected, and the following year the Seaton furnace was lighted in Cumberland. At this time the price of iron again took an upward turn, and within a few months it had advanced by more than £2 a ton. At Ketley the demand for pig iron was such that it was not unusual for waggons to be kept waiting while the furnaces were tapped, and for the pig iron to be carried to the forges while yet hot. In 1762 the Bersham works were reconstituted, and John and William Wilkinson began to cast cannon, shell, and grenades here on a scale that was soon to gain for them a reputation throughout Europe.[1]

The Peace of Paris, signed in February, 1763, was followed by a few months of continued prosperity; but in July came the inevitable crash, heralded by the failure of merchants in Amsterdam and Hamburg, and passing rapidly to this country.[2] A long period of bad trade followed, in which, if we may accept the almost unanimous testimony of both contemporaries and modern scholars, the unhappy relations with the American colonies played an important part.[3] It is true that relatively little iron and steel was exported in an unfinished state, but large quantities of ironwares—nails in particular—were sent to America in years of normal trade. In December, 1765, Samuel Garbett informed William Burke that some thousands of artificers in the neighbourhood of Birmingham were suffering from want of remittances from America; and, in the following year, a merchant, who usually sent nails to the value of £50,000 a year to the colonies,

---

1. Scrivenor, *App.*, 359; Evidence of John Floory before the Committee on the Exportation of Buckle-Chapes. *J.H.C.*, xxviii, 883; *V.C.H. Shropshire*, 465.
    2. Macpherson, ii, 366.
    3. See *Aris's Birmingham Gazette*, 31 Dec. 1765; and Daniels, *Early English Cotton Industry*. Petitions to Parliament in 1766 from Birmingham, Coventry, Wolverhampton, Dudley, and Stourbridge attributed the trade depression to the dispute with the colonies; *J.H.C.*, 865. *Cal. Home Office Papers 1765*, 2,000.

declared that owing to the countermanding of orders he had then 300 workmen unemployed.[1] With the hardware trades in this condition it was difficult for the iron producers to find an outlet for their product, especially as there was little compensatory demand for ordnance until the outbreak of actual hostilities in 1775. The position of the iron industry is reflected in the almost complete cessation of furnace erection. In a list of furnaces compiled in 1790 the date of building of each was recorded; according to this no fewer than eleven smelting works had come into being during the Seven Years' War, while during the succeeding eleven years of peace only four new works were recorded.[2] No doubt in both periods some furnaces had been constructed which were subsequently abandoned; but the fact that the number of survivors from the earlier period was so great is striking testimony to the manner in which industrial activity was concentrated in the years of war.

Apart, however from the trouble with the Americans, it was almost inevitable that the period following the great struggle should be marked by social discontent. From all sides came protests against the high costs of living; and vigorous attacks were made on the forestallers and engrossers, who, as the agents of high prices, were generally regarded as the controllers of the price level. That the explanation lay elsewhere is clear enough. It has been too lightly assumed by some writers that during struggles like that of 1756-63 the current of national life flowed on with little interruption, and that the production of commodities in general was but little affected by the war. What appears more likely is that the withdrawal of energies to war purposes, such as that of cannon-founding, led to the holding up of public works of other kinds, and that the execution of these was thus delayed and crowded into the post-war years. How otherwise, indeed, is one to explain the sudden surge of schemes for the making and improving of roads, canals, bridges, harbours, and other means of communication, during the two or three years that followed the

1. *Aris's Birmingham Gazette*, 24 Feb. 1766.
2. Scrivenor, *loc. cit.*

peace?[1] The deflection from agriculture of the labour and capital required for these enterprises could not fail to have been a potent factor in causing and maintaining the rise of food prices of which so many bitter complaints were made.

But there was yet another cause. Finance by inflation is no modern discovery; and here and there, even in the eighteenth century, were men who recognised that the over-issue of currency was bound to result in rising prices. " Was there not a Coinage of fifty Millions of Paper Money during the late War, and a vast Increase of real Money by rich Captures, and an extended Commerce, to the Amount of many Millions more? " asked a writer[2] in 1766. " Have not the Prices of Butter, Cheese, Eggs, Meat, and even Corn, gradually *advanced* upon us, according to the great Increase of our Paper and Money Currency.—For the more we abound in Money, of the less Value it is (for it will have its Market Price, as well as any other Commodity;) and as it decreases in its Value by its Plenty, you must give more of it in Weight or Tale, to purchase what you want; and this *has,* and (as the Evil goes on) *will raise* the Prices of Estates, of Rents, and of every Thing else." In a period when money wages remained fixed over many years and responded but slowly to changes in the cost of necessaries of life, the evils of inflation were greatly intensified, and much of the distress and unrest between the Seven Years' War and the American Revolution must be attributed to this cause.

A harvest failure in 1766 made matters worse. " The trade hath a melancholy prospect," wrote Samuel Garbett in November,[3] and from other parts of the country came reports of dead trade and unemployment. Ironmasters in particular had to face the fact that some of their markets had, for a time at least, ceased to exist, and that new outlets must be found if production were to be continued. Hence it was that in 1767 the Coalbrookdale Company used its surplus metal to make rails of iron to replace those of wood on its waggon ways. This was done partly in order to keep the men in employment,

---

1. *J.H.C.*, xxx, and xxxi *passim.*
2. *Aris's Birmingham Gazette,* 1766.
3. *Cal. H.O. Papers,* 1766, 325, 332.

and with the knowledge that if iron again rose in price the rails could be taken up and sold, but also, no doubt, in the hope of creating a new commodity for general use.[1] In 1768 the industry was still under the shadow of depression, and with the commercial crisis of June, 1772, came a yet deeper gloom. "The trade of Birmingham is so dead at this juncture," wrote Matthew Boulton,[2] "that the London wagons have to make up their loading with coals for want of merchandise. The country has received a severe shock since June last, such a one as it will not recover from for many years, scarcely any one of considerable trade in Great Britain but has felt the consequences of it in some respects." According to a letter addressed by a freeman of Bristol to the King, the well-to-do of the town were buying provisions to sell below cost price to the poor—with the effect, it was alleged, of further raising prices by reason of the greater consumption.[3] Evidence of the depression exists at every turn. Boulton himself suffered financial embarrassment, and the Carron Company was severely hit and had to be reconstructed in the following year.[4] " I hear nothing but bad accounts (as they are generally called) respecting the pig iron trade, and predictions of its being still worse," wrote Richard Reynolds to his wife in 1773; and that trade followed but a sluggish course in the following year is indicated by other correspondence of the same ironmaster.[5] In 1775 all industries alike suffered something approaching paralysis under the threat of the storm that was about to break out in the West. " I aver," wrote John Wesley in August,[6] "that in every part of England where I have been (and I have been East, West, North, and South within these two years) trade in general is exceedingly decayed, and thousands of people are quite unemployed.

---

1. Dukes, *Antiquities of Shropshire App.*, lxxxiii ; *V.C.H. Shropshire*, 465.

2. *Hist. MMS. Comm.*, Rept. XV, App. I, 178.

3. *Cal. H.O. Papers*, 1766-72, 1202. Was it the dangerous, if sound, political economy of this statement that led the writer to add : " There is no one knoweth of this letter ; no not the wife of my bosom !"?

4. *Information for Samuel Garbett against the Carron Co.*, 10th Oct. 1778.

5. Rathbone, *Memoir*, 126, 31. Lloyd, *The Lloyds of Birmingham*, 100. *Hist. MSS Comm.*, xv, App. I, Vol. 3, 200.

6. *Hist. MSS. Comm.*, Rept. XV, App. I, Vol. 3, 220.

Some I know to have perished for want of bread; others, I have seen creeping up and down like walking shadows . . . ."

But again to the ironmaster the actual clash of arms sounded the advent of a new prosperity. In 1776 iron rose in price, and the works were soon fully employed. Though James Watt, whose foreign commitments were being delayed, might exclaim to Wilkinson[1] that " the diabolical war will ruin every thing," the assent of the latter may well have been somewhat lacking in conviction; for Bersham and Bradley were working at pressure, and over in France his brother was setting up new furnaces and boring-mills, and helping to remodel the ordnance works at Le Creusot.[2] The demands made by the Russians, the Danes, and the Spaniards on the Carron Works in 1777 have already been noticed; and that the small-arms trade was similarly active is indicated by the statement of a French traveller that, in Birmingham, at least 300 new houses were required annually during the war.[3] The revived incentive to iron production resulted in a fresh flow of new enterprises : in 1765 Anthony Bacon set up his furnace at Cyfarthfa, and from this time till the end of the war he was constantly engaged in casting for the Office of Ordnance.[4] In Shropshire new works were put up at Snedshill, the Calcutts, and Benthall in the vicinity of Coalbrookdale, as well as at Cleehill, near Cleobury. In Staffordshire a furnace was lighted at Tipton, and in Scotland the Wilsontown works were established. But it was Yorkshire and Derbyshire that saw the most widespread development at this time. In 1777 Smith & Co. put a furnace in blast at Chesterfield; during 1780-2 others were built in the same district at Stone Gravel and Wingerworth; and in 1782 the Athersley furnace near

1. Watt to Wilkinson, 26 June 1779.
2. Dickinson, *John Wilkinson*, 49.
3. Saint-Fond, *Travels*, ii, 34.
4. According to Wilkins (*op. cit.*) the contracts were withdrawn from Anthony Bacon owing to his having supplied the Americans also with munitions. No evidence, however, is presented in support of the statement. A similar story is told of John Wilkinson: in 1775 he had secured the contract for the supply of water-pipes to Paris, and, according to tradition, he succeeded in smuggling cannon, in the guise of water-piping, from Broseley, down the Severn to the French frigates which awaited the arrival of his barges in the Bristol Channel. But it is not made clear by any of the writers who repeat the tale that this was done at a time of actual hostilities with France.

Derby was started. Further north new smelting works were erected at Chapeltown in 1778, and two years later similar enterprises were initiated at Seacroft, near Leeds, and at Birkenshaw in the Halifax district.[1]

This activity in construction was largely due to the intensification of the war : between 1778 and 1780 France, Spain, and Holland had taken up arms against Britain, and hostilities had also broken out in Ireland and India. These events increased the demand for iron at a time when the supplies from America were cut off, and the English makers of pig and bar iron were thus able to take full advantage of the situation. It is true that the metal could still be brought in from the North of Europe, but even here circumstances arose that seemed to hold forth promise of further prosperity to the English ironmaster. In 1780 the claims of Britain in the matter of blockade, of the taking of contraband and enemy goods carried in neutral vessels, and of the right of search of all merchant vessels on the high seas, called forth vigorous protests; and Russia, Sweden, and Denmark joined to form the First Armed Neutrality, in which they were afterwards supported by Holland, Prussia, Austria, and Portugal. For a time it appeared possible that commerce with the North might also be severed, and Britain be left to depend on her own resources for the vital supplies of bar iron. But the trade was a matter of great moment to the Northern Powers no less than to Britain, and Catherine II was too astute to allow the dispute to develop into actual warfare.[2] Nevertheless the diplomatic position was probably not without its effect in stimulating the English ironmasters to increased production at this time.

The period succeeding every great war is marked by demands for the protection of domestic industry; for not only is the spirit of nationality strengthened by the conflict, but the coming of peace removes a very effective barrier to the competition of the foreigner with the home producer. It had

---

1. Scrivenor, *op. cit.*, 360.
2. The year 1781 actually marked the high-tide of the century as regards the importation of bar iron from Russia—perhaps as the result of fears lest the trade should be prohibited.

been so after the Seven Years' War. In 1765 Dr. Roebuck
and Samuel Garbett had voiced the opposition of the ironmasters to the practice of the Customs Officers in treating
plate-iron from Sweden as unmanufactured bars, and so
allowing it to enter the country on payment of a lower duty
than that imposed on manufactured iron. A little later,
further complaint had been made of the importation, subject
to the payment of the lower duty, of iron partially shaped into
ship-bolts, of iron formed into three gun-barrel skelps in a
single bar, and of other semi-manufactured wares brought in
from Russia.[1] And the same fear of the foreign manufacturer
had been exhibited in the hot pursuit of workmen who, at this
period of depressed trade in England, had attempted to
transfer themselves to ironworks in Sweden, Russia, and other
foreign parts.[2]

After the American War the same spirit of economic
nationalism was equally active among all kinds of manufacturers. Though statesmen like Pitt might help to introduce
the first stages of a more liberal commercial system, and
might receive some measure of support from the purely
commercial classes, the demands of the industrialists for an
exclusive policy against outsiders made their task one of the
utmost difficulty. In 1783 the members of the Russia
Company petitioned the Government for lower duties on
imports, or drawbacks on the re-exportation of Russian iron,
in compensation for the losses with which the coming of peace
appeared to threaten them. British merchants and manufacturers in general seem, indeed, to have developed exaggerated
fears of American competition, now that the trade of the New
World could no longer be supervised from Westminster.
" The iron manufacturers in this country," wrote William
Robertson of Glasgow in February, 1783, " having Slitting
Mills and other valuable extensive establishments for manu-

1. *Cal. H.O. Papers* (1760-5), 2,000 ; *ibid.* (1766-9), 82, 112, 124.

2. *Infra* 201-5. At the same time it was enacted that such part of the duties
paid on iron imported in foreign ships as exceeded that paid on iron brought
in British ships should no longer be drawn back upon re-exportation ; and
although this measure was obviously designed as part of the navigation policy,
it had incidentally the effect of strengthening the tariff defences of the British
iron industry. *J.H.C.*, xxxii, 381.

factured goods from Russian iron for exportation are exceedingly alarmed at the present state of the iron trade—paying a heavy duty on the iron at importation not drawn back at exporting the goods made from it, and America left free to trade with other Countries, perhaps paying no duties, whose provisions are cheaper and taxes less.'' The Scottish manufacturers of Russian iron thus supported the Russia Company in its request for lower duties. But the ironmasters concerned with the production of pig and bar iron were hostile to at least the first of the alternative policies suggested by the merchants; for a considerable proportional increase in the size of the industry had resulted from the war constructions, and they were put to it to find a vent for their iron, without the added difficulty imposed by intensified competition from Russia.[1] The familiar cleavage of interest between the producer on the one hand, and the merchant and manufacturer on the other, can also be observed in the discussions as to the trade with Ireland and with France, details of which will be given in a later chapter.[2]

The peace had found the industry with a productive capacity in excess of demand at remunerative prices; and during the years 1783-5 the trade in iron was undoubtedly depressed. This was especially true of the section of the industry located in South Yorkshire and Derbyshire, where, as already mentioned, the erection of furnaces had been most marked : the cessation of war contracts is reflected in the statistics of the Chesterfield Canal, along which the transportation of iron declined in volume at a time when that of commodities in general exhibited a steady increase.[3] Elsewhere also there are indications of bad trade. Early in 1785 two of the ten blast-furnaces owned by the Coalbrookdale

---

1. Cited Lloyd, *The Lloyds of Birmingham*, 30.
2. *Infra* 166-174. The same protectionist impulse resulted in the Act of 1785, which prohibited under heavy penalties the exportation of tools and engines used in the manufacture of iron and steel. Macpherson, iv, 75.
3. *Abstract of Tonnage—Chesterfield Canal*, Jackson Coll., Sheffield.

			Tons of Iron.	All commodities.
1781	...	...	2,046	34,077½
1782	...	...	2,654	45,892
1783	...	...	715	46,483½
1784	...	...	590	39,798½
1785	...	...	1,001½	50,365

group had been put out; and the continuance of conditions of over-production is shown by the fall in the price of castings that took place in August of the same year.

Nevertheless there is no evidence of such a disaster as that which was to fall upon the industry at the close of the Napoleonic War. To the ironmasters of the Midlands the reopening of trade with America brought some measure of compensation, for the demand of the Americans for nails and hardware soon reverted to the English market. The rapid extension of the use of the steam-engine created new business for the ironmasters, and the Wilkinsons, who benefited most, also held large contracts for the supply of water-pipes for Paris and New York.[1] At this time one of the brothers visited Germany and introduced the coke-smelting process into Upper Silesia. The Carron Company found a vent in the increased use of their domestic stoves, and other firms also extended the production of similar commodities. New uses for cast iron were being sought on every hand: in 1787 John Wilkinson achieved a seven-days' wonder by launching his first cast-iron barge on the River Severn, and at Carron William Symington was constructing the steam-ship which, in 1789, was to make a famous first voyage along the Forth and Clyde Canal.[2]

But it was the application of cast iron to the building of bridges that constituted the chief preoccupation of the ironmasters during the eight years in which the industry lay becalmed between the storm of the American War and the whirlwind of the Revolution. No cannon were made by the Coalbrookdale Company, and during the war the firm had found leisure to complete the cast-iron bridge across the Severn which had been projected in 1776. The structure had attracted considerable attention, and schemes for bridging other rivers by similar single-span arches, so avoiding the inconvenience of piers in mid-stream, were soon set on foot. In the planning of these the most interesting figure is that of

1. John Hall, of Mount Ironworks, New York, to James Watt, 18 Mar. 1786.

2. Dickinson, *op. cit.*, 24, 53. *A Century and a Half of Commercial Enterprise*, 12, published by the Carron Company, 1909.

Tom Paine, and no account of the iron industry of the period would be complete without at least passing reference to this somewhat erratic genius.

After the conclusion of the American War, in the prosecution of which he had taken so prominent a part, Paine turned his attention to civil engineering; in 1786 he presented to Franklin the model of a bridge to be erected over the Schuylkill—a single arch with thirteen ribs, typifying the unity and strength of the thirteen states of the new republic. Before the scheme could be executed, however, Paine left for Europe, and soon afterwards he is found exhibiting before the Academy of Science in Paris, and the Royal Society in London, models of a bridge intended for a river of four or five hundred feet in width. From both these bodies he received a cordial reception; and the collapse—due to a failure of the piers—of two bridges built by Smeaton over the Tyne, rendered opinion favourable to Paine's project for a single arch.[1] In 1788 he obtained a patent for his design,[2] and immediately looked about for an ironworks where his scheme could be executed. It was his original intention to give the contract to the Wilkinsons, but they were, at the time, on a visit to Germany and Sweden; arrangements were therefore made with the Walkers, who set aside in the works at Masborough a room in which Paine was free to make his drawings and erect his toy bridges. It was at Masborough also that an arch of 90 feet was constructed to span the River Don; and another of 110 feet, cast by the Walkers to Paine's design, was removed by sea and exhibited to the public at Paddington.[3]

But by this time other and more clamant calls were being made on Paine. Already Lafayette had entrusted to him the key of the fallen Bastille for transference to Washington;[4] towards the end of 1790 Paine again turned his constructive energies from bridge-building to political philosophy; and shortly afterwards he left the seclusion of his office at

1. Conway, *Life of Thomas Paine*, 218-22, 242, 254.
2. No. 1667.
3. Conway, 258.
4. It was sent in May 1790, along with half-a-dozen razors made of Walker's cast-steel. *Letter to Washington*, Conway, *op. cit.*, 275.

Masborough to plunge once more into the perilous waters of revolution in France. From a modification of the designs he left behind in England the bridge over the Wear at Sunderland was cast by the Walkers in 1796; and, in the same year, a similar structure was erected by Telford at Buildwas, of castings made at Coalbrookdale.

II.

The outbreak in 1793 of the struggle with revolutionary France resulted in a brief but acute commercial crisis : between the beginning of March and the end of July no fewer than 768 bankruptcies were recorded, and over a hundred British banks were obliged to close their doors.[1] In this dislocation of normal trade ironmasters, no less than others, were involved; and even so firmly rooted a concern as that at Coalbrookdale found itself in financial difficulties. In December the partners were obliged to call on Richard Reynolds for a loan of £4,000; but the temporary nature of the crisis, and the new prosperity that the war had brought to ironmakers as a whole, enabled the debt to be repaid in the following May.[2] Between this time and 1796 the industry appears to have been free from stress or anxiety, though the scarcity of corn in 1795 obliged the Shropshire ironmasters to provide wheat and maize for their workpeople at 25 per cent. below cost price;[3] and the proposal of Pitt to place part of the growing financial burden of the war on the shoulders of the iron magnates, by taxing coal and pig iron, caused a temporary flutter in the ironmasters' meetings at this time.[4]

Again in 1797 a commercial crisis—largely the result, as Mr. Hawtrey has shown,[5] of events in France—led to temporary embarrassment of the manufacturers in the chief centres of production. The cessation of cash payments by the Bank of England caused considerable alarm : Boulton and Watt, for

1. Macpherson, iv, 266.
2. *Coalbrookdale MSS.*
3. Rathbone, *op. cit.*, 259. In districts in which no such provision was made serious rioting occurred. For the riots at Tipton see *Aris's Birmingham Gazette*, 11 Sept. 1795.
4. *Infra*, p. 175.
5. *Economic Journal*, xxviii, 52-65.

example, wrote post haste to Mrs. Matthews, their London banker, asking for £3,000 in gold, and stating that, failing British coin, they would make shift with Spanish dollars which could be made to circulate with their mark upon them. Hearing, however, the following day of the issue of guinea notes they wrote instructing her not to pay more than five per cent. premium for cash.[1] But at the same time Boulton addressed a letter to George Rose pointing out that manufacturing towns were in a very different situation from commercial centres since they had wages to pay, and offering, if the Government would supply bullion, to coin it " on any terms rather than our town should be ruined or in flames." There was, however, little danger of such dire results : on 2 March at a general meeting of townspeople it was resolved to accept Bank of England notes to any amount, as also the bearer notes of the local banks; and the subsequent provision of smaller token currency put an end to any fears of disaster.

Financial disturbances like those of 1793 and 1797 could have but a passing effect on industrial activity ; and as regards the iron trade there were more potent causes producing an abounding war-time prosperity. Between the opening of hostilities and 1796 the price of iron had remained fairly steady; for the increased output of British works, combined with the imports from Sweden and Russia, enabled supply to keep pace with the accelerating demand. It was moreover generally believed that the war would be of short duration. In October the younger Watt expressed the opinion " that we shall have peace in the course of three or four months, as soon as the French are in possession of Holland and consider themselves secured against us. This may not be very agreeable to certain gentlemen about St. James', but is indispensably necessary to the welfare, if not the existence, of this country."[2] In 1796, however, a rise of about 30 per cent. took place in the price of foreign iron,[3] and a veritable boom in domestic production developed. In every centre of the industry there were indications of abnormal activity; press

1. B. and W. to Mrs. Matthews, 1 and 2 Mar. 1797.
2. J. Watt, Junr., to Mrs. Matthews.
3. Tooke, *High and Low Prices*. Cited Scrivenor, 404

L

notices and advertisements for labour show that the casting branch of the industry was developing so rapidly that the existing supply of labour was inadequate to cope with the orders that were pouring in.[1] The successive increases of 1796, 1797, and 1798 in the customs duty on bar iron, amounting in all to 19s. 3d. a ton, brought added gains to the English ironmasters,[2] and not only were existing works extended but the formation of new businesses was again marked. In 1798 an ironmaster declared that no fewer than twenty-one fresh furnaces had been put in blast since 1796, and that nineteen others were in process of construction.[3] In 1799 and 1800 there was the same story to tell: " There are new furnaces for the smelting of iron constantly erecting; and it is now difficult to get pitmen to work the Coals," said a Shropshire ironmaster before the Committee on the Coal Trade in December, 1800; and the newspapers give evidence to the same effect.

Among the causes which had led to this condition of industry the demand of the Government for ordnance must, perhaps, take first place. Hardly less important, however, in this respect were the relations of Britain with the Northern Powers, which still controlled a substantial proportion of the iron required in the smaller metal trades of Sheffield and the Black Country. By this time Russia had become a more important source of supply to the British ironworker than Sweden, and for many years the Russians had shown a disposition to raise the terms on which they were prepared to sell their iron. The imposition of export duties, the establishing of a credit bank for Russian exporters, and the insistence on the purchase of a fixed quantity of timber for every hundred tons of iron allowed to leave the country, were among the measures taken by the Russian Government to secure for its subjects the major part of the gain arising from the trade with England. Even more important as a source of friction between the two countries was the re-opening of

---

1. See, *e.g.*, advertisements in *Aris's Birmingham Gazette*, 13 Nov. 1795, and 11 Apr. 1796; *Sheffield Iris*, 26 Aug. 1796.
2. Watt to Barnes, 17 May 1796.
3. *Thoughts on Taxation in 1798 by an Ironmaster.* Printed in Dr. Macnab's *Letter on the Coal Trade of London*, 65.

the question of contraband and the right of search at sea : in the later months of the year 1800 Russia, Sweden, Prussia, and Denmark drew together to form a Second Armed Neutrality to combat the claims of Britain in these matters. The future of Malta was yet another matter of dispute ; and when at length the island fell into the hands of the British fleet, Paul I retaliated by placing an embargo on all British ships in Russian ports and throwing the captured British seamen into prison. To this the British Government replied by the imposition of an embargo on Russian vessels, with the result that by the end of the year trade between the two nations was entirely suspended. But for the sudden death by assassination of Paul I in March, 1801, Britain and Russia might have been involved in war on a large scale.

Throughout the period 1796—1801 the possibility of a stoppage of the currents of trade with the North—and its realisation during the winter of 1800-1—was a factor stimulating Englishmen to increased production and to the discovery of improved methods of iron-making. " It was at the time that we had quarrelled with the Northern Nations," observed Sir John Wrottesley later,[1] " that the greatest exertions were made to work our native iron, and that that trade flourished the most." To the British ironmaster the situation must, indeed, have appeared far from displeasing. Pitt's attempt to find a new source of revenue for a straitened exchequer by imposing a tax on pig iron had failed; and the only result of the proposal had been an increase in the import duty imposed on foreign iron, while the English ironmasters, thanks to their capacity for organised propaganda, had escaped untouched.[2] In 1796 the import duty was raised from £2 16s. 2d. to £3 1s. 9d. a ton; in the following year it was increased by a further 2s. 10d.; and in 1798 it stood at £3 15s. 5d.[3] In the first of these years a sudden advance of about thirty per cent. had taken place in the price of Russian iron, and the embargo at the end of the century had brought about an increase of yet another ten per cent ; so that, whereas

1. Report of Parliamentary Debate, *Sheffield Iris*, 9 May 1806.
2. *Infra*, p. 175.
3. Tooke, *High and Low Prices*. Quoted Scrivenor, App., 404.

in 1795 it had been possible to purchase it for from £13 to
£15 10s., the manufacturer had now to pay between £23 and
£26 10s. for the iron from Russia, and at least the same for
that from Sweden. The effect on the English ironworks is
obvious. "It appears by the Scarcity and Dearness of Iron
since the Dispute with Russia and Sweden, that there is not
Iron enough made in Great Britain to supply the Consumption. The Iron Masters take every Advantage of a Scarcity
to raise the Iron, while the Manufacturer of Goods cannot
raise his Price, which is very hurtful, and keeps many
industrious Tradesmen from reaping the fruits of their
Labours." So wrote an advertiser in a Birmingham paper
in May, 1801, in putting forward a proposal for the erection
of an ironworks by the consumers of iron, each manufacturer
to provide his share of the capital, and to undertake to
purchase his quota of the metal produced.[1] Such a scheme,
it was claimed, "would keep the Iron at a more certain Price."

In view of the experience of the trade in periods following
the close of the earlier wars of the century, it might have been
anticipated that the conclusion of peace in October, 1801,
would have resulted in loss to the ironmasters and unemployment to their workers. In this and the following year, it is
true, the secondary iron trades suffered. But the impetus
derived from recent developments was sufficient to carry iron
production across the gulf, and at this time Dr. Macnab[2] could
draw a contrast between "the astonishing growth of the iron
trade in the large way, and the palsied state of the manufactures of copper and iron in the small way." In 1801 and
1802 there were no fewer than 22 new furnaces in blast, and
25 in process of erection, and the resumption of the war in
May, 1803, gave to several of these a guarantee of full employment for many years to come.

The intensity with which the struggle with Napoleon was
now conducted, and the restraints on intercourse with
European nations, led to a substantial fall in the volume of
foreign iron imported; while the fact that in 1803 English
iron was, for the first time, substituted for that of Russia and

---

1. *Birmingham Scrap Book,* ii, 263.
2. *Letter on the Supply of Coal to the Metropolis,* 52.

Sweden by the navy and other Government services[1] led to further reductions in the demand for the latter. The amount of foreign iron retained for home consumption during this period varied as follows:[2]

Tons.		Tons.
1799—33,162	....	1807—14,338
1800—29,116	....	1808—15,877
1801—46,181	....	1809— 8,816
1802—39,834	....	1810—19,852
1803—18,682	....	1811— 7,470
1804—22,950	....	1812—Not known.
1805—27,411	....	1813—11,634
1806—17,194	....	1814— 7,361

The figure for the year 1803 obviously registers the dislocation occasioned by the outbreak of war. The year 1806 saw the beginning of the Continental System, and in July, 1807, by the Treaty of Tilsit, Russia threw in her lot with France—events which were mainly responsible for the steady fall in the figures between 1806 and 1810.

Thus shielded from the competition of their foreign rivals the English ironmasters were able to sell the output of their busy furnaces and forges at prices that were more than remunerative. In 1805 " the iron trade in the smelting of pig iron was exceedingly profitable," according to Thomas Attwood;[3] and similar, though less marked prosperity, continued for at least five more years. Even as late as June, 1810, the partners in the Coalbrookdale Company found that their orders were greater than they were able to execute without buying iron, and it was decided that a disused furnace should again be put in blast.[4]

On the manufacturers of ironware and the producers of steel the effect of the war was more equivocal; for though

1. *Observations on the Proposed Tax on Pig Iron* (1806) 10.
2. Scrivenor, *op. cit.*, App., 420. The year assigned to each quantity is the one prior to that given by Scrivenor, who omits to point out that the fiscal year ended on 5 January. Thus, for example, his nominal year 1800 really relates to 1799.
3. *Minutes of Evidence against Orders in Council,* 16
4. *Coalbrookdale MSS.*

they might benefit from the increased demand for weapons,
like the textile manufacturers they normally found a vent for
a substantial part of their product in foreign countries. In
April, 1806, it will be recalled, Britain declared a blockade of
the German coast between the Elbe and the Ems; in November
of the same year Napoleon issued the Berlin Decree, closing
European ports to British vessels and declaring the British
Isles to be in a state of blockade. In January and November,
1807, the British Government replied by the Orders in Council
which in turn called forth Napoleon's Milan Decree of
December, 1807. It is well known that these attempts to put
an end to trade with subjects of enemy countries were far from
successful, and breaches were made in the fortifications of
both belligerents.[1] Licences to neutrals were sold by both
British and French Governments, and contravention of some
of the decrees which were impracticable of enforcement
was winked at. Further, though some of the channels
of trade between Britain and the Continent were effectively
dammed, the streams of commerce quickly cut for themselves
new courses. Though from the end of 1807 to 1811 the
Napoleonic system was enforced with more or less rigour
along practically the whole continental littoral, the possession
by Britain of Malta and Heligoland, and the occupation by
British forces of Sicily, provided points of strategic importance
in the commercial war. Each of these islands became a
gigantic warehouse from which goods could be carried, as
occasion offered, to the ports of the mainland and thence to
the interior; and the popular resentment in several nations
against the Continental System, which tended to increase the
prices of several necessaries of civilized life, rendered smuggling of this kind a matter of no great difficulty.

In 1807 hardware in considerable quantities was exported

---

1. The closing of Hamburg by the British blockade led to the sending of
goods via Tonningen. " Henry Vander Smissen's Sons Altona Beg leave
to announce to their Friends, that in consequence of the renewed Blockade of
the Rivers, Elbe, Weser, and Ems, they have again united themselves with
T. H. Tetens, Esq., of Tonningen; where, as heretofore, their Business as
General Agents, will be carried on under the Firm of ' T. H. Tetens & Co.,'
and beg to solicit a share of those Commands, with which they favoured them
during the period of their last Establishment at the said place—Altona, Apr.
22 1806." *Sheffield Iris*, 15 May 1806.

by British merchants to both Malta and Sicily, where it was transhipped to neutral bottoms and carried to Trieste or Fiume.[1] After the seizure of Heligoland, in September of the same year, British goods of all kinds were run in from the island to Hamburg, where the authorities were less than lukewarm in their administration of Napoleon's decrees; and from Hamburg English wares passed with ease into the heart of France itself. By this route, for example, William Huntsman continued to carry on a large trade with Pierre Louis Sahler of Montbeliard, who purchased steel for watch springs and other purposes. The casks were sent in the first instance to one Abraham Ellermann at Heligoland, who passed them on to a Ludwig Wilhelm Beauvais of Hamburg, who in turn forwarded the steel to Sahler at Montbeliard.[2]

In 1810, however, the French took measures to stop these holes in the dyke : a stricter supervision was exercised over the Mediterranean ports, and a new French administration was established at Hamburg. Nevertheless in 1811 British ironwares were still reaching the Continent—though probably in smaller quantities—via Malta;[3] and alternative doors of entry to that of Hamburg were found in Tonningen in Denmark and Carlshamn in Sweden, where the decrees were heartily disliked and sympathy was felt for those who disregarded them.

Although, therefore, British traders suffered from the delay resulting from circuitous routes, from the high level of freights, from the necessity of paying convoy duty, and in some cases from the confiscation of goods by the enemy, commerce was still carried on; and the iron manufacturing centres enjoyed a quiet prosperity during the whole of this period. The attempts of the British Government to enforce the Orders in Council were, however, to produce a serious situation for those who found their chief market in the United States. It is unnecessary to consider here the relations betweeen the two countries or the fluctuations in general trade during the American Embargo of December 1807—March

---

1. Lord Sheffield, *The Orders in Council and the American Embargo*, 4.
2. Letters among *Huntsman MSS*.
3. Attwood. *Evidence against Orders in Council*, 3.

1809, and the subsequent period of Non-Intercourse. Suffice
it to say that the dislocation of commerce resulted in a fall
in exports to the States of no less than fifty per cent, and that
exporters were only partially compensated by the speculative
boom in trade with South America, the collapse of which in
the later months of 1810 led to the general trade depression
of the following year.[1] In this the smaller iron trades were
involved no less deeply than the textile and other industries
that depended on outlets to foreign markets. If we may
accept a loose estimate made by Thomas Attwood, the total
value of wares produced in Birmingham at this time was
about two million sterling per annum. Of these wares about
half were disposed of in the home market; others to the value
of £800,000 went to America; and the remainder were sold in
the European market.[2] Nails in particular were an important
article of exportation to America, where the use of wooden
buildings occasioned a widespread demand for this staple
product of South Staffordshire.

During the early days of Non-Importation nails and sheet
iron were specifically excepted from the prohibition, and
during the period of the Embargo the smuggling of such
wares into the United States by way of Canada had some
measure of success; but in 1811 similar attempts failed
utterly[3]: and the outbreak of actual war, in June, 1812,
rendered the position of many of the domestic ironworkers
desperate in the extreme. In 1811 over 9,000 people were in
receipt of poor relief in Birmingham alone.[4] During 1809
and 1810 the Sheffield cutlery trade had been at the height
of prosperity : in spite of the offer of high wages there had
been an acute shortage of labour, and demands had even been
put forward for the relaxation of apprenticeship regulations,
which, it was alleged, were hampering entries to the trade.[5]
But in 1811 and 1812 a profound gloom had settled on the
town, and the distress among the metal workers was intense.

---

1. For an account of this see Professor Daniels : " The Cotton Trade at the
Close of the Napoleonic War," *Trans. Manchester Statistical Society*, 1917-18.
See also Lord Sheffield, *op. cit.*, 11-26.
2. *Minutes of Evidence against Orders in Council*, 13.
3. *Minutes of Evidence against Orders in Council*, Potts, 30-31.
4. *Ibid.*, Attwood, 4.
5. Lloyd, *Cutlery Trades*, 339.

Such a fall in the activity of the iron manufacturing trades could not fail to have some reaction on the production of iron and steel, with which alone we are here concerned. "Even the smelting, that till within these two years, afforded some degree of profit, now affords no profit whatever," declared Attwood[1] in April 1812. "The stock of iron has increased; every manufacturer is overloaded with stock, and if he sells his iron he only sells it at his own loss." The effect on labour was serious: ". . . great numbers of labourers have been dismissed within the last twelve months; . . . labourers that twelve months ago could obtain in the iron-works 20s. a week, cannot now obtain more than 10s. or 12s.; and hundreds of them are to be had at 12s." Short time was general in Staffordshire, and many concerns were only kept running by the proprietors' foregoing all profits. At their meeting in November 1812 the Coalbrookdale Partners decided to blow out one of the furnaces at Horsehay on account of the low price of iron;[2] and a similar fall in the price of steel led to a reduction of output by the Sheffield converters and refiners, amounting to almost fifty per cent.[3]

Notwithstanding all this, there is good reason for believing that in iron production the trade depression was but a temporary affair; and never during the war were the smelters, forgemen, and rollers in a plight similar to that of the cotton or lace operatives. There are no riots to record; no Luddites made onslaughts on the plant of the ironworks;[4] and there are none of the midnight meetings and hurried movements of troops that light with a picturesque gleam the somewhat sordid story of the textile workers during these years. The fact is that the iron industry still found its principal market in England; foreign trade was not of immediate importance to more than a minority of the ironmasters; and the outbreak of war with America held for the others the compensation of a

1. *Evidence against Orders in Council*, 12. In 1811 the firm of Popplewell, Pullam and Shaw of the Royds Ironworks, near Leeds, failed. Ling Roth, *The Genesis of Banking in Halifax*, 18.
2. *Coalbrookdale Minute Book.*
3. *Minutes of Evidence Against Orders in Council*, John Bailey, 133.
4. Evidence of Luddite activity in South Yorkshire, however, appears in a letter from one of the partners in the Thorncliffe Ironworks addressed to George Newton. *Thorncliffe MSS.* The letter is dated 18 Nov. 1813.

further demand for the production of cannon and shot. In 1812 the depression cleared; a substantial increase in output took place in South Wales; and in Staffordshire, where the iron industry was most closely associated with trades dependent on exports, the rising demand for cast-iron pipes for the new water-supply companies, afforded work to the value of at least £100,000. Moreover, by this time Sweden had been forced into war with Britain, and the sudden fall in the imports of bar iron from the Baltic provided, until the middle of 1812, a gap for the English forges to fill.[1]

From this time until the cessation of hostilities with America and France the English iron industry continued its path of prosperity. The re-opening of relations with Russia and Sweden resulted in no serious inroad into the home market, for in 1813 the tariff defences of the British producer were again strengthened by an increase of £1 per ton in the existing duty of £5 9s. 10d. But whether protected or not the English ironmaster had now little to fear from foreign competition, except in the highest grades of steel-making irons. During the war period the processes of rolling and puddling had come into general use, and the peasant forges of Northern Europe could not hope to keep pace with the coke-refineries and rolling-mills of the new industrial England. Secure in the home market, and not yet feeling the necessity for other outlets, the English ironmasters could give their energies to the production of munitions and of iron for structural purposes at home, without the perpetual dread which must have haunted other industrialists, that some new turn in politics might sever their supplies of raw material or block their access to a foreign market.

Advocacy of the thesis that the claims of war and the weakening of foreign competition by tariff barriers and high freights were stimulating to the iron trade must not be taken to imply the heresy that war may be productive of national wealth. What the ironmaster gained at this time the British consumer, in large measure, lost. Moreover, a stimulus is not necessarily invigorating in the long run; and it is arguable

---

1. See the Statistics of iron moved down the Monmouth Canal. Scrivenor, 126-7, App. 420; Attwood, *Minutes of Evidence.*

that if the industry had not been subject to the feverish touch of war during the period of growth its constitution in later years would have been more robust, and its final stature would have been no less great. War conditions resulted in a rapidity of development that was far from healthy; and the effects on the industry are to be read not only in the fortunes amassed by the ironmasters, or the relatively high earnings and opportunities for advancement of their workers, but also in the convulsions and distresses of the early years of peace. Just as the war of 1793—1815 had been most effective in energising the ironmakers, so it resulted in poverty and disorganisation more intense than that which had followed the earlier struggles, and more lasting than that which fell upon other British industries in the post-war years.

At the end of the war the English iron industry again found itself with a capacity for production in excess of the immediate peace-time needs of the country. In spite of attempts made by the associated ironmasters to maintain prices, a general fall in values took place and such sales as were effected were at figures below those recorded in the books of the various " Meetings," which are the chief source from which information has generally been drawn.[1] But with the prices of their product falling, the ironmasters found further production impossible; for rents and royalties were generally subject to long-period contracts which had, for the most part, been drawn up in the profitable years when war-prices prevailed. In these circumstances ironworks everywhere were being shut down : many works were sold at a sixth or a seventh of their original cost; the plant of others was broken up and sold for whatever it would fetch; and in some cases whole ironworks were abandoned and allowed to revert to the landowner.[2] " It appears that in Shropshire at this moment [August, 1816] there are 24 iron furnaces out of blast, and only 10 in blast. It also appears that the works of Mr. Reynolds (the oldest family in the trade in the Shropshire

---

1. In 1817 the price of bar iron in Shropshire fell from £18 to £7 a ton. *V.C.H. Shropshire*, 469.

2. *Report on Manufactures, Commerce and Shipping* (1833). Evid. of William Matthews, 9,637.

district) have totally ceased; and that out of 34 furnaces (each casting 50 tons of pig iron per week, and each employing about 300 men) only 10 are at present in work; and of these the Colebrookdale company has given orders for the discontinuance of two; and others must inevitably do the same, for it is estimated that the company at Lilleshall has 5,000 tons of iron on hand, and the one at Madeley-Wood not less than 3,000. These extinguished works consumed not less than 8,000 tons of coal per week, so that a corresponding number of colliers are also destitute."[1] After a few months Joseph Reynolds dismantled the Ketley works and sold the machinery —with results disastrous to the social life of the Wellington district. In Staffordshire the story was the same; and a visitor to Bradley speaks of the " silence of unmingled desolation " of the great ironworks which John Wilkinson had brought into being there. The miseries of the workers have often been detailed : their savings spent and their household furniture sold, many wandered about the district literally starving. In Bilston alone there were 2,000 unemployed, and the death-rate increased fifteen per cent. In Walsall, Wednesbury, Tipton, Dudley, and Wolverhampton at least 12,000 were out of work. At Merthyr Tydfil, where rioting took place, military had to be called in to preserve order, but elsewhere the poverty and dejection were too intense for the spirit of revolt to assert itself.[2]

Slowly and painfully some measure of readjustment was brought about. The continued need for water-pipes gave some employment to Staffordshire and South Yorkshire foundries; and the Walkers of Rotherham received a contract for castings, weighing over 5,000 tons, for the Southwark Bridge which Rennie was erecting at this time. Part of the contract was sub-let to the Thorncliffe enterprise and to William Yates—a relative of the Walkers—who owned the Gospel Oak Ironworks in Staffordshire; so that these firms

1. *Annual Register* (1816), 131.

2. *V.C.H. Shropshire*, 460; *Annual Register* (1816), 111; Lawley, *History of Bilston*, 175. For the distress in Monmouth and South Wales see *Economica*, ii, 163; for that of Birmingham see the *Birmingham Weekly Post*, 31 August 1889.

were helped in some measure during the worst period of depression.[1] In 1818 the cloud appeared to be lifting and there were a few months of brightening trade extending into the following year;[2] but gloom once more settled on the industry; and though between 1819 and 1822 conditions were never as bad as in 1816, works were still being closed, plant was being sold, and new construction was practically at a standstill.[3] Not until 1823 did the first signs of improvement show themselves; in the following year trade was definitely good; and in 1825 the boom was at its height. The story of the subsequent collapse and stagnation of the late 'twenties hardly falls within the scope of this chapter.

The fluctuations of the iron trade during the early part of the nineteenth century are not easily represented in statistics of output; for the volume of iron produced is no criterion of profit. In periods of good trade there was, needless to say, a tendency for production to increase, but it required a very serious depression to bring about a large diminution in the output of pig and bar iron. One ironmaster, indeed, even went so far as to assert that when trade was bad ironmasters increased the volume of their product—partly because of the need to sell more iron when prices were low, to cover the instalments of the purchase price of minerals in the soil, and of the works themselves.[4] Although this statement need not be accepted in its entirety, there was certainly an inelasticity in iron-production that renders crude statistics of output somewhat delusive. Prices are a better index of the prosperity of the ironmasters, and the existence of periodic meetings in each locality has provided records of price changes over a long series of years, though, as already mentioned, there was a tendency in times of bad trade for individuals to break away from the associations and to sell at

1. Guest, *Historic Notices of Rotherham*, 491.

2. " The iron trade is also so much revived in most of its branches that the present works are not able to supply the demands." *The Cambrian*, 19 Dec. 1818. Cited Matthews, *Historic Newport*, 170.

3. " There are two periods of very extensive ruin : one was from the latter end of 1815 to about 1817, and the other in 1820, 1821, and 1822." *Report on Manufactures* (1833), Evidence of William Matthews 9639

4. *Rept. on Manufactures*, William Matthews, 9641, 9671, 9705.

something below the official values. With this fact in mind, the following figures relating to the average prices of forge pig iron in the Midlands may be taken as a rough indication of industrial vicissitudes during fifteen years of war and the succeeding fifteen years of peace.[1]

£	s.	d.		£	s.	d.
1801—6	15	0	....	1816—3	15	0
1802—6	0	0	....	1817—4	5	0
1803—6	0	0	....	1818—5	10	0
1804—5	16	6	....	1819—6	2	6
1805—6	8	0	....	1820—4	10	0
1806—6	15	0	....	1821—4	0	0
1807—6	1	3	....	1822—3	15	0
1808—6	5	0	....	1823—4	0	0
1809—6	5	0	....	1824—5	0	0
1810—6	6	0	....	1825—7	10	0
1811—6	5	0	....	1826—5	0	0
1812—5	10	0	....	1827—4	10	0
1813—5	2	6	....	1828—4	0	0
1814—6	0	0	....	1829—3	12	6
1815—5	0	0	....	1830—3	8	9

III.

The ebb and flow of the tide of trade under the influence of forces ultimately political in origin have so far been considered in their bearing on the industry as a whole. How a single industrial unit fared in its voyage over these changing seas may be learned from a study of the records of Messrs. Newton, Chambers and Co., of the Thorncliffe Ironworks; and with a brief account of the history of this remarkable undertaking between the time of its formation on the eve of the war to the end of the post-war depression in 1823, this chapter will be brought to a close.

In the year 1792 Thomas Chambers, formerly an employee of Samuel Walker, entered into partnership with George

1. *Ibid.*, Barclay.

Newton, a manufacturer of spades and trowels in Sheffield; and in December the Phœnix Foundry was set up, where articles such as stoves, ranges, wheels, and machinery for cotton mills were cast by the partners. Like many Sheffield craftsmen of the late eighteenth century, Newton had combined his industrial operations with retail shopkeeping and dealings in tea, cutlery, and miscellaneous goods; and it was through him that a wholesale tea merchant of London, named Maskew, came to invest some two thousand pounds in the new venture. In the following year, however, Maskew withdrew from the partnership, and his place was taken by Henry Longden, a razor-maker, who in 1796 supplied further capital out of a bequest of twelve or fifteen thousand pounds from his uncle, a wealthy West Indian merchant of Sheffield. And in 1799 two brothers, Robert and John Scott, woollen-draper and haberdasher respectively, of London, brought additional resources to the firm.

In December 1794 the capital of the new enterprise was £2,128, and during the year a profit of about 23 per cent. had been made. Encouraged by this success, and finding difficulties in obtaining adequate supplies of pig iron for the growing foundry, the partners, who were now assisted by Longden's capital, determined to set up smelting works of their own : a lease of land, coal, and ironstone for twenty-one years was arranged with Earl Fitzwilliam, and the Thorncliffe Ironworks at Chapeltown came into being. The first furnace was put in blast in 1795, and seven years later the foundry was moved from Sheffield to Chapeltown.

Almost from the first the firm specialised in the production of iron rails for the waggon-ways of collieries in the South Yorkshire area; contracts were obtained for the supply of cast-iron pipes to the West Middlesex Water Company and many similar undertakings; and, as already mentioned, the firm co-operated with the Walkers of Rotherham to supply materials for the construction of Southwark Bridge. But perhaps the chief source of profit was the making of pipes, lamp-posts, and apparatus for gas-lighting, to assist in the production of which James Malom, who had received his training under Murdoch at Soho, was brought into the

business. Contracts for the supply of ordnance were under-
taken during the later stages of the war; but at no time,
apparently, did these fill a large place in the order-books of
the firm.

Longden and Robert Scott seem to have taken no active
part in the conduct of the business, but—at least after 1806—
each of the other partners had definite duties assigned to him :
Newton directed the counting-house and attended to the
correspondence; Chambers superintended the furnaces and
dealt with all matters relating to work and wages; and John
Scott controlled the warehouse and saw to the dispatch of
goods to customers. It was agreed that each of the heads
of the business should receive a salary, but this was fixed at
a sum almost absurdly small in view of the services rendered
and the magnitude of the operations of the firm.   From 1799
to 1811, for example, George Newton received £80 per
annum; and though in 1812 his stipend was raised to £200,
it remained at this figure for four years only, and in the
post-war depression it was reduced to the original amount.
With regard to profits, a similar arrangement to that of the
Coalbrookdale Company was adopted, whereby the partners
received a fixed interest of five per cent. on their capital, and
the surplus was then divided into nine shares, of which three
went to Longden, two to Chambers, two to Newton, and the
remaining two to the Scotts. In 1811, when Longden withdrew from the partnership, his share of the joint capital
amounted to £25,222—more than double his original holding.
Money was borrowed to pay off this sum, and it was agreed
that henceforth all profits should be divided equally among
the three remaining partners.[1] The policy of leaving profits
to accumulate in the firm at 5 per cent. was generally adopted,
both before and after the withdrawal of Longden; and thus
the capital increased automatically with the growth of
profitable business.

These details of organisation and finance are necessary
to an understanding of the figures shown below, which
have been drawn up from the partnership book of George

1. John Scott had left the firm in 1808, and his share had been taken over
by his brother.

Newton, still in the possession of the firm. After 1799 the profits shown are net: they represent the surplus after 5 per cent. had been paid on capital. In the last column these have been expressed as percentage on capital in the manner of a modern joint-stock company; but it should be borne in mind that no such dividends were ever drawn from the concern: had they been there would have been nothing in reserve and no growth of capital could have taken place. Moreover, it must not be forgotten that the "wages of management" were extremely small, and that much of what appears to be a relatively high profit would have been absorbed by salaries had these been on what would now be considered an adequate scale. The profits do not by any means represent the gains of passive shareholders: they are mainly the fruit of the efforts of hard-working men and are in no sense fortuitous.[1] Such earnings are hardly comparable with those of a modern company, and attention is directed not to the absolute amounts but to the fluctuations that occurred from year to year.

1. That the active partners were alive to the fact is indicated in the correspondence of the firm. In 1813 Scott had written Newton from London complaining that his interest had not been received when due, and in the course of a sharp reply the other partners remark: "We *think* we have good grounds for expecting that for the *privilege* of being a sleeping Partner (which in these times is certainly a great *privilege*) you ought to let your Capital be made up to the strict Letter of the Articles of Partsp especially as we do not require you to make any *real* advances, but permit it to be made up with Int. which is spun out of the Bowels of the Concern itself."

M

Period.	Capital at beginning of period. £	Net profits or losses.* £	Profits or losses.* per cent.
Dec.—Dec.			
1793—1794	2,270	494	22.3
1794—1795	4,974	1,228	24.7
July—July			
1799—1802	14,500[1]	9,746	67.2[2]
1802—1805	24,379	2,300	9.4[3]
1805—1806	27,401	3,224	11.8
1806—1807	30,686	3,984	13.0
1807—1808	33,939	Nil	Nil
1808—1810	34,280	8,208	24.0[3]
1810—1811	41,649	7,471	17.9
1811—1812	46,481	6,000	12.9
1812—1813	27,720[4]	6,000	— [4]
1813—1814	34,576	6,501	18.8
1814—1815	39,527	6,600	16.7
1815—1816	49,672	Nil	Nil
1816—1817	50,031	−3,856	−7.7
1817—1818	47,234	2,700	5.7
July—Dec.			
1818—1820	50,377	7,415	14.7[5]
1820—1821	58,260	2,800	4.8[5]
Dec.—Dec.			
1821—1823	63,306	662	1.0[3]

* Losses are indicated by a minus sign.

It could not be expected that the log of any single craft should record every cyclonic and anticyclonic movement

1. Approx.
2. 3 years.
3. 2 years.
4. Longden withdrew in 1811, and during 1812-13 the other partners were paying off his share—over £15,000—of the joint capital. The £5,000 taken as profit was therefore a nominal figure, and to express this as a percentage of the reduced " share capital " would be misleading. The partners were in the position of a modern company which increases its debentures instead of its ordinary shares, for the debts owing were greatly enlarged by the transaction. By July 1813 £11,685 had been repaid to Longden.
5. Eighteen months.

across the ocean, for each vessel is liable to meet stray winds and sudden calms outside the courses steered by others. Nevertheless most of the main influences affecting the industry during this period are represented in these figures. The boom of the period 1800—1801 is reflected in the relatively high profits of the Thorncliffe partners, as is also the general fall of prosperity—not however resulting in actual loss—after 1810. The post-war depression is clearly marked in the cessation of all profits, and in the losses of 1816-17. In December, 1814, new leases had been entered into with Earl Fitzwilliam for the working of coal and ironstone, on terms which indicate the expectation of good trade; and the difficulties of the partners after the war are shown by the fact that, in September, 1816, they appealed for the postponement of royalties till the spring, " as the great Scarcity of Money and decline of Business renders our situation truly embarrassing at present." Another document, dated 18 March, 1817, also illustrates the conditions of the industry : in an appeal for a lenient assessment of rates the ironmasters declare that the works " are much depreciated in Value by the present deplorable state of the Iron Trade, having only one Furnace in Blast, doing above two-thirds less Business than usual, so that a great part of the buildings are unoccupied." The temporary revival in 1818 is represented in the increased, but by no means abnormal, profits of the eighteen months following July of that year; and the return of dark days again led to the reduced gains of 1820-3. Fortunately the firm was directed by men whose energy and judgment enabled it to weather these storms in which so many others went down; and the Thorncliffe Works have survived to become one of the best-known and most efficient undertakings in the iron and coal industries of to-day.

CHAPTER VII.

COMBINATIONS OF CAPITALISTS.

I.

THE organisation of the ironmasters into associations for the regulation of the industry began in early times, and the fusion of local nebular groups into those powerful national bodies that are typical of modern iron industrialism was largely accomplished during the period with which this volume is concerned. Even in the seventeenth century, and probably before, agreements as to the terms on which trade should be conducted were reached between neighbouring ironmasters; and in May, 1665—to cite one instance—George Sitwell made an arrangement with two rival capitalists whereby the selling price of bar iron was fixed in the markets which they served in common.[1] In the charcoal-iron industry one of the chief incentives to concerted action was derived from the limitation of fuel, and it was undoubtedly this that drew together the industrialists of the Furness region.

In 1712 the only two firms in the district—the Cunsey and Backbarrow companies—came to an understanding as to the price to be paid to woodowners and the quota of the local supplies of charcoal to be taken by each : if either received quantities in excess it undertook to compensate the other at the rate of half-a-crown per dozen sacks; and when woods were purchased outright the companies agreed not to bid one against the other. Such a combination of buyers was obviously hostile to the interests of the woodowners; and in 1748 several of the larger proprietors set up a furnace of their own, in order to afford an outlet on better terms for the charcoal supplies they produced. Almost all the lesser woodowners also undertook to boycott the " combinators " and to deliver only to the new furnace, at a price regulated, under a

1. Sitwell, *Journal Derbyshire Arch. Soc.*, x 31.

sliding scale, by the price of pig iron in the Bristol market.[1] This agreement lasted for thirty years, and in 1781 the three chief iron firms in Furness again entered into a concordat which continued until the year 1818, when all the surviving ironworks came into the hands of a single firm and a local monopoly was established. Agreement as to charcoal naturally led to concerted action in other matters; and soon after the middle of the eighteenth century regular meetings of local ironmasters were held at the Sun Inn, Penny Bridge, to deal with trade affairs, prices, and conditions of employment. In 1757, for instance, it was agreed " that no bar iron at home be sold under £19, at Liverpool £17 per ton."[2]

But so long as charcoal remained the only fuel used in the making of iron, works were necessarily widely dispersed, combination was difficult, and regulation of price on anything approaching a national scale impossible.[3]

In the coke-smelting industry the causes of the development of combinations of ironmasters are to be found elsewhere. At all times ironmaking required a relatively large amount of fixed capital: in 1812, according to Thomas Attwood, a complete set of ironworks could not be constructed for less than £50,000;[4] and in 1833 one with a productive capacity of 300 tons of bar iron a week—with the necessary mines of coal and ironstone—would cost anything from £50,000 to £150,000.[5] At this time about one-fourth of the cost of bar iron was said to consist of royalties on the raw material, and of interest on the capital sunk in the plant; and although such charges had probably increased very considerably, it is certain that in earlier periods also the ratio of fixed to circulating capital was high compared with that of other industries. In these circumstances not only was it ruinous for an ironmaster to withdraw from the industry during a period of depression, when his plant would fetch little in the market, but it was also expensive to shut down the works even for a

1. Fell, *op. cit.*, 142-5.
2. *Ibid.*, 254, 279, 288.
3. This and the preceding paragraph are reprinted from an article by the present writer in the *Economic Journal*, xxx, 331-339.
4. *Evidence against Orders in Council*, 18.
5. *Committee on Manufactures* (1833), Ev. of William Matthews, 9657.

limited period. In times of bad trade, works were continued so long as the selling price of the iron would cover even a little more than the prime costs of production—raw material and labour. Competition in sales was consequently felt to be harmful, and there was a strong incentive for ironmasters to combine with the object of maintaining prices.[1]

It was considerations such as these that as early as 1762 led Abraham Darby to enter into an agreement with Isaac and John Wilkinson whereby a uniform price was to be charged by the companies of Coalbrookdale, Willey, and Bersham, for cylinders, pipes, and other articles in all markets other than that of London.[2] And it was very probably by a welding of this with similar groups that an association of ironmasters covering the Midland area shortly afterwards came into being. The exact time and circumstance are unfortunately forgotten, but a reference in one of the published letters of Richard Reynolds shows that this union of producers was in existence in 1777, and that it had already adopted that system of quarterly meetings by which the iron trade was regulated till well into the nineteenth century.[3] It is more than probable that, from the first, these meetings were concerned with the determination of prices and of the conditions of sale. But within a few years political circumstances forced them to pay attention to other matters; and, in common with similar groups of capitalists formed in other industries, the organised ironmasters took a by no means insignificant part in the shaping of public policy during the last two decades of the century. In particular, the Midland ironmasters were intimately associated with the Birmingham Commercial Committee which was set up in July 1783 under the presidency of Samuel Garbett.[4] For many years Garbett had deplored the neglect of industrial matters by the Government; and after failing in an attempt to persuade Burke " to take the lead in considering our commerce as a subject of politics," he

---

1. *Ibid.*, Evid. of Anthony Hill, 10230-36 ; Sparrow, 10777.
2. *V.C.H. Shropshire*, 464.
3. Rathbone, *Memoir*, 126. See also letters written in 1789 and 1791, pp. 179, 185-6.
4. Wright, *Chronicles of the Birmingham Chamber of Commerce*. See notice in *Birmingham Scrap Book*, Vol. v. 12 Aug. 1783.

threw himself into the new movements by means of which the industrialists were themselves seeking to defend their supposed interests in the political arena.[1]

In 1784 manufacturers throughout the country were unanimous in their condemnation of Pitt's ill-devised excise scheme; and on 7 January, 1785, the Quarterly Meeting of Ironmasters held at Stourbridge passed a resolution that might well have been framed by some modern advocate of the Estate Duty as a substitute for the Corporation Profits Tax, or other taxes bearing heavily on business life : " That property acquired by trade and manufacturers is a fit object of taxation ; but not the manufactures themselves." In the same spirit the Commercial Committee of Birmingham, after commending the Ironmasters' resolution, declared

" That manufactures and commerce should only be considered as a means of acquiring that real property which is the proper subject of taxation. That property, while exposed to the extreme uncertainty which it is necessarily subject to, cannot be justly deemed substantial until it is withdrawn from those dangers . . . That, in general, every Excise law is irreconcilable with the freedom and secrecy every manufacturer has a natural right to demand, in his own workshops and in the exercise of his business. . . "[2]

But it was naturally with the proposed tax of 2s. a ton on coal that the ironmasters were primarily concerned : at any time such a duty would have been highly objectionable, but to bring it forward at the very moment when mineral fuel was being substituted for charcoal in the refining process, and when puddling and rolling were on the point of being put into practice, was surely most inopportune.[3]

This point of view was vigorously expressed by Richard Reynolds in a letter to Earl Gower, President of the Council,

1. *Cal. H.O. Papers* (1766-72, 134).
2. Wright, *op. cit.*, 15-16.
3. At a later date it was estimated that in making a ton of pig iron about 10 tons of coal were consumed ; and that (including the fuel used in torrefying the raw material, that used for the steam engine, and that consumed by the workers in their homes) no less than 19 tons were required to produce a single ton of iron in the form of rods. Estimate of Dr. Macnab. Cited Meade.

in which, after pointing out the advantages that had already flowed from the use of coke, he urged that " the only chance we have of making iron as cheap as it can be imported from Russia, is the low price of our fuel."[1]   Such considerations carried weight even with politicians, and coal remained exempt from the burden of the new Excise.

Taxation of raw material was not, however, the only question on which the industrialists ranged themselves in opposition to the policy of the Government.   Whether well-founded or not, there was a general belief among Englishmen at this time that the economic policy towards the colonies had been a principal cause of the American War; and while that war was still in process an attempt was made to revise the Irish policy, lest a similar unhappy issue should appear across St. George's Channel.   The outbreak of the war now shut the American market against the Irish linen manufacturers, and the embargoes imposed by Britain struck a severe blow at the Irish provision trades.   Distress was acute and a demand for the removal of trade restrictions arose in Ireland. This was voiced in the English House by Lord Nugent, Burke, and others, and was met in April, 1778, by the proposal of the Ministry to set Ireland on the same footing as England in respect of the colonial trade, and to remove certain disabilities against Irish traders.

Vested interests in England were quick to organise themselves in opposition : the traders of Bristol, who were concerned with the importation of hemp and iron from the colonies, appear to have taken the lead, and to have sought to enlist the iron-masters in the ranks of the opponents of the measure.   In April 1778, William Gibbons of Bristol, one of the outstanding figures in the iron trade at this time, wrote to Birmingham and other centres of the industry to urge the importance of con-certed measures against the new policy.[2]   It was pointed out that the Irish duty on imported iron was about 10s. a ton, whereas the English duty was about five times greater ; the Irish had lower rents, cheaper food, and smaller wages ; and internal taxes—so it was alleged—remained at a low level in Ireland

1.   Rathbone, *op. cit.*, 280.
2.   *Aris's Birmingham Gazette*, 27 April 1778.

at a time when Great Britain was bearing the heavy burden
of a National Debt incurred mainly in the service of imperial
defence. The proposed breach in the Colonial System would
give to Ireland an enormous advantage in the production of
iron; labour would tend to move there, and emigration to the
Shannon would be as frequent as in the past it had been to
the American seaboard. The writer ended by urging the
immediate preparation of protests to Parliament; a draft
petition was enclosed; and an indirect tribute was paid to the
political sense of the Birmingham industrialists in the apology
offered for these detailed instructions, which had been drawn
up for the guidance of little bodies of manufacturers—" a
Hint useless to places of greater Consequence, and Men of
Information."

In view of the antagonism which the measure aroused, the
Government acted with discretion : direct importation from
the colonies to Ireland was prohibited, and the list of commodities that might be exported from Ireland to the colonies was
curtailed. Further, the opposition of the iron interests was
allayed by an undertaking that exportation of iron and iron
wares should be allowed only on condition that the Irish
Parliament imposed duties equivalent to those in force in
Britain[1]—a principle that was applied generally when further
relief was conceded to Irish trade under the threat of the
Volunteers in 1779 and 1780.

More serious, however, was the struggle over the Commercial Propositions, which, formulated by the newly
enfranchised Irish legislature, were brought to the notice of
the House of Commons in February, 1785. In essence these
proposed a reciprocal lowering of tariffs between Britain and
Ireland; and the intention of Pitt and other sponsors appears
to have been, in particular, to encourage the importation of
Irish linen into England. The remaining disabilities of the
Irish exporter to this country were to be removed; the colonial
trade was to be opened to Irishmen; duties in the two
countries were to be equalised; and, in accordance with Pitt's
dictum of " community of benefits, community of burdens,"

1. *Aris's Birmingham Gazette*, 25 May 1778; 18 Geo. III, c. 55

Ireland was to contribute part of the anticipated increase in her revenue to the British Exchequer.[1]

To these proposals English manufacturers as a body were bitterly opposed. In February, 1785, the Birmingham Commercial Committee met to consider the matter, and immediately afterwards general meetings were arranged to which traders from the surrounding district were summoned.[2] Resolutions were formulated, and a petition against the Irish Propositions asked that the revenue systems of the two countries should be brought into conformity, and that, in particular, the duties on the importation of bar iron should be assimilated. Those actually levied on importation into Ireland were, as already pointed out, substantially lower than the English duties, and it was obviously possible to achieve equality either by raising the former or by lowering the latter.[3] Asked by George Rose " whether if the manufacturers of iron of Great Britain and Ireland were made subject to the same duties upon importation into each country respectively, the manufacturer of Great Britain would have any reason to fear a competition? " Richard Reynolds replied in the negative—" so long as our fuel is untaxed and our national spirit of industry and exertion continues." But both he and other ironmasters insisted that a common tariff must be reached only by a raising of the Irish duties :

" A reduction of the duty on the importation of foreign iron into England to the same rate that is paid in Ireland would not only immediately and greatly decrease our revenues, but still more extensively, as well as more importantly, injure it and the country also, by ruining the iron works of this kingdom; and therefore, the Irish paying an equal duty to ours on all foreign iron imported, as it is the shortest, so it is the truest . . . . way of putting the iron trade of the two countries on an equal footing."[4]

In other parts of the country meetings similar to that in Birmingham had been called, and, in particular, the manufac-

1. Murray, *op. cit.*, 238-40.
2. Wright, *op. cit.*, 18.
3. The Irish duty was 9s. 7½d. a ton, the English £2 16s. 1½d. See *A Complete Investigation of Mr. Eden's Treaty*, 74.
4. Rathbone, *op. cit.*, 259, 284.

turers of Manchester, under the leadership of Thomas Walker, were actively resisting the policy of the Propositions. At the suggestion of Josiah Wedgwood delegates from the various districts met to co-ordinate the opposition; and on 14 March, 1785, there appeared that most ambitious issue of the corporate sense of the rising industrialists, the General Chamber of the Manufacturers of Great Britain. The activities of this body and the part played by it in the defeat of the Irish Propositions have recently been described in the admirable thesis of Dr. Witt Bowden.[1] As, however, Dr. Bowden had access only to newspaper reports and treated the body mainly as the creation of the cotton men, it may not be out of place to give additional details from the publications of the Chamber itself and to emphasise the part played in it by the ironmasters.

" It seems hitherto to have escaped the notice of the manufacturers " [declared its founders [2]] " that whilst the *landed* and the *funded interests,* the *East India,* and other *commercial bodies,* have their respective advocates in the great council of the nation, *they* alone are destitute of that advantage; and it is probable from this source that many of their grievances have arisen—that they have so repeatedly and perhaps inadvertently been oppressed by ministers unacquainted with their real interests, and misled by the designs of interested individuals."

The Chamber laid special stress on the organisation of local bodies, and those of Manchester, Birmingham, and the Potteries, formed the backbone of the national movement.[3]

---

1. *The Rise of the Great Manufacturers of Great Britain.* Doctoral thesis presented to the University of Pennsylvania, 1919. See also article by the same writer in *American Historical Review,* xxv.
2. *Plan of the General Chamber of Manufacturers of Great Britain,* Municipal Reference Library, Birmingham.
3. The Regulations declare : i. That the Chamber shall consist of Manufacturers and such Delegates (being commercial men of the same description) as may be appointed by Provincial Chambers. Every member not subscribing to a Provincial Chamber shall pay a guinea. Provincial Chambers are to pay to this institution 5s. per annum per member. ii. A General Meeting shall be held soon after the meeting of Parliament every year. A Committee shall be appointed to consist of 21 Manufacturers, residing in London, who shall meet on the first Thursday in every month ; and of this Committee, the President, Vice-President, and all Delegates from Provincial Chambers shall be members, and be entitled to vote ; any 5 of whom shall form a Committee. *Plan of the General Chamber.*

Informal meetings of leaders in the different trade groups were also frequent; and it was, no doubt, as representatives either of the Chamber itself or of the Ironmasters' Association that on 11 May, 1785, William Gibbons of Bristol, Richard Reynolds, and Matthew Boulton obtained an interview with George Rose. " After we had talked over this Matter " [wrote William Gibbons, evidently referring to the Irish Propositions as a whole[1]] " we had a little Chat ab^t the Iron Trade and from it I have no doubt, that if the Irish Proposition pass into Law, We shall have a Bounty on Iron Ware to equalize us with Ireland. I saw Mr. Garbet in Town and told him hereof and he will second the Idea in an Interview he expects in a day or two with Mr. Pitt." If, as seems likely, it was intended to buy off the opposition of the iron manufacturers by a Danegeld, the policy resulted in failure, for the incursions of the industrialists into the domain of the politicians became more pronounced. In their petition of 7 June to the House of Lords, the Birmingham Chamber boldly entered the open field in full day and declared " that the only expedient which can firmly and lastingly unite the interests of the two kingdoms in commercial matters is a complete union of the two states."[2]

This demand for the reversal of the Irish policy as a whole was too audacious to find acceptance, but the strategy of the General Chamber was successful first in obtaining the postponement of a Parliamentary decision, and subsequently in securing such a modification of the Propositions as to render them unpalatable, and so bring about their rejection by the Irish themselves.[3] The massed force of the new manufacturers, captained by such men as Wedgwood and Boulton, had achieved a signal victory.

On the question of the Eden Treaty and freer commercial relations with France there was no such unanimity. William Eden himself, under instructions from Pitt, was careful to ascertain the opinions of the industrial and commercial leaders before entering into negotiations with the French; and this

1. William Gibbons to Matthew Boulton, 17 May 1785, *B. and W. MSS.*
2. Wright, *op. cit.*, 21.
3. Bowdon, *op. cit.*, 75.

time the weight of the cotton, iron, and pottery interests was as strongly thrown in favour of the Government policy, as in the case of Ireland, it had been against that policy. For all these trades had much to gain by a wider entry to the French market, while none had cause to be afraid of serious competition from French manufacturers. " With respect to the iron trade, I apprehend the intercourse between the two nations cannot be too free." [wrote Reynolds to Lord Sheffield[1]] " From its most imperfect state as pig-iron, to its highest finish in the regulating spring of a watch, we have nothing to fear if the importation into each country should be permitted without duty." During the autumn of 1786 the matter was debated from every point of view; and though the Committee of the Chamber, on 28 November, expressed doubts whether sufficient safeguards had been provided against the migration of English workmen to France, that of 9 December, with Wedgwood in the chair, passed a resolution strongly supporting the Treaty.

This resolution cleft the Chamber from top to bottom, for the capitalists in the older industries, and those of London in particular, were bitterly hostile. On 5 February 1787 a General Meeting was called, and since this was held in London, it was easy for the manufacturers of the older type to outvote the industrialists of the Midlands and the North. At another meeting, five days later, the chamber expressed its alarm on hearing that Parliament was about to make an immediate decision; and a petition was framed asking for a postponement of judgment, and pointing to "the providential effects" of delay in the settlement of the Irish question a few months earlier.[2] At the General Meeting which followed, special attention was given to the iron trade, and here again the protectionist manufacturers of ironware, as distinct from the "liberal" producers of pig and bar iron, were in a decided majority. It was asserted that since 55,000 tons of bar iron were imported annually, whereas only 30,000 tons were produced in this country, the existing duty was absolutely necessary if the

1. Rathbone, *op. cit.*, 287.
2. *Public Proceedings of the General Chamber of Manufacturers*, 25.

English ironmaster was to keep pace with the Russian. But, so loaded with duty on his raw material, the English manufacturer found it difficult to maintain a footing in the French market : for the Frenchman paid duty of 15 livres only on his imported bar iron; and even when the special stamp duties imposed in certain areas were included, the total taxes on the manufacturer were considerably less than those shouldered by the Englishman.[1] The ancient jealousy of Irish industry also once again raised its head. If the treaty were ratified Irish ironwares would enter France burdened only with the lower duty imposed in Ireland[2]; and, further, it would then be possible for Irish goods to be brought into England at the lower tariff rate proposed for the French, by the simple expedient of making the vessel in which they were carried touch at Dunkirk on its way to this country. From the fears expressed lest the trade in anchors to Portugal should be lost to England, it appears that the anchor-smiths of the Thames Estuary—always a body standing apart from other iron industrialists—were among the opponents of freer commercial intercourse.[3]

The attitude of the Birmingham group, on the other hand, was expressed by James Watt in a letter of enthusiastic praise and high hopes that the proposed treaty would lead to lasting peace between the two nations.[4] To Wedgwood, Watt wrote on 26 February, 1787, with assurances of the support of himself and his associates :

" I am very sorry to see by the public papers that there are two opinions in the Chamber of Manuf^{rs} about the Treaty with France. As your opinions on that subject seem to coincide with my own I thought it might be some small support to you to inform you of it and also to assure you that Mr. Boulton, Mr. Garbett and I believe all the town of Birmingham are of the same sent^t at least I was present some time ago at a public meeting with above 100 of the principal inhabitants, Merchts and manufacturers, where

1. Fifteen livres was about 12s. 6d., and the stamp duties amounted to about £1 5s.
2. *A Complete Investigation of Mr. Eden's Treaty*, 74.
3. *Public Proceedings*, 37, 66.
4. James Watt to De Virly, 4 Feb. 1787, *B. and W. MSS.*

success to the Treaty and a perpetual peace between Britain and France was drunk and followed by three hearty and unanimous cheers. Mr. Garbett also informs me that he is pestered with his townsmen calling on him anxiously enquiring when he thinks the ports will be opened."

Three weeks later, in face of the continued agitation against the treaty, Watt counselled withdrawal from the General Chamber and the formation of a new body. In this only delegates from associations should find a place, and no direct representation of individuals should be allowed. The Birmingham Committee unanimously condemned the General Chamber for its action in sending to Parliament a petition against the treaty.[1] And on 25 July, in a letter which indicates clearly the cleavage between the older centres and the new industrial regions, Watt informed Wedgwood of his project :

" At a private meeting of some of the principals of our Commercial Committee to-day I was desired to write to you concerning the establishment of a Chamber of Manufacturers on a better footing than the last, on which head they wish to be possessed of your ideas and if convenient wish you to spend a day here on your return home giving them timely warning. The Idea now started but not any ways fixt is the union of the Chambers of Manchester, the Iron masters, Sheffield, the Pottery, Nottingham, and such others as are in the neighbourhood to meet at Manchester, Birm^m, the pottery, &c., either in rotation or as may be convenient and to maintain a regular correspondence and to have nothing to do with Londoners except on particular occasions."

There is no evidence that any such organisation as that here suggested was actually brought into being, though representatives of various provincial commercial committees sometimes met to concert a policy when trade interests appeared to be threatened.[2] The fact that the groups

1. Wright, *op. cit.*, 26.
2. In 1796, for example, delegates from Manchester, Liverpool, Leeds, Halifax, Birmingham, and Exeter met to consider the confiscation of British property in Southern Europe. Helm, *History of the Manchester Chamber of Commerce*, 34.

enumerated in Watt's letter had seceded from the General Chamber meant that its power was shattered, and the Government was thus able to complete the agreement with France, undeterred by the resistance of the protectionist Londoners.

With reference to the action of the dissentients the phrase " commercial liberalism " has been used; it may not, therefore, be superfluous to point out that it was no consistent economic theory or enlightened social ideal that dictated the attitude of Wedgwood, Garbett, the Ironmasters, and the Manchester manufacturers—though it is true that here and there appeared a dim consciousness that industrial prosperity and peace in Europe were not entirely unconnected. The mercantilist bias of these men had already been exhibited in their attitude to the Irish Resolutions; and it was now one of the main counts in their indictment against the anti-treaty party that the latter had published their deliberations in the press, and had thus given information to the French concerning several British industries.[1]

The pro-treaty group were no less determined than their opponents in resisting the repeal of the laws prohibiting the exportation of tools and machinery: Boulton and Watt, engaged though they were in exporting what surely was of far greater moment than any single tool or piece of textile machinery, joined with others to prevent British instruments of production getting into the hands of the foreigner; and their only concern was lest steam-engine parts " be construed by some ignorant Custom House Officer into Hardware Tools," which were among the prohibited implements.[2] The truth is that expediency and immediate self-interest determined their " liberalism ": the new, no less than the old order of industrialists was protectionist at heart.

For a few years hereafter no ill-wind from Westminster arose to ruffle the surface on which the ironmasters were

1. Watt to Wedgwood, 26 Feb. 1787, *B. and W. MSS.* " In any case no conduct can be more absurd than news paper publications on the subject. Why should we inform the French ministry of the secrets of our trade or our private sentiments?'

2. Garbett to Watt, 24 June 1786; Watt to Phillips, 26 Apr. 1787. A meeting of the Birmingham Commercial Committee was considering the matter in March 1790. *Birm. Scrap Book*, vii, 94.

floating to fortune; but, in 1796, the proposal to impose a tax on coal at the pit-head, followed as it was by the suggestion of an excise of 20s. per ton on pig iron and a corresponding customs' duty, raised a new storm in the industry. On 26 October, 1797, when Pitt's full intentions became known, Boulton and Watt directed urgent letters on the subject to William Reynolds of Ketley, Joseph Dawson of Low Moor, and the Walkers of Rotherham, counselling immediate action by the Ironmasters' Meeting and suggesting that the opposition would be more effective if it were brought to the notice of Pitt by Members of Parliament before the matter should be raised in the House itself. A meeting of ironmasters was held at Wolverhampton, and John Wilkinson, William Gibbons, and Richard Crawshay were deputed to meet members of the Ministry.[1] "We understand the Welsh Ironmasters have been informed" [wrote Watt to Dawson, 11 November, 1797] "and we hope the Scotch ones have been—Mr. Hawkins Browne would be a proper member to apply to among others—the Marquis of Stafford has large revenues from Iron Works—From what we have heard if good reasons are given to Mr. P. the matter will be dropt for the present, but it behoves the Iron Masters to be upon their guard and not to suffer themselves to be deceived by a delusive calm." Pitt was, in fact, persuaded to abandon the proposal for an excise on iron, and since the customs duty was raised, as originally suggested, the ironmasters gained an additional measure of protection as the result of their action.[2]

By the year 1806 the financial burden of the war against Napoleon was becoming a matter of general concern, and increased taxation had become a necessity of sound finance. The Income Tax which had been reimposed at a higher rate, and to a lower exemption level in 1802, was not sufficient:

1. B. and W. to Reynolds, 13 Nov. 1797; Watt to Walker, 9 Nov. 1797.
2. How quick to scent a danger were the ironmasters at this time is shown by their opposition to the seemingly harmless proposal to allow coal to be carried by canal to London, free of duty. Dr. Macnab, Richard Crawshay, William Gibbons, William Reynolds, John Wilkinson, and other leaders of the industry insisted that the measure would produce such a rise in the price of coal as to force the ironworks of the Midlands and South Wales to cease operations. See *Letters of Dr. Macnab to William Manning on the Supply of Coal to the Metropolis.*

N

there was urgent need for new sources of revenue. Hence the proposal for an excise on pig iron was revived by Lord Henry Petty; and it was estimated that, as the output had now reached a quarter of a million tons per annum, a tax of 40s. a ton would yield £500,000 a year to the Exchequer.

The ironmasters were quickly in arms once more in defence of their trade interests. A committee of fourteen, representing the various areas of iron-production, was set up in London; pamphlets were prepared, and statements were drawn up to disprove the estimates made by the Ministry.[1] On 14 April, the High Bailiff called a meeting of protest in Birmingham, and deputations were sent to interview Lord Henry.[2] It was pointed out that the proposed tax was objectionable on grounds of both equity and economy: it would lead to the substitution of timber—which was scarce—for iron, and of horses for machinery; it would hamper the development of railways in the collieries, of canals, and of bridge- and ship-building; it would penalise the agriculturist who used implements of iron to the advantage of the grazier who made but small use of it. British industry was the mainstay of national defence, which it would be sheer madness to weaken. The presence of excise officers in the ironworks would be vexatious, and the fact that the tax would be one on raw material ran counter to the Smithian canon of Economy, since the burden would tend to increase with each successive stage in manufacture. Embezzlement of metal by workmen was already a serious matter: " being at work all hours in the night, and having the opportunity, in a few moments, of completely concealing the stolen metal, it is not likely to be less practised hereafter "; but the removal of metal in this manner might make it appear that the excise was being evaded, and penalties would fall on the ironmaster as the result of events over which he had no control.

These and other arguments—many fundamentally sound, others somewhat specious—were urged by representatives of associations in various parts of the country; and though the

1. Scrivenor, 97. See also *Observations on the Proposed Tax on Pig Iron*, by an Ironmaster. Published 3 May 1806.
2. Langford, *Century of Birmingham Life*, ii, 221.

bill was at first successful—and even in the Committee stage there was a majority of ten in its favour—it was thought wise, in face of the determined opposition, to withdraw it. An innocuous tax on brewing was substituted, and the ironmasters were able to register yet another victory over the politicians.

II.

It should not be imagined that the activities of the associations of ironmasters were solely, or even mainly, political. That of the Midlands had almost certainly come into being as the result of purely industrial forces, and, quarter by quarter, its members had been meeting in one or other of the towns of Staffordshire and Shropshire to regulate the price and condition of sale of their iron, and also to negotiate sales with the rod-ironmongers who were the principal customers of the ironworkers in this region. It was probably indeed for this latter purpose that, after 1790, a weekly dinner was held in the Ironmasters' Room of the Union Tavern in Birmingham.[1] In the industrial politics of the 'eighties and 'nineties the capitalists of districts other than the Midlands had taken their parts not as representatives of permanent organisations, but as individual ironmasters, or, at best, of temporary *ad hoc* committees. But whether as the result of political pressure or simply as a natural consequence of assimilative growth, associations like that of the Midland ironmasters came into being in both the South Wales, and the Yorkshire and Derbyshire industries, during the waning hours of the old, or the small hours of the new century.

In 1802, at a meeting of ironmasters held at Abergavenny, at which Tait, of Dowlais, and Homfray, of Penydarren, were present, it was resolved to institute a Welsh Quarterly Meeting, and a constitution was adopted : members agreed to pay an annual subscription of a guinea, and each new member had also to provide a bowl of punch for the gathering.[2] The later meetings of the Association were held at Newport, and prices were fixed for foundry and forge pigs and for bar

1. *Old Taverns of Birmingham*, 77.
2. Wilkins, *Iron, Steel, and Tinplate Trades*, 66.

iron each quarter from 1803 onwards.[1] In 1810 the prices
were left "open for every one to sell as he likes," but
regulation was resumed in 1811, and continued till 1824, when
the meetings at Newport came to an end : it is possible that
the Welsh association was absorbed by the larger gathering
of British ironmasters held that year.   The local association,
however, appears to have been revived in the 'thirties, and in
1836 resolutions were passed at Newport that the make of
pig iron be reduced 20 per cent., that twenty-two furnaces be
blown out, and that the price of pig iron be continued at £10
per ton.   "The Staffordshire, Shropshire, North Wales, and
Scotch ironmasters were requested to join in this arrangement,
to which they acceded."   Again, in 1840, an agreed reduction
in output of 20 per cent. took place.[2]

Perhaps no form of organisation is so reticent and elusive
as a trade association; it neither seeks nor obtains publicity in
the Press or in official records, unless its conduct is such as
to call forth protests from the consumer; and its history has
generally to be pieced together from casual references made
by writers interested primarily in other matters.   But, as
regards the third main area of iron production—that of
Yorkshire and Derbyshire—our information is more definite,
and it is possible to trace the origin and progress of the
combination movement in greater detail from an original
source.   There is, in the Sheffield Public Reference Library,[3]
a volume containing, in manuscript, the minutes of meetings
of the principal ironmasters of Yorkshire and Derbyshire held
between 1799 and 1828; and most of the material for the
remainder of this account has been drawn from this document.

The "Friendly Association," modelled like that of South
Wales on the older Midland body, came into existence on
11 August 1799.   Its constitution provided for an annual
subscription of one guinea, and 2s. 6d. had to be paid for
dinner—whether taken or not—at each of the quarterly
meetings which were held on the first Wednesday before the

1. For South Wales Prices, from Newport Quarter-Day Book, see Scrivenor,
op. cit., Appendix, 410.
2. *Ibid.*, 314, footnote.
3. *Jackson Collection*, 1297.

full moon at inns in such centres as Sheffield, Rotherham, Barnsley, Leeds, Bradford and Wakefield. The meetings were arranged in advance and a printed card was sent to the members stating the time and place of each.[1] At the first meeting Mr. Joseph Dawson of Low Moor was elected President, Mr. Littlewood of the Sheffield Park Ironworks, Secretary, and Mr. Thomas Chambers, of Thorncliffe, Treasurer. On the suggestion of the President it was decided that dissertations on the processes and practices of ironmaking should be read at each meeting, and that a gold medal be awarded for the best of such essays each year.[2] But it was not only technical questions that brought the ironmasters together, nor was it the prospect of winning medals that formed the subject of their thought and conversation as they rode home in the moonlight. From the first commercial practices were discussed; and, although no record of any trade agreement occurs during the first few entries in the Minute Book, there is independent evidence that the principal producers of pig iron had formulated a concerted policy as to prices at least as early as November 1800.[3] The Minute Book itself shows that by the following month, if not earlier, castings also had been brought within the sphere of regulation, for the President was instructed to see to the printing and circulation to each member of an agreed list of prices. Owing to their diversity, however, castings were less susceptible of regulation than pig iron. Special meetings of founders, as distinct from the producers of pig iron, were called from time to time, but never

1. The following is a copy of one such notice of meetings. *Thorncliffe MSS.* The dates are filled in by pen.

Meetings of Iron Masters
will be held
in the Year 1827
January 17th at the Tontine Inn, Sheffield.
April 11th „ „ Hotel, Leeds.
July 11th „ „ Tontine, Sheffield.
October 17th „ „ Hotel, Leeds.
At the King's Head Inn, Gloucester.
March and September

2. The first essay was read by Mr. Dawson on "The Effects of Air and Moisture on Blast Furnaces"; Mr. Murrah followed with "The Best Method of Burning, Destroying and Condensing Smoke"; and Mr. Emmott, of Birkenshaw, considered the question "Whether it was better to use one or two Tuyere Pipes by which to throw Air into Blast Furnaces."

3. See *Minutes of Meeting of Yorkshire Ironmasters*, App. D.

were all the founders in the area brought within the net of the association ; and frequent charges were made against members of having sold castings below the agreed prices. After 1809 prices were also fixed for bar iron, and schedules for squares, flats, and rods were constructed.

In the case of pig iron control appears to have been most completely exercised, and quarter by quarter the changes in demand were reflected in movements in the value of each grade : between 1808 and 1824, for example, the price of No. 1 pig was altered no fewer than seventeen times and varied between £7 and £10 a ton.

As early as 1808 the meeting urged "a good understanding" with the ironmasters of Wales, Salop and Staffordshire ; and from 1810 representatives of Yorkshire and Derbyshire attended the meetings at Gloucester, a levy of two guineas being imposed on each furnace in blast and on each forge to defray expenses. In 1813 a resolution was passed welcoming an increase in the price of pig and bar iron by the Gloucester meeting, and asserting that the members "will at all times coincide with their Brethren in the districts of Wales, Shropshire and Staffordshire in any regulation for the benefit of the Iron Trade at large through the Kingdom." Frequent reference is made to these meetings, and on one occasion a donation of twenty guineas is sent to the *Society* of Iron Masters for Wales and the Counties of Salop, Stafford, York and the North.

But national uniformity was not easy to maintain, and in the trade depression that followed the peace, not only was contact with other districts lost, but the dissolution of the local association was even debated early in 1822. At a later meeting it was resolved that "in case it should be clearly ascertained that any charge is made in this district less than agreed prices, any firm may sell to same house *only* at such reduced price, notice being given of such deviation to the secretary." But the trade boom which culminated in 1825 was already incubating ; and in 1824 the association was suddenly galvanised into new life. With the cessation of the demand for munitions in 1815, some of the more prominent firms in the district—such, for example, as Messrs. Newton, Chambers and Co., of the Thorncliffe Ironworks—had specialised in the production of gas apparatus, gas-pipes, and lamp-posts. Gas lighting had been known in parts of London since 1807, but it was during 1824 and 1825 that the flotation of new companies was specially marked, and the House of Commons was besieged with petitions for Gas Light Bills from all parts of the country.[1] News of the speculative outburst had reached the North early in 1824, and on January 21st it was resolved that a special meeting be called at Sheffield on February 1st, and " that in the meantime the parties here present pledge themselves not to sell pipes in London or elsewhere for less than £9 per ton, Money." The February meeting drew up a list of prices for pipes and lamp-posts, and Messrs. Jessop, Leah, Field and Hartop were appointed to meet the iron-masters of the Midlands at Birmingham with a view to effecting an advance in prices in the London market. A year later it was resolved " that £1 per ton be added to the list of prices for London Contract Castings," and six members were appointed to attend a general meeting of British ironmasters in London.

During the frenzy of 1825 and 1826 the supply of iron for purposes of all kinds was far below the demand at customary prices—a fact insisted upon by the Chancellor in 1825 when proposing a drastic reduction in the import duties on iron[2]— and the price of No. 1 grade of pig, for example, was raised from £7 early in 1824, to £12 10s. in April, 1825. But the subsequent fall was only less rapid, and by the summer of 1827 the price again stood at £7. Even at this figure frequent complaints of under-selling were made against members of the local association, and one of these was expelled. The record ends dolefully in 1828 with the assertion that " the only effective remedy for the present ruinous low price of iron is in a diminished make."

No such concerted curtailment of output as that practised in South Wales appears to have been adopted by the northern group of ironmasters; but in 1811 it had been agreed that all members of the association should inform the secretary of the

---

1. *J.H.C.*, 1823, 1824, 1825, *passim.*
2. Hansard, 25 March 1825.

extent of their unexecuted orders so that prices might be adjusted accordingly; and in the same year the practice of price discrimination was introduced. Pig iron for coastwise transit to Newcastle and elsewhere was delivered at Hull at a price sometimes as much as £1 below that charged to local foundries, and London merchants were similarly favoured.[1] In the case of No. 3 pig, which could be used indifferently for forge or foundry purposes, discrimination was made in favour of the forge masters.

Throughout the period regulations as to terms of credit were frequently made, and the granting of more favoured terms was then, as now, an easy method by which the banished demon of competition could re-enter the house. At this time a credit of nine or twelve months, or more, was quite common, and a vigorous attempt was made to reduce this too liberal allowance. In 1809 it was agreed " that on the sale of each parcel of Pig Iron an acceptance shall be taken for the amount at eight months from the date of invoice, or an allowance of 5 per cent. for ready money "; and the credit for cast iron goods was fixed at six months, or 5 per cent. for payment within one month. No allowance whatsoever was to be made to " engineers, millwrights, and others." For forge pig the maximum credit was fixed at nine months. In 1815 the terms for pig iron were altered to " six months, or discount of 5 per cent. for bill on London at 2 months within one month of date of Invoice "; and resolutions reaffirming this were passed from time to time.[2]

To determine whether the type of combination assumed by the iron industry was economically justified, or socially beneficial, would require a more detailed study than is possible here. There is plentiful evidence that competition was never entirely eliminated, and even the firms that had been most active in the movement were sometimes open to charges of failing to observe agreements reached at the quarterly meet-

---

1. In 1813 Messrs. Darwin and Co. are accused of having sold 50 tons of No. 1 soft pig for £7 10s. to Sheffield manufacturers under the pretence of these being London merchants.
2. This account from p. 177 is, with some small additions, taken *verbatim* from the article in the *Economic Journal*, xxx, 331-339. Specimen minutes of the Ironmasters' Meetings are given in Appendix D.

ings. The consumer was never entirely without remedy. In the boom of 1825 prices were raised abnormally; but since those of other commodities also increased, it might seem that the ironmasters merely took advantage of market conditions which were determined by forces beyond their control, and that, at best, combination enabled the rise to take place somewhat more rapidly than it would have done under competition. " It is to this combination that we must, in a great measure, attribute the present enormous price of English iron," said a writer in 1825.[1] " A great consumption for the iron rail-ways is anticipated, and the consumers of iron have no doubt displayed a considerable eagerness to purchase. Of this anxiety the iron masters have not failed to take due advantage; and the consequence is that the price of English iron has advanced from £9 to £15." The fact that foreign iron which, in 1782, was imported on payment of a duty of £2 16s. 2d. now had to pay £6 10s. a ton gave special powers to English producers when they entered the lists against the consumers; and it was suggested that the duties might not unreasonably be reduced in view of the prices prevailing in the market. Proposals for such a lowering of the tariff were put forward by the Chancellor of the Exchequer, and Huskisson claimed that the diminution would be advantageous to the producer, no less than to the consumer, since it would tend to check those violent fluctuations in prices which had been so disturbing to the course of trade.[2] From January, 1826, the duty on foreign bar iron was lowered to 30s. a ton.

In spite of this partial removal of an undoubted aid to combination, and in spite, too, of the disaffection and secession of individuals during the depression of the late 'twenties, the ironmasters' meetings remained to provide a basis for those associations, combines, and amalgamations of iron and steel producers that are so familiar a feature of the more recent history of the industry.[3]

1. Prescott, *Letter to Joseph Hume on the State of the Iron Trade*, 4, 5, 11.
2. Hansard, 25 March 1825.
3. In July 1831 at a meeting of the ironmasters of Staffordshire, Shropshire, and South Wales, a proposal was made for a concerted reduction of output, but the members failed to reach agreement. *Committee on Manufactures* (1833). Evidence of Anthony Hill, 10295, 10310, 10344.

By many writers the combination movement has been treated as a new-born product of the late nineteenth century, and the unrestricted competition of some of the early economists has been translated by those of a later generation from the sphere of hypothesis to the supposed realm of facts. Nothing could be more false. The combination of the iron-masters was by no means unique. That the cotton and pottery industries had developed corporate institutions is implied in the account given above of the Chamber of British Manufacturers. In the copper industry two great groups, representing the Anglesey Company and the Cornish Metal Company, divided the English market, and came to terms as to the price to be charged for their product ;[1] and the Newcastle Vend in the coal industry is another instance that at once flies to the mind of anyone conversant with the history of this period. In London the booksellers had, for a time, a regulative association,[2] and similar groups probably existed elsewhere. In the subsidiary metal trades the development was specially marked : as early as 1790 the steel manufacturers of Birmingham, with the active support of Matthew Boulton, had formed an association for the regulation of their trade ;[3] by 1812, and probably much earlier, the nail manufacturers of Staffordshire were organised and were gathering together in quarterly meetings ;[4] in Sheffield the cutlers had retained their organisation from the seventeenth century ;[5] and between 1773 and 1784 the silver-plate manufacturers held monthly meetings at which price-lists were prepared.[6] The Stubs records indicate that long before the end of the century the steel-tilters prepared similar lists; and associated file-makers and tool-manufacturers of Sheffield were in close contact with those of West Lancashire. In 1814 a Mercantile and Manufacturing Union of all Sheffield trades was instituted, with the object of regulating wages and suppressing combinations of work-

1. *The Letter Books* of Boulton and Watt for the year 1787 contain detailed information as to the relations between these two companies.
2. Babbage, *Economy of Manufactures*, Ch. xxxi.
3. Langford, *A Century of Birmingham Life*, i, 358.
4. *Minutes of Evidence against Orders in Council.*   Evidence of Mr. Whitehouse, 20.
5. Lloyd, *Cutlery Trades*, 110.
6. Leader, *Sheffield in the Eighteenth Century*, 88.

people.[1] Among commercial men and dealers the same
associative impulse was at work, represented in the Chambers
of Commerce of Birmingham, Manchester, Leeds, Halifax,
and Exeter;[2] and organisations of merchants dealing in
particular commodities, or trading with particular markets,
were not unknown.[3]

So numerous and diverse, in fact, were the forms in which
the corporate sense of the early industrialists found expression,
that justice could be done to them only by a special study,
which, carried out by a competent student, might throw a
flood of new light on the economic life of the late eighteenth
and the early nineteenth centuries. At the time with which we
are here concerned local organisations were breaking up and
giving way to larger bodies, or themselves expanding and
assuming a form in which they could play a part on the
larger stage of national politics. The emphasis placed in this
chapter on the political and economic potency of organised
capital in these early days may perhaps save some from that
crude interpretation of economic history, according to which
an original system of free competition has been meta-
morphosed into a new system of industrial monopoly, itself
destined to evolve into the state socialism of our dreams or
nightmares. The truth is that at all times some measure of
rivalry has existed in industry and trade; and at all times
have men sought to tame and control the forces of competition,
so that they might regulate—whether for good or ill—the flow
and direction of the currents of economic life.

1. Lloyd, *op. cit.*, App., xii.
2. Wright, *Chronicles of the Birmingham Chamber of Commerce*, 46.
3. See, *e.g.*, *Minutes of Evidence against Orders in Council*, Shore, 40.

CHAPTER VIII.

The Ironworkers.

" We tore the iron from the mountain's hold,
    By blasting fires we smithied it to steel ;
    Out of the shapeless stone we learned to mould
    The sweeping bow, the rectilinear keel."
                    —*John Masefield : The Ship.*

I.

THE workers in the iron industry form a far less homogeneous group than their employers, and it is not easy to delimit the area of labour which should form the subject-matter of this chapter. It would obviously be impossible to describe the economic condition of all the employees of the ironmasters, for the latter sometimes pushed their activities into spheres quite remote from that with which we are here concerned. Agriculture, fisheries, cotton spinning and manufacture, brewing, the mining and smelting of lead and copper, shipping and banking, were among the operations carried on, at one time or other, by prominent ironmasters; and even the processes connected with iron itself occupied a chain of workers of very diverse types. Charcoal-burners, carriers, ironstone-miners, colliers, limestone-quarrymen, blast-furnace-men, forgemen, puddlers, rollers, moulders, smiths, enginemen, general labourers, and manufacturing craftsmen—all had a place in the industry. In the following pages a bare outline will be given of the economic circumstances of the chief only of these groups, and a few statements of a very generalised character will be made.

The relations between the ironmasters and those who produced the raw material for the industry varied from time to time and from place to place. Some of the charcoal-iron-masters, such as the Foleys, owned the woods that supplied their works with fuel; others purchased wood standing in coppices owned by landlords, and employed men to cut, pile,

coal, and carry to the furnace or forge; and others again
bought the charcoal from farmers and small landowners, who
were themselves responsible for all these processes. The last
was the method of the early iron-smelters of Furness: at
Backbarrow, for instance, there were in 1714 no fewer than
130 people supplying fuel to the works—sometimes in almost
minute quantities.[1] Where labour was employed direct, it
was occasionally paid by the day, as at Coalbrookdale, but
generally the workers received a piece-wage: in South Wales,
about the middle of the century, 1s. 6d. per short cord was
paid for cutting, and 3d. for cording, or piling, the wood; the
charcoal-burners obtained 4s. a load of twelve sacks, and there
were additional charges for carriage varying with the distance
from the furnace. In Derbyshire, and perhaps elsewhere, it was
sometimes the custom to make payment to both charcoal-
burners and carriers in the form of bar iron; but in the
eighteenth century money payments were the general rule
throughout the country.[2]

Whatever the form of organisation, there was ample
opportunity for disagreement between the producers and the
consumers of charcoal. In the nineteenth century this was
usually carried to the works in large hampers, known as
"banisters," slung on each side of a horse or galloway. In
Yorkshire "they were made with a bottom to pull out for
the convenience of emptying. They were wide at the top,
narrow in the bottom, which gave the colliers an opportunity
of cheating, by filling them hollow, so that they were left
of, and sacks used in their stead: this was in the year 1660."[3]
Nevertheless charcoal baskets were still in use a hundred years
after this date in South Wales. Where sacks were employed
they were supplied by the ironmasters, who hired women to
make them to prescribed measurements and to keep them in
repair;[4] but, even so, causes of friction were by no means

1. Fell, *Early Iron Industry of Furness*, 130.
2. Percy, *Metallurgy: Iron and Steel*, 876; Sitwell, A Picture of the Iron
Trade in the Seventeenth Century, *Derby. Arch. and Nat. Hist. Soc. Trans.*, x,
31.
3. An account given to John Hobson of Dodworth Green, near Barnsley,
by an aged banister maker, who died in 1732. *Surtees Soc. Coll.*, lxv, 311.
4. Percy, *op. cit.*, 898. Elizabeth Spollion, who prepared the "blacking"
at Coalbrookdale, made bags for use at the works.

eliminated. In North Lancashire the wood-owners complained of " the great imposition of the Iron Masters upon us and the Country in respect of the excess of measure insisted upon by them, which really made our Woods of much less value than they formerly were. The sacks or bags they imposed were some four or five inches wider than common, and they insisted on their being filled five ft. high by which means the bags contained nearly one-fourth more than usual." This difference it was that led to the setting up in 1748 at Penny Bridge of a furnace controlled by the woodowners themselves; and further controversy as to the price to be paid for charcoal was obviated by a sliding-scale according to which it was made to vary with the price of pig iron.[1]

When mineral fuel came to take the place of wood the same diversity of organisation presented itself. Sometimes mining and smelting were carried on by independent groups of adventurers, and firms like the Coalbrookdale Company bought both coal and ironstone from master colliers or from mining companies. Yet even from early times it is possible to trace a tendency towards that integration which is so marked a characteristic of the modern iron and steel industries. As wealth accumulated, groups like the Reynolds, the Wilkinsons, the Walkers, the Carron Company, the Thorncliffe partners, and the Low Moor Company, purchased mines of their own ; and in some cases the sale of coal was as important a source of revenue as the production of iron itself. Similarly hæmatite mining in Cumberland and Furness was controlled by the smelting companies, and a considerable proportion of their profits was drawn from the shipping of ore to other districts.

Like the charcoal-burners, the colliers and ironstone-miners were paid according to output. Disputes as to piece-rates were both frequent and acute ; and when trouble arose between the ironmasters and their employees it was always the homogeneous, " class-conscious " body of coal-miners that took the lead, while the smelters and forgemen, if involved at all, were rarely conspicuous in the struggle. A description of the

1. Fell, *op. cit.*, 145.

economic circumstances of the miners would, however, lead to regions far beyond the boundary-stones of the iron industry; and no adequate account of them could possibly be given here.

In considering the rates of wages paid to ironworkers it is necessary to bear in mind the fact that real wages were often substantially greater than nominal wages, since it was generally the practice to make part payment in goods. In almost all cases houses were provided by the firm, either without charge or at low rents[1]; fuel for domestic purposes was also generally supplied, and where this was not gratuitous or given at cost price, the workers helped themselves to it. Allowances in the form of ale were made at times when special exertion was called for; indeed a brew-house was an essential part of the plant of every well-equipped furnace or forge undertaking. Often a grocery store was set up in conjunction with an ironworks, and part of the wage paid was in the form of tickets exchangeable into goods only at such a shop. If the goods were provided at cost price this might mean—as it probably did at Chapeltown—an increase in real earnings; but the truck system was obviously open to grave abuse; and there is abundant evidence that it was often used as a means of surreptitiously reducing earnings and of increasing profits by exploitation.[2]

At a furnace of moderate size in the early years of the century about seven men would be employed. Two of these, known as keepers, had the duty of determining the charge of ore and fuel, of regulating the blast, and of tapping the furnace when the smelting process was complete. Two bridge-servers filled the baskets with ironstone, or ore, limestone, and fuel, and two or three fillers carried the baskets to the bridge and charged the furnace. In addition, casual labour—often the wives and children of the regular workers—was employed for such purposes as preparing the ore and picking out fragments of iron and charcoal from among the furnace cinders.

The money wages paid to furnace workers were strikingly

1. In March 1792 the Coalbrookdale Company was putting up forty houses for its workpeople.
2. *Report on Manufactures* (1833), 9792, 9868-71, 9888; Habershon, *Chapeltown Researches*, 163.

uniform in different districts, and relatively stable over periods
of time. In North Lancashire from early in the century to
1755, the keepers received 10s. a week, and from the outbreak
of the Seven Years' War to the end of the century, 10s. 6d.
Between 1720 and 1785 the bridge-servers had 6s., during the
next ten years 7s. 6d., and after 1800, 9s. The fillers received
7s. a week between 1720 and 1795, then 8s. till 1800, and
thereafter 9s.[1] In the coke-smelting industry of Shropshire
wages were somewhat higher. In 1767 two keepers at Coalbrookdale were paid 11s. a week, and the fillers 10s. 6d. At
Horsehay, between 1774 and 1781, the keepers obtained 12s.
a week, together with a small bonus. Thus the earnings
of Richard Jones, one of the furnace keepers, were as
follows for monthly periods taken at random in a survey
of the Wages Books at Horsehay : 1774, £2 9s. 6d.; 1778,
£2 13s. 9d.; 1780, £2 4s. 0d.; 1781, £2 16s. 7½d. As late as
September, 1797, the same keeper's monthly earnings were
£2 16s. 3d. In 1774 two fillers were paid 10s. 6d. a week; but
by 1797 a filler's wages had risen 33 per cent., and he now
received, in addition, a small bonus on output. At Ebbw
Vale in 1798 keepers were paid 14s. weekly with an allowance
of 4d. a ton for moulding and cleaning the pigs. Over the
same period furnace labourers were paid 1s. to 1s. 6d. a day
at both Coalbrookdale and Horsehay.

The upward movement in general prices, and the special
demand for iron to which the Napoleonic war gave rise, led
to an increase in the wages of each of these classes of furnacemen; and although earnings fell very considerably after 1815
money wages remained permanently at a higher level than
before the war. In 1826 the keepers at Horsehay had £1 a
week, the fillers 15s., the furnace labourers 14s., and the cokers
and other unskilled workers 2s. to 2s. 6d. a day. A keeper
employed by William Matthews at Kingswinford in 1833
made about 30s. and unskilled labourers at the same furnace
13s. a week, while in South Wales fillers were receiving 15s.
or 16s.[2]

1. *Fell*, 234, 296.
2. *Wages Books at Coalbrookdale and Horsehay; Ebbw Vale MSS.;
Committee on Trade* (1833), 2774-2782, 10273-10280.

Those engaged in converting pig into bar iron were known as finers or hammermen, and at each forge there were at least two men assisted by one boy. In this branch of the industry apprenticeship was considered essential, and a youth was generally required to serve seven years, though occasionally three were deemed sufficient. In return for a premium and the services of the apprentice the master hammerman was under the obligation of supplying sustenance and instruction. Newspaper notices relating to runaway apprentices describe the delinquents as being able to make " only the half-bloom," or as " Master of the Bloom," according to the stage of training they had reached.[1] The master hammerman himself was among the aristocracy of labour, for his position approximated rather to that of the small employer than to that of the ordinary wage-earner. He usually entered into an engagement for a term of years with some landowner or proprietor of mines, and, in practice, the conduct of the undertaking was under his sole control. The inventions of the last three decades of the century wrought great changes, especially in the fining processes; the scale of business was vastly increased; new grades of workers were required for the puddling and rolling processes; trained engineers were necessary when steam power was introduced; and increased supplies of unskilled labour were called for to handle raw material and finished product and to assist the skilled workers in their operations. In these circumstances the master hammerman disappeared : either he evolved into the works manager or foreman, or he was superseded by a new type of administrative official. But in the early years of the century he was of vital importance in ironmaking, since on him devolved the varied functions of industrial leadership, technical training, and sometimes commercial dealing, in addition to the ordinary executive duties of the forge.

The engine-men who were required at the larger ironworks

---

1. See, for example, notices inserted in *Aris's Birmingham Gazette* by John Lavender, master-hammerman to Lord Foley at Wildon Forge, 14 May 1750 ; by Robert Wilson of Bromwich Forge, 9 Dec. 1751 ; by Peter Davenport of Keynton Forge, 15 Dec. 1766 ; by Thomas Cranage, master-hammerman of Bridgnorth Forge, 5 May 1766 ; by Caswell and Gibbons of Sutton and Pitchford Forges, 8 Sept. 1766.

O

were relatively well-paid; and as many of them were trained
by James Watt at Birmingham, before taking service under
the ironmasters, it is possible to obtain information as to their
conditions of employment from the records of Boulton and
Watt.   In April 1786 the Walkers of Rotherham complained
that a servant of the Soho partners had endeavoured to entice
some of their employees to Birmingham; and, after repudiating
any knowledge of the matter, James Watt adds, " As to the
affair of 18/ per week, coals and house I think it highly
improbable any such offer could be made as I do not know
who would give it them.   The only one of our Customers who
wants an Engine man parted with a good one merely because
he would not stay under 18/ p^r week."   Fifteen or sixteen
shillings was probably about the average for this grade of
labour.

At the same time, young smiths were paid 11s. a week, and
the wages were increased by 1s. a year to a maximum of 16s.
In 1796, when wages as a whole had risen, "middling hands"
received 15s. and 16s., good smiths 17s. and 18s., and even
a guinea might be paid to a man when working away from
home.   In the same year the Ebbw Vale Co. engaged a
blacksmith at 24/- a week, out of which, however, he was
required to pay 1s. for house and firing.   In 1833 smiths
employed by William Matthews were given 2s. 4d. to 3s. 6d.
a day.[1]

Whenever practicable, piece-wages or time-wages with
a bonus on output were adopted.   "The only security and
check an Iron-master has over the workman, who is carrying
on his business while he is asleep, to compel a proper
performance of his duty, and prevent him, by neglect, from
suffering the metal being burnt, or unduly wasted in the fire
and spoiled " [wrote one employer[2]] " is, by limiting him to,
and frequently proving his yield, and paying him a bounty,
in proportion to the degree of care and skill shewn . . ."
Thus, both in the foundry and at the forge, payment by the

---

1.   *Committee on Trade* (1833), 2774-2782, 10273-80; Watt to Matt. Stark,
27 Aug. 1787; Watt to Barnes 17 May 1796. John Parker, afterwards one of
the wealthy ironmasters of Staffordshire, began as a smith to Boulton and Watt
at 12s. a week.

2.   *Observations on the Proposed Tax on Pig-Iron* (1806), 16.

piece was the general practice : two forgemen at the Seaton
works in 1779 were together paid 15s. for each ton of merchant
iron produced, out of which sum 2s. 6d. or 3s. had to be paid
to the boy who assisted them. In the preliminary processes
the same system prevailed : at Ebbw Vale, for example, in
1796 a coker received 1s. 4d. a dozen barrows. At Carron
piece-work was apparently almost universal, and when Jars
paid his visit in 1765, the chief workmen were able to earn as
much as 20s. a week. In steel-making the same method was
general, and the two workmen who were required at each
cementation furnace in the Newcastle district at this time were
together paid 4s. a ton of steel produced.[1] James Watt was a
firm believer in payment by results, and whenever possible
smiths and others employed by him were put on piece-work.
The method was not, however, without its drawbacks,
especially when applied to the furnace and foundry workers :
when the bonus system, which had been abandoned, was
re-introduced at Coalbrookdale in 1832 it was observed that
equipment such as rails, wheels, and all kinds of loose castings
and tools disappeared into the blast furnace in order to swell
the output, and similar evil practices arose also among the
founders.

Generally the ironworkers were men of strong physique;
and although the operations were arduous, labour was free from
those specific diseases that were so prevalent in the cutlery
trade, as well as from the general ill-health that marked the
industrial career of many of the textile workers.[2] Women and
children were employed in small numbers only, and their
lives were not unduly strenuous. At Kingswinford,
William Matthews employed about fifty boys, aged from 9 to
15, under conditions, which—if we may accept his own
statement—were not objectionable even according to modern
standards. "They work their own time; if they are tired they

---

1. *Voyages Métallurgiques,* 279, 224.
2. The strength of the workers was a matter of pride to the industry. One
of the arguments against the tax on pig iron proposed in 1806 was that such
an imposition would tend to crush these "men of athletic make and great
bodily vigour, which was a consideration of no small consequence . . . since it
had been justly said that too many of our manufactures tended to deteriorate
the physical constitution and produce a feeble and degenerate race of men,
without spirit or ability to defend their rights." Scrivenor, *History,* 102.

go home, and their fathers do their business; but generally they work six or seven hours, and sometimes eight or ten; they work and play pretty much as they like, subject to the control of their parents." They were generally paid 3s. to 7s. or 8s. a week.[1]

For adults the working day was long. In the early years of our period Ambrose Crowley's men were required to begin at 5 a.m. and work till 8 p.m., with a break of half an hour at 8 in the morning, and an hour at noon—$13\frac{1}{2}$ hours a day, or 80 hours for a full week. Towards the end of the century the working day at Coalbrookdale was from 6 a.m. to 6 p.m., with similar stops of a half, and one hour, for breakfast and dinner respectively; and quarter of a day's wages was forfeited by any workman who spent longer over his meals.[2] These conditions exhibit substantial improvement over those prevailing in a model factory at an earlier period; and they contrast very favourably also with the hours of toil required to wring subsistence earnings from domestic nailmaking. For here, during the war period, it was said to take the labour of an able man from six in the morning to eleven or twelve at night to make the 12s. which constituted the average earnings of the trade.[3]

Of these manufacturers of iron—the workers engaged in transforming the metal into nails and other finished products—the account given here must necessarily be brief. Generally such workers were engaged by nail-ironmongers or other middlemen, and they carried on their operations in their own homes, or in small workshops under that type of economic organisation which, for want of a better term, is spoken of as the domestic system. Raw material was given out by the ironmonger, and the finished product collected by him, the worker receiving payment strictly according to his output. These ironmongers constituted a body of capitalists distinct from those considered in this essay; but here and there the two industrial groups overlapped, and in the early part of

1. *Report of Committee on Trade* (1833), 9790.
2. *Law Book of the Crowley Ironworks. Rules for the Preservation of Good Order in the Works of William Reynolds and Co., Horsehay MSS.*
3. *Minutes of Evidence against the Orders in Council,* Whitehouse, 20.

the period there was a tendency for the manufacturers to come under the control of the iron producers. Thus in the late seventeenth century the Sitwells of Derbyshire were concerned not only with the production of bar iron, but also with the manufacture of such articles as saws, nails, guns, iron bullets, chimney plates, mortars, sugar stoves, and rollers for crushing cane in the Barbadoes. Some of these commodities were evidently of cast iron and were produced directly from the blast-furnace; but others were the product of manufacturers in Gainsborough, Eckington, and other places, to whom the Sitwells gave out iron and from whom, in return for a piece-wage, they received the finished nails and saws. This was obviously the domestic system in its pure form; but in the case of one large undertaking—that of the Crowleys—the arrangement was modified so as to include some at least of the features of the factory system.

In many respects the enterprise carried on by Sir Ambrose Crowley and his son John, at Swalwell and Winlaton, was surprisingly modern. In its integrated structure, its internal administration, its methods of ensuring industrial peace, and even in such *minutiæ* as the provision of standardized gauges, the concern appears properly to belong to the twentieth, rather than the seventeenth or eighteenth century. Within the same business unit the domestic system and factory production can be seen side by side, and the history of the concern is largely that of transition from one to the other. In the foundry, in the converting of steel, and in the heavy forge processes, the men worked in buildings and with machinery provided by the capitalist; they were sometimes paid time-wages, and were in other respects similar to the modern factory worker. But many of those employed in manufacturing the smaller wares were on a somewhat different footing. Iron was supplied by the Crowleys to master workmen, who, aided by hammermen employed by themselves, worked it up in their own homes, or in little workshops, with tools of their own—often purchased by means of advances from the Crowleys. They then carried the finished goods back to the warehouse, where they received the difference between their value and that of the raw material originally advanced to them.

But though these workers were thus independent small masters, the conditions of work and the hours of labour were closely regulated by the firm itself. This benevolent supervision applied especially to those workers who lived in the community known as the "Square," for, in their case, leisure no less than work was under paternalistic control. Surveyors were appointed to see that the standard of workmanship was maintained, and it was their function also to inspect the shops and to advise newcomers as to place of residence and work. Arbitration courts, consisting of nominees of the firm and of the workers, were set up to enquire into grievances; and contracts made between the master workmen and their hammermen were drawn up in these courts. Very early in the eighteenth century a system of contributory insurance against death, sickness, and old age was compulsory on all workers; and a doctor, a clergyman, and a schoolmaster were maintained jointly by the firm and its employees.

It is tempting to discuss in further detail the organisation of this remarkable undertaking, especially in view of the fact that it has not received from economic historians the attention which the range of its experiments in welfare methods would appear to merit.[1] But most of the activities of this kind

1. Brief descriptions of the Crowley Ironworks are given in Surtees, *History of Durham*, and in the *Victoria County History*. A few quotations, selected almost at random, may be made from the *Law Book* drawn up by Sir Ambrose and his son John Crowley, for the conduct of their works.

"It is here declared that all Masters are to receive of their Hammermen Twopence p. Week, neither more or less, and those Hammermen that have paid by themselves or Masters for 2 months Time Successively in health shall have Relief in Time of Distress."

"The Surveyor of what they make is to recommend them [*i.e.*, new workmen] to the fittest place to Work, Live or Board. The Ironkeeper is then to Deliver each Newcomer such a Quantity of Iron as the Nailkeeper or Surveyor shall Direct till the next Stock List Shall be made."

"When any danger of loss by Trusting any Workmen, you are to recommend their working Journey work to such persons as you think proper to employ them."

"When any Workman cometh that is much wanted and hath not Credit . . . and is at work, but is not in his power to make a Reckoning in 4 days, the Councell may Direct the Workkeeper to Credit him one third part of what he and his hammermen may and probably do earn."

"When you take Bond of any Person [*i.e.*, workman] you must never make your penalty less than double the Number of pounds in the Condition."

"You are not to pay any Workman anything till he hath paid mistakes, his Hammermen for Service done in that Reckoning . . . and before the Master is paid—also Grinder and Toolmaker."

related not to the producers but to the manufacturers of iron.
The organisation of the metal workers of the Newcastle
district, no less than of those of South Staffordshire,
Yorkshire, North Derbyshire, and the villages between Leigh
and Warrington in Lancashire, should form a fertile territory
of research for some future investigation.

II.

In early days, as already pointed out, a close connection
existed between ironmaking and agriculture; and in the
eighteenth century it was still from the ranks of men bred on
the soil, rather than from those of the town, that labour for
the iron industry was recruited. Furnaces and forges were
often stopped during the summer months in order that the
workers might assist with the harvest; and many labourers
themselves held small plots of land which they cultivated in
their spare time and which saved them from idleness when
shortage of water, or other cause, brought the ironworks to a
temporary stand. Even during the period of most rapid
expansion following the technical changes of the 'seventies
and 'eighties the main source of labour was the same: the
ironworks about Birmingham drew labourers from the agricultural parts of Staffordshire and Warwickshire; and in
Hereford the level of wages paid to land workers was higher
in the South than in the North, by reason of proximity to the
coal and iron industries of Monmouth and South Wales.[1]

In the charcoal iron industry the dispersion of works
meant that whenever a locality was depleted of wood, and the
works were transferred to another district, labour had to be
transported over considerable distances; and although information relating to individual workmen is meagre in the
extreme, such evidence as exists suggests mobility of a somewhat suprising degree.[2] When about 1688 Ambrose Crowley

1. See A. Redford, *The Migration of Wage-earners, 1800—50.* Doctoral
thesis presented to the University of Manchester.
2. Even in mediæval times there are instances of such movement. Reference has already been made to the *forgiae errantes* of the Forest of Dean, and
to the transference of labourers from South Yorkshire to the Bishop's forges
in Weardale in the early years of the fifteenth century. Migration of French
and Dutch ironfounders to the industry of the Weald and the Forest of Dean

established his ironworks, first at Sunderland, and then at
Swalwell and Winlaton, he obtained skilled workers not only
by importations from Liège, but also on a considerable scale
from London and its outlying districts.   In order to facilitate
this movement Crowley's agents in London were instructed
to accept goods in pawn and to advance against them sums
sufficient to cover the cost of the voyage to the Tyne; the
surveyor at Winlaton had the duty of finding the newcomer
suitable housing accommodation, of lending a sum not
exceeding 3s. 6d. to cover immediate needs, and of providing
tools and material after having first secured a bond for
repayment.   Other illustrations of the transference of workmen
are provided by the Backbarrow Company which commenced
operations in 1711 : the furnace was constructed and superintended for many years by a skilled man brought from Ireland,
and a little later additional labour was sought by the company
in South Wales, Yorkshire, Staffordshire, and Shropshire.
In 1727, when the Furness ironmasters established works at
Invergarry in the Highlands, founders were again brought
from Barnsley and South Wales, and charcoal-burners from
Ireland[1]—not the first migration of ironworkers to Scotland,
for in 1607 Sir George Hay had established a colony of
English workmen to tend his blast-furnace at Letterewe in
Ross.[2]

   In the coke-smelting branch of the industry the same
fluidity of labour is to be observed.   The first Abraham
Darby is said to have induced founders from Holland to assist
him in his undertaking at Bristol, and when, in 1708, he

1.   Fell, *op. cit.*, 362.
2.   Swank, *Iron and Steel in All Ages*, 54.

was marked in the sixteenth century (*S.A.C.*, xiv, 159). This influx of
foreigners continued during the following century : German miners from the
Keswick district moved into Furness (*V.C.H. Lancs.*, ii, 354), and a new colony
of German ironworkers and cutlers was established at Shotley Bridge, in
Northumberland, during the reign of William III (*British Association Rept.*
1863, 737).   Apart from such immigrations there is evidence of early movements
of English workmen within the industry.   At least one family moved from
Sheffield to the Rossendale Valley (*V.C.H.*, ii, 361) and another from
Northumberland to Sussex ; and during the slow death by exhaustion of the
Wealden Industry labour and capital transferred themselves from Sussex to
South Wales (*S.A.C.*, xiv, *loc. cit.*).

removed to Coalbrookdale, workers like John Thomas were transferred also. Later influxes into the Coalbrookdale district were on a larger scale. In the 'eighties the Company was obliged to build extensively in order to provide houses for the incoming workers; and the following figures illustrate the growth of the parish of Madeley, which includes the village of Coalbrookdale and the ironworks themselves.[1]

	Jan. 1782		Mar. 1793
Houses	440	......	754
Families	560	......	851
Persons	2,690	......	3,677

The fact that the proportionate increase of persons is somewhat greater than that of families almost certainly represents an influx of unmarried men into the district; and the same cause was responsible for the growth of the population around John Wilkinson's works at Bradley, which, by reason of immigrations from Wales and Shropshire, increased from 3,000 in 1780 to 12,000 in 1821.[2] As already pointed out, these industrial areas of Coalbrookdale and Bradley themselves served as centres of dispersion for the industry, and workers moved thence to Carron in 1760, and at a later period to other districts. In the train of John Guest and the Homfrays from Shropshire, and James Cockshutt from Yorkshire, many skilled ironworkers from the Midlands—and from Stourbridge in particular—made their way by road and canal to the land of promise in the upland valleys of Glamorgan. And, towards the end of the century, there was a less marked, but nevertheless important, infiltration of agriculturists and lead miners from Derbyshire into the growing iron region about Sheffield.[3]

The transition from charcoal to coke was obviously one of the chief causes of these movements of population; and the opening up of new sources of ironstone and coal also necessitated migration. Of aimless vagrancy there is no indication

1. Rathbone, *Memoir*, 44. Quoted from Plymley's *Survey of Shropshire*.
2. Lawley, *History of Bilston*, 171.
3. Wilkins, *Iron, Steel, and Tinplate Trades*, 56; Habershon, *Chapeltown Researches*, 139.

whatsoever. Indeed during the greater part of our period the demand for skilled labour was such that the supply could not keep pace, and wage rates were not sufficiently elastic for such an increase to result as would equate the two. Hence, after about 1770, employers everywhere were conscious of a shortage of trained workmen, and there are numerous complaints in the letter-books of the period of attempts made by one firm to entice labour from another. Evidence to the same effect is afforded by the willingness of the employers to pay travelling expenses to workers moving from a distance, and by their efforts to protect their men, from both the blandishments of the recruiting sergeant, and the rapacity of the pressgang. During the American and the Napoleonic Wars the seductions of the army and navy were a source of anxiety to ironmasters in various districts; and Boulton and Watt, who, from the nature of their business, were obliged to make use of itinerant engine-builders, suffered serious inconvenience from the attentions of His Majesty. Even so valued an employee as William Murdoch dared not move about the country without the special protection of the magistrates.[1]

But such hindrances to the geographical movement of labour were of small account when weighed against the possibilities of advancement in life offered in the newly-opened areas of iron-production; and even the barriers raised against the migration of English ironworkers across the national frontiers were by no means entirely effective in checking the expansive tendencies of the new industrial population. Here, it is true, there were more formidable obstacles: patriotic sentiment, legislation, and the supposed interests of the British industrialists, all opposed migration

---

1. In 1779, in particular, there was danger of men being pressed, and Watt sought the protection of John James of Bristol and a Mr. Flood of Exeter for William Murdoch, who was making a journey into Cornwall. See letters dated 22 Sept. 1779, and 11 and 16 July 1779. The last of these related to an engineman, Jack Strafford, who had left his master because his request for an advance of a shilling a week had been refused. " I think him very reprehensible in leaving Mr. Scott without proper warning " [wrote Watt] "have advised the latter to give him 13s. pr. Week, which the other ought to accept of as he can get no immediate employment and there is now a very hot press here of every Idle Man, in short he could never have pickt out a worse time to throw himself out, both by leaving the Bog when burthened with Water and coming off when every body is glad to work for anything, fear of being pressed."

of labour to other countries. At the time when Peter the Great was introducing the industrial methods of Western Europe into his dominions, his agents visited Sheffield, Newcastle, and Birmingham to secure skilled men for transference to Russia. No complaint appears to have been made until 1719 when, following upon the death of Charles XII, the hostility of Englishmen turned from Sweden to Russia. In January of that year the Cutlers' Company of Hallamshire protested against the emigration of English cutlers and ironworkers, and the placing of foreign workmen and apprentices in iron and steel undertakings in this country. Their petition was followed by others from the ironmongers of Birmingham and London, and a Parliamentary Committee was appointed to enquire into the matter.[1]

Before this committee evidence was given by John Crowley and others, and a Bill was introduced " to prevent the Inconveniences arising from seducing Artificers in the Iron and Steel Manufactures into foreign Parts; and from taking Foreigners Apprentices in the said Manufactures." At this point the London clockmakers complained that, bribed " by large Promises, and in hopes of great Profit to themselves," men of their craft were leaving England for France; and, after a second reading, it was agreed to make the Bill applicable to British manufactures generally, though the clauses relating to the apprenticing of foreigners in this country were omitted. The Act, 5 Geo. I., c. 27, imposed a fine not exceeding £100 and three months' imprisonment on those guilty of attempting to seduce workmen; and these penalties were substantially increased by 23 Geo. II., c. 13, which also prohibited the exportation of tools and utensils employed in certain British industries.

In spite of this legislation many ironworkers were from time to time carried to the Continent. In 1753 the King of Sweden offered special privileges to foreigners who should engage in the iron and steel industries in his dominions,[2] and a number of workmen left England for the North of Europe. In 1763 a passenger from Birmingham to London left behind

1. *Supra*, p. 115; *J.H.C.*, xix, 57, 78 *seq.*
2. *Aris's Birmingham Gazette*, 17 Sept. 1753.

in the fly in which he had travelled a pocket-book which contained papers relating to the proposed transference of English workmen to an iron foundry that was to be set up in Sweden. Among these documents was a testimonial of good character signed by the proprietors of the Carron Works; the finder of the wallet therefore sent the whole to Dr. Roebuck of Birmingham and Carron, who at once communicated the facts to the Home Office. It appeared from these papers that a Johan Cahman of Stockholm had entered into correspondence with one Downing of Little Dawley in Shropshire, with a view to obtaining labour for the erection of an air furnace at Gothenburg; and a workman, Francis Lloyd, had been induced by an offer of a guinea a week, all expenses, and a bonus on the output of the furnace, to take service under Cahman. Lloyd was instructed to take with him two other labourers—who were each to be paid fifteen shillings a week—together with the necessary tools, and even bricks and mortar for the furnace. At the time when news of the conspiracy reached official quarters, he was actually in London engaged in negotiations for the purchase of Windsor bricks for Sweden. Before he could be apprehended, however, Lloyd had left again for Shropshire to make final arrangements for departure; and instructions were given that on his reaching home he should at once be brought before a Justice of the Peace to give security not to leave the country. Downing was to be dealt with according to law.[1]

A fortnight later Samuel Garbett, whose son was then touring the Low Countries, Norway, Sweden, France, and Germany to study foreign trade processes, informed Stanhope of other efforts made by the Swedes to secure British workmen, and, in particular, of a lucrative offer made " to one of our most considerable manufacturers in Birmingham." The latter was none other than Matthew Boulton, to whom, in the following year, Dr. Solander, the Swedish librarian of the British Museum, again made proposals for a removal to Sweden.[2] To these Boulton vouchsafed no reply : in a letter to William Burke he declared that he would spare no expense

1. *Calendar H.O. Papers*, 1760-5, Nos. 1339 and 1347.
2. *Ibid.*, 1476, 1818, 1821, 1919.

in detecting schemes to entice Englishmen abroad, and would
keep a close watch on any foreigners who might visit
Birmingham. At the same time, Roebuck and Garbett were
having some measure of success as amateur detectives, and
had tracked down at Montrose two of their own workmen from
Carron, who were on the point of leaving for Gothenburg.
It is easy to see why the proprietors of Carron should have
been specially concerned with this question of emigration : the
works were the best equipped of their kind in the country, and
their early success had been very widely advertised; the
position of the ironworks near the sea provided special facilities
to workmen who wished to escape; and the laxity of the petty
officers of justice in Scotland, and their secret hostility to the
English ironmasters, reduced the risk of capture and punishment. On several occasions the partners deplored their own
lack of local prestige, and suggested this might, to some extent,
be remedied if they had the right of appointment to such
minor posts as those of tide-waiter and salt officer. Failing
such personal influence they besought the Home Office to
induce the Lord Advocate of Scotland to pay special attention
to the prosecution, and to mete out exemplary punishment to
aiders and abettors of the emigrant workmen.[1]

A Scot named Croswell was apprehended as an instigator
of the men who were caught at Montrose, and on his failing
to appear before the court, after release on bail, sentence of
outlawry was passed upon him. At the same time General
Conway, at the instance of Garbett, wrote the Lord Advocate
urging, in the case of one of the detained workmen, that the
bail taken of him should be sufficiently heavy to be effective.
In spite of such vigilance one of the Carron workmen had
managed to get through to Gothenburg; and in May 1766
it was stated that he, or one of a number of other emigrants,
had sent twenty guineas to his wife in Scotland, and that
this was having an unsettling effect upon labour at Carron.
Later in the year attempts were made to compel the return
of the runaways : acting on instructions from the British
envoy, the English chaplain at Gothenburg interviewed five of
them and pointed out the serious consequences of their

1. *Cal. H.O. Papers*, 1765-9, No. 1941.

remaining abroad.   None of them, however, could be induced
to return and Garbett had to console himself with the reflection
that the promulgation of their outlawry would serve as a
warning to those at Carron who might otherwise have followed
the delinquents to Sweden.[1]

The Swedes were not alone in their attempts to secure
trained labour from England.   In 1765 complaints were made
that a manufacturer of coach springs had been enticed to
Holland by an Edward Cator, a native of Banbury, who had
set up an iron manufactory near Amsterdam.   Again, in
1766, Garbett is found enlisting the services of an English
jockey in an attempt to track down three British workmen who
had settled in Vienna;[2] and later, when he became Chairman
of the Birmingham Commercial Committee, he found new
opportunities of " knight errantry."   In view of Garbett's
persistent efforts to arouse his fellow-countrymen to a sense
of the foreign peril, it is not without ironical interest to observe
that his own son-in-law, Charles Gascoigne, turned apostate,
took service under Catherine II, and carried skilled workmen
from England to manufacture guns and shells for the armies
of Russia.[3]

Many other instances could be given of movements of
individual workmen to foreign countries.[4]   During the early
years of the nineteenth century prosecutions were frequently

1.   *Cal. H.O. Papers*, 1766-9, 134, 251, 414.   At a later date it was asserted
that the workers who went abroad rarely stayed long, and, if this were the
case, the threat of outlawry was a serious matter.   " In starting a fresh
manufactory it is universally the practice, especially in the iron trade, to employ
a few English workmen, but after their own workmen have obtained the same
skill and knowledge which the English workman possesses, the prices of
English workmen being much higher than that of native workmen, it is of
course the interest of the manufacturer either to expect the English workman to
come down to the native workman, or to let him return to his own country.   I
am acquainted with Mr. Cockerill, a large manufacturer at Liège and Seraing,
and when they commenced their manufactory they employed a great number of
English workmen, but I believe most of them have now returned to England.
He had to pay for English workmen 7s. and 8s. a day, and his native
workmen are employed at one and two francs a day."   *Rept. of Comm. on
Manuf.* (1833), Evid. S. Jackson, 2973.
2.   *Cal. H.O. Papers*, 1766-9, 107, 309, 332.
3.   Mayer, *Iron and Steel Inst. Journal* (1872), Vol. iii
4.   For attempts to attract miners from Cornwall to Portugal see *H.O.
Papers* (1766-9), 1115, 1267, 1278.   See also 1077.   Other cases are recorded in
the newspapers.   See *Aris's Birmingham Gazette*, 9 Apr. 1750, and 22 June 1778.
The attempts to attract both Smeaton and James Watt to Russia are well
known.

conducted at the instance of the associations of ironmasters, and, as late as 1823, the Yorkshire ironmasters passed a resolution of thanks to Messrs. Walkers of Rotherham for their "public-spirited action" in prosecuting one who had enticed artisans to France. But by this time the crude nationalism of the eighteenth century had begun to lose ground before the assault of newer ideas of personal freedom; and, in that first flush of economic liberalism that lightened the otherwise sombre 'twenties, the obnoxious legislation was repealed, and workmen became free to sell their labour in the most profitable market, whether at home or abroad.

In most discussions of eighteenth century industries attention is given to the combination of workers in clubs and trade unions; and it might well be expected that some account of associations of labour would be given in this place. Recent research has brought to light the existence of a surprisingly lusty impulse towards unionism at an early period in the history of the textile industries; and that the mining industry and metal manufacturing trades possessed organisations of a similar character is clear from numerous passing references in the Journals of Parliament and the press. Thus, as early as 1738, John Bannister complained of the frequent rebellions of the nail-makers, "five hundred and a thousand of them together,"[1] though whether anything more than a temporary combination was effected must remain a matter of doubt. Benefit clubs, which probably exercised industrial functions, existed among the cutlers and the filesmiths in 1732, if not earlier, and a Grinders' Society came into being in 1748.[2] Later in the century, other groups of metal workers organised and pursued a concerted industrial policy. In his evidence before the Committee on the Exportation of Buckle-Chapes, in 1760, Matthew Boulton stated that the iron chape-makers had entered into combination and declared that they would raise their prices 3s. in the pound.[3] In 1777 the Kenyons, steel makers and tool manufacturers of Sheffield, explained a

1. *J.H.C.*, xxiii, 111.
2. Lloyd, *Cutlery Trades*, 239.
3. *J.H.C.*, xxviii, 882.

delay in the execution of orders by referring to the combination of their workmen[1]; and in the following year there are indications that the locksmiths of Wednesbury and the surrounding district were also organising themselves.[2] From this time onward unions developed rapidly among the craftsmen of Sheffield. In 1787 the cutlers engaged in a regular strike; in 1790 a combination was formed by the scissors-grinders, and in 1791 the scissors-smiths also took action.[3] Four years later an active wages policy was followed by the journeymen spring-knife makers[4]; and in 1797 the saw-smiths formed a union which was still in existence in 1833, by which time, indeed, all groups in the cutlery and silver-plate industry, with the solitary exception of the spring-knife cutlers, were properly organised.[5]

All these instances of early unions are on the fringe of the iron industry : there is no evidence of similar activity among the smelters, founders, and forgemen of the industry itself, though the presence of apprenticeship seems to imply that something of the form and spirit of the gilds of ironmongers and founders had survived in the eighteenth century. Of active trade unionism there could obviously be little among the workers in the charcoal-iron industry, scattered as they were, in half-dozens, at forges and furnaces dotted about the country and but rarely clustered at any one spot. Moreover the class distinction between the skilled keepers and founders, on the one hand, and the colliers and labourers on the other, would operate against concerted action. As the larger ironworks sprang up on the coalfields the facilities for the formation of combinations of labour were, indeed, greater; but the autocracy of the employers was exercised benevolently on the whole, and at Coalbrookdale, Carron, Thorncliffe, and other great works there were probably few serious grievances to evoke industrial unrest. John Wilkinson was reputed to be a good master; but what would have been the outcome of any associated effort on the part of his

1. See note in *Sheffield Telegraph*, 4 Dec. 1919.
2. *Aris's Birmingham Gazette*, 1 June 1778.
3. Lloyd, *op. cit.*, 241-7.
4. *Sheffield Iris*, 8 July 1796.
5. *Committee on Manufactures* (1833), Ev. of Jackson, 2749-50.

ironworkers can be gathered from his attitude towards the demands of the Cornish copper-miners and the colliers of Staffordshire. In October, 1787, the struggle between the Anglesey Company and the Cornish Metal Company—in which Boulton, Watt, Garbett, and Wilkinson were shareholders—had produced a disastrous fall in the price of copper; and thousands of miners in Cornwall, faced with starvation, were threatening their employers with personal violence. At one moment Matthew Boulton, who was on a visit to Cornwall, was in serious danger from a mob of some four hundred miners, and it was only by making them a present of twenty guineas for drink that he managed to escape with his life. To Watt and Wilkinson, in the security of Birmingham, this action savoured of weakness: " Mr. Wilkn. called here yesterday . . ." [Watt informed his partner[1]] " he condemns the gift of 20 Guineas, recommends a press gang, says what must be true that they cannot be in much distress yet, that the most profligate being disposed of elsewhere It will be salutory to the miners by lowering the price of wages—That He can employ 100 of them in this Country. N.B. the Bilston Coaliers are now in rebellion to have their wages made 3s. a day, he will stop his works rather than comply." Watt's early career had been impeded by craft regulations, and his embitterment against the journeymen engineers and millwrights made him also a vigorous opponent of labour combinations. " Get some sober Man to attend the Engine," he advised one of his clients,[2] " some Man of common Gumsion [*sic*] tho' not a professed Engineman." And at the time of a strike of the journeymen employed in erecting the Albion Mills, he urged upon Rennie the importance of employing carpenters rather than millwrights, and of presenting the " document " to all workmen—" that they shall not under a heavy penalty become members of the Millwright Club nor attend the meetings of the same while they are your servants."[3]

1. Watt to Boulton, 11 Oct. 1787. At the same time, in a letter to Garbett, Watt urged that " a powerful military force shd immediately be sent, and press gangs to take away the active rioters. They make excellent sailors or soldiers . . . and his Majesty wants men."
2. Watt to Henderson, 15 July 1779.
3. Watt to Rennie, 2 July 1786.

Whether it was the scattered nature of the industry, class cleavages, or the antagonism of employers, some force apparently impeded the growth of trade unions among the ironworkers, or at least sufficed to keep them underground. According to a well-informed ironmaster, William Matthews, no combinations of workmen existed in the industry during the Great War; and though in 1831 the riots at Merthyr Tydfil were attributed in part to the activities of trade unions, references to agitators who came from Wigan make it clear that it was the coal miners, rather than the ironworkers, who were involved.[1] But the fact that no evidence of united action by the ironworkers can be presented for a period earlier than the nineteenth century must not be taken as proof that no industrial combination existed. For this would involve an error similar to that of those writers who assumed that free competition of employers prevailed during the eighteenth century, simply because the evidence to the contrary was not to be found by a superficial glance. In all periods, and in all industries, the urge towards association of labour is at work : sometimes it produces a shoal of trade clubs that are visibly lively at the surface of society; at other times the movements take place more obscurely, and, though the trawl of the investigator be cast deep, he may catch nothing. A more skilful fling of the net by some future student may perhaps show that even the area of labour roughly charted in these pages was not devoid of active associational life.

---

1. *Committee on Manufactures* (1833), 9819. The Friendly Society of Iron-founders was formed on 6 Feb. 1809 at Bolton (Lancashire). From the first its members engaged in trade activities, and, to ensure secrecy, the books were buried in the peat of the neighbouring moors. See 420th Monthly Report of the Friendly Society of Ironfounders—Goldsmith Library.

CHAPTER IX.

THE IRONMASTERS.

" They need their pious exercises less
Than schooling in the Pleasures . . .'
—Meredith, *A Certain People.*

IN the introductory chapter reference was made to the sources from which the capital and enterprise engaged in the iron industry were drawn; and the intimate connection between ironmaking and the ownership of land was pointed out. During much of the eighteenth century this association continued, though in a much diluted form: the landed proprietors had long ceased to participate in the industry directly, but they continued to provide much of the fixed capital by leasing mines of coal and ironstone, and sometimes furnaces and forges, to the active industrialists. This practice enabled those with relatively meagre accumulations to engage in iron production, and the principal figures in the industry were men who had climbed from humble circumstances, often assisted by the liberal terms on which their leases had been granted.[1]

From what classes were these entrepreneurs drawn? Writing of industry in general, Toynbee and Mantoux have attributed to them a yeoman origin; but in iron production there is little support for the generalisation. Most of the successful men in the industry entered it from the secondary metal traders—successful craftsmen seeking control over the sources of their raw material—or from the merchanting of iron and steel wares. There were, of course, many exceptions. Andrew Yarranton was originally a linen-draper's assistant; John Pemberton came of a family of goldsmiths; Charles Lloyd was a farmer; John Roebuck a doctor of medicine; Joseph Dawson a minister of religion; and Samuel Walker a

1. Samuel Walker and Anthony Bacon are outstanding examples. See Guest, *op. cit.*, 461; and Scrivenor, *op. cit.*, 121

schoolmaster. But that the generalisation laid down is true of
the body of ironmasters is incontrovertible. Henry Darby,
the father of the first Abraham, was a locksmith, and
Abraham himself was, for a time, a maker of malt-mills. Aaron
Walker was a nailer; William Hawks, of Newcastle, and
John Parker of Staffordshire began their industrial life as
blacksmiths;[1] Peter Stubs, the founder of the well-known firm
at Rotherham, was originally a filemaker and innkeeper at
Warrington;[2] Spencer, who held Barnby Furnace in Yorkshire, began as a maker of hay-rakes;[3] and George Newton of
Thorncliffe was a maker of spades and shovels, who was drawn
to iron production by the high price of the material with
which he had to work.[4] To steel-making came Benjamin
Huntsman from the manufacture of clocks; and the steel firm
of John Kenyon and Co., of Sheffield, was started by two
sons of a Chapel-en-le-Frith watchmaker.[5] From the
miscellaneous metal trades of Sheffield and Birmingham
proceeded a numerous array of iron and steel producers:
Samuel Garbett began life as a brass worker;[6] Roebuck's
father was a manufacturer of small wares in Sheffield; Richard
Baddeley combined the ownership of a furnace at Rushall with
the operations of button-maker and gunsmith in Birmingham;
the Brades steel-works was set up by the four brothers Hunt
with capital made by their father out of buttons;[7] and the
conversion of Matthew Boulton from a maker of Birmingham
" toys " to an engineer and ironmaster has been described in
some detail above. Ambrose Crowley and Richard Crawshay[8]
had their early training in ironmongers' shops; Richard
Reynolds was the son of an iron merchant of Bristol;[9] and
Anthony Bacon had made money as an exporter of iron and
ore at Whitehaven, and as a merchant in London, before he
became an industrialist at Merthyr Tydfil.

1. Parker was described by Watt in 1779 as a " tollerable smith and
professes boiler making, wages about 12s. a week."
2. *Sheffield Telegraph*, 10 Dec. 1919.
3. *Surtees Socy.*, lxv, 312.
4. *Supra*, p. 157.
5. *Sheffield Telegraph*, 4 Dec. 1919.
6. Wright, *op. cit.*, 34.
7. *Memorials of the Old Square*, 62.
8. Smiles, *Industrial Biography*, 132.
9. Rathbone, *Memoir*, 5.

Such was the origin of the ironmasters. Most of them had risen by dint of constant industry and unremitting thrift; their early life and struggles left a definite mark upon their minds and outlook; and the narrowing effect of long years devoted to the single object of producing pig iron meant that few of them could feel at home in circles where art and literature and the lighter graces of life were cultivated. This same experience determined perhaps the spiritual, as well as the intellectual tendencies of the ironmasters: in religion, no less than in politics and social life, they stood aloof from official and fashionable groups, and tended to form societies where they could express their own aspirations in forms which sometimes appeared crude and strange to those nurtured in a more genial climate.

The close affinity between capitalist enterprise and religious nonconformity has been emphasised by several writers.[1] "One drop of Huguenot blood in the veins is worth a thousand a year," exclaimed Huxley; and that the spirit of dissent naturally led to industrial success might appear a safe enough generalisation. Sombart, however, has argued that Puritanism was in itself hostile rather than favourable to capitalist development, and that it was rather their exclusion from public offices and the state church that led the dissenters to turn their energies into industrial and commercial channels. "Only from this source could they hope to derive the means for winning for themselves respected positions in the body politic. What wonder, then, that in this 'excluded' class money was valued more highly, other things being equal, than among the rest of the population? For these people money was the sole means to power." Is it not probable, however, that the connection was more direct? In the great manufacturers of the eighteenth century the qualities of self-reliance, assertiveness, and adventurous enterprise were strongly developed; and the dignity and reticence of the service of the Established Church made small appeal to men of this type, whose ardent spirit called for more individualism, more spon-

1. See, *e.g.*, Sombart, *The Quintessence of Capitalism*, 287-290; Levy, *Economic Liberalism*, Ch. V; Ashley, *Economic Organisation*, Lecture VII, and *British Association Handbook* (1913), 354-8.

taneity—one might almost say more venturesomeness—in public worship. Quakerism, Methodism, Unitarianism, answered their need better.[1]

Whether the cause was enforced isolation; or Puritan thrift and energy; or simply that men who were innovators in matters of doctrine tended also to be progressive in technical affairs; or whether, finally, as Sombart[2] suggests, "nonconformity and capitalism are both the expression of biological characteristics, and . . . . nonconformity may be traced to economic causes," it is not necessary for us here to determine. Whatever the form of the connecting-link, there can be no question as to the fact of the alliance; and no industry is more fertile in illustrations of it than that of iron-making in the period 1700—1825.

Abraham Darby, Isaac Hawkins, Benjamin Huntsman, Shadrach Fox, Samuel, Aaron, and Jonathan Walker, Sampson and Nehemiah Lloyd, Daniel Colton, Job Rawlinson, David Mushet, Beriah Botfield, Jeremiah Homfray, Joab Parsons, Zephaniah Parker—the very names of the ironmasters are redolent of the Old Testament, and imply for those who bore them a Puritan parentage. Sir Ambrose Crowley, it is true, belonged to the Church of England : a chaplain was appointed to minister to his workers at Winlaton, and he was interested in the erection of a church at Greenwich.[3] But Crowley,

1. A somewhat harsh, but perhaps not entirely false, characterisation of the early dissenters is that given in Chamberlayne's *Angliæ Notitia*. Cited Dove, *Account of Andrew Yarranton*, 82.

"When we speak of any of these sectaries indiscriminately we call them *Dissenters* and *Nonconformists*, and they that speak more freely term them fanaticks and enthusiasts. It must be confessed that in all these sects there are some good moral men ; nay, some of them zealous towards God, but in such a zeal as is not according to knowledge ; neither are they all equally blameable in all respects. The Presbyterians come nearest to the Church; the Quakers are the most peaceable ; the Papists are the most mannerly, and the like ; but take them all generally, and they are all *envious* at the Established Church, desirous perpetually of a change of government, willing to fish in troubled waters ; *opiniating*, relying much upon their own judgment; ungrateful, as not holding themselves beholden to any man, saying it is God that put such and such beneficence into their benefactors' hearts, which they therefore could not avoid doing; *proud* as thinking themselves the only favourites of God, and the only wise or virtuous among men ; *obstinate* to all manner of arguments and entreaties ; *selfish, pragmatical, censorious* and the like."

2. Sombart, *op. cit.*, 290.

3. *Law Book of the Crowley Ironworks.* See also *Hist. MSS. Comm., Portland MSS.*, v, 222.

after all, like the Foleys of Worcestershire, belonged rightly
to the seventeenth, rather than the eighteenth century : he
was typical of the wealthy merchants of the Restoration
period, rather than of the rising industrialists of Georgian
days. Yet many, even of Crowley's contemporaries in the
iron industry, found their spiritual home in the meeting-
houses of the dissenters.[1]

In the early years of the eighteenth century perhaps the
most numerous, and certainly the most successful and progressive group of ironmasters was that made up of Quakers :
indeed the more important chapters in the early history of the
iron industry might be written almost without passing beyond
the bounds of the Society of Friends. At one time or other
Quakers were to be found conducting ironworks in each of the
chief centres of production : in the North there was William
Rawlinson of Backbarrow[2]; in Wales Charles Lloyd of
Dolobran and his descendants; in the Midlands John Pemberton and Isaac Spooner of Birmingham, Richard Parkes
and John and Samuel Fidoe of Wednesbury, and Booth
Hodgetts of Dudley; in the South, Gardner Manser & Co., of
Rotherhithe; and among Sheffield steel-makers the Hunts-
mans, the Doncasters, and others.

But the outstanding example of several generations of
Quaker industrialism is afforded by the Darby family. All
three Abrahams were devout Friends, all were unceasing in
the prosecution of industry, and in works of piety, and all
were married to women of the same strong cast of character
and religious fervour. Abiah Darby, the wife of the second,
was, moreover, something of a theologian and engaged in
long disputations on doctrinal matters with Fletcher, the
saintly Vicar of Madeley. And Rebecca, the wife of the
third, has left us many happy letters testifying to her varied
interests, to her practical Christianity, and to the shrewdness

---

1. The family of Cotton, of Silkstone and Denby in Yorkshire, who were
for long connected with the iron trade and ultimately worked the Rockly
furnace on lease from Lord Strafford, were Nonconformists " eminently dis-
tinguished for the support they rendered to the ejected clergy." *Surtees Society
Coll.*, lxv, 262, footnote. Thomas Pemberton, ironmaster of Birmingham
(1625-93), was one of the earliest followers of George Fox. Hill and Dent,
Memorials, 22.

2. Fell, *op. cit.*, 269.

and kindliness of her outlook on life. The death of the first
two Abrahams, before their children had reached maturity,[1]
placed the control of the Coalbrookdale firm for many years
in the hands of Richard Ford and Richard Reynolds, both
relatives by marriage, and both Quakers ; and among other
members of the Friends who were connected with the Darbys,
either as employees or as associates in ironmaking, were John
Thomas, Charles Lloyd, John Hawkins, and William Rawlinson[2] in the time of the first Abraham, and later in the century
the Cranages, Dearmans, Lloyds, and Parkers.

Mantoux has spoken of the Darbys as a dynasty of ironmasters, and the phrase is well-chosen; for not only was the
sovereignty at Coalbrookdale handed down from father to
son for several generations, but, like a royal family, the
Darbys allied themselves by marriage with other powers in
the iron world; and collateral branches as well as the direct
line of descent were connected with the industry. Thus the
first Abraham was allied, by the marriage of his wife's sister,
with Thomas Harvey, who, after his association with the
notorious William Wood, controlled forges at Sutton and
Upton; and a son of this union subsequently married a
daughter of Joshua Gee. Darby's own sister, Esther, married
in 1706 Anthony Parker, a nailer of Hagley, who afterwards
moved to Coalbrookdale, and one of whose daughters was to
become the wife of one of the Cranage brothers, and another
the wife of a son of John Thomas, Abraham Darby's first
assistant in Bristol. Parker's son, also named Anthony, died
in 1766, leaving five young sons, all of whom received their
early training at Coalbrookdale and who, about 1783, established the firm of Parker Bros. of Tipton, and drew a large
fortune from the industry. But to return to the Darbys
themselves : in the second generation Mary, eldest daughter
of the first Abraham, was married in 1718 to Richard Ford,
and her sister Ann became the wife of John Hawkins of
Bersham ironworks. Hannah, the eldest daughter of the

---

1. The first was born in 1678, and died in 1717; his son, born in 1711,
died 1763 ; and the third Darby was born in 1750, and died 1789.

2. Abraham Darby visited William Rawlinson at Graythwaite in 1714, **and**
took back to Coalbrookdale a parcel of Furness ore. *Fell, op. cit.*, 269.

second Abraham, married Richard Reynolds in 1757; and a little later the family became connected by marriage with the Dearmans of the Eagle Foundry in Birmingham. Iron, it would seem, was in the very blood of the Darbys, and the permeation of the industry by men of this stock is indicated in the form of a genealogical table on p. 216.

Other examples of the inter-marriage of Quaker iron-masters are afforded by the family history of the Lloyds. Charles Lloyd (1662—1748), the third of that name, married in 1693 Sarah, daughter of Ambrose Crowley of Stourbridge; and two years later his brother Sampson (1664—1724), who established the forges at Powicke and Burton, and the slitting-mill in Birmingham, took as his second wife another daughter, Mary Crowley; while their sister Elizabeth established a further link with the industry by her marriage with John Pemberton. Of the sons of Sampson, Charles (1696—1741) married Sarah Carless, daughter of an ironfounder, and Sampson II (1699—1779) joined his fortunes to those of a well-known family of ironmasters by his marriage with Sarah, daughter of Richard Parker. The same process is to be observed among the later generations of the Lloyds. Charles, the son of the second Sampson, married Mary Farmer, daughter of an ironworker who had risen to wealth as a gunsmith in Birmingham; and their son Charles Lloyd, the poet, married in 1775 into the Pemberton family; while at a later date George Braithwaite Lloyd married one of the Dearmans of Birmingham.

The families with whom the Lloyds intermarried were themselves connected with other ironmasters by similar matrimonial alliances. On the death of his first wife in 1711 John Pemberton became betrothed to a daughter of Ambrose Crowley (of Stourbridge), but the engagement was broken, and in 1713 Hannah James of Bristol—probably a member of the family of ironmasters of that name—became his second wife. A daughter, Rebecca, married an ironmonger, John Fidoe, and another daughter, Jane, was wedded to Samuel Lloyd. In 1727 Thomas Pemberton, son of John, married Jane, daughter of Richard Parkes, who himself had married a Fidoe. The Pembertons, Parkes, Fidoes, Lloyds, Crowleys and other

— Sergeant

John Darby

Anthony Parker = Esther Darby
1706
NAILER OF HAGLEY

Abraham I
1678-1717
OF COALBROOKDALE WORKS
1699 = Mary Sergeant

Hannah Sergeant
1699 = Thomas Harvey
OF SUTTON AND UPTON FORGES

Benjamin Harvey = d. of Joshua Gee
OF TERN AND FRIZZINGTON IRONWORKS

Abraham II
1711-1763
COALBROOKDALE WORKS
1718 Mary = Richard Ford
COALBROOKDALE WORKS

Ann = John Hawkins
OF BERSHAM WORKS

Samuel
1755-1796

Edmund
1782-1810
COALBROOKDALE

Abraham
EBBW VALE

Alfred

Richard = Esther Phillips
IRONMASTER OF WELSHPOOL

Anthony

Ann = Cranage
OF BRIDGNORTH FORGE

George   Richard   John   Abraham   Benjamin
IRONMASTERS OF TIPTON
(CONEYGRE FURNACE) AND APEDALE

Richard Reynolds = Hannah
KETLEY AND HORSEHAY

William Reynolds
KETLEY AND HORSEHAY

Abraham III
1750-1791
COALBROOKDALE

Richard Darby
COALBROOKDALE

William Henry   Charles Edward
IRONMASTERS OF BRYMBO WORKS

John Henry Darby

William Darby
BIRMINGHAM

Quakers were, indeed, so intermixed that only the formal presentation of their pedigrees could lay bare their manifold relationships.[1] This would be inappropriate in a work dealing specifically with industrial history. It will suffice to say that a close study of such pedigrees helps to explain the longevity of the iron concerns owned by the Quakers, and perhaps to some extent also the relative ease with which trading agreements and price associations were effected in this industry.

With the other ironmasters matrimonial alliances were often used as a means of establishing their families in a higher social grade; and once the ambition was achieved and they had been admitted to the serene clime of the English nobility, the ladder of iron by which they had mounted was kicked away, and henceforth they obtained their incomes from the more respected and less arduous functions of land-ownership. Examples of this social ascent might be given in large numbers, but one or two will suffice. Sir Ambrose Crowley himself took a first step towards aristocracy with results which —if Addison's satire may be accepted literally—were not devoid of discomfort to him.[2] Two of his daughters were

1. For the pedigrees of the Lloyds, Pembertons, and other families see Hill and Dent, *Memorials*. Appendices.

2. He is depicted by Addison in *The Spectator*, No. 299. A letter from Sir John Envil, married to a Woman of Quality.

" I am a person of no extraction, having begun the world with a small parcel of rusty iron, and was for some years commonly known by the name of Jack Anvil. I have naturally a very happy genius for getting money, insomuch that by the age of five and twenty, I had scraped together four thousand two hundred pounds, five shillings and a few odd pence. I then launched into considerable business, and became a bold trader both by sea and land which in a few years raised me a very considerable fortune. For these my good services I was knighted in the thirty-fifth year of my age, and lived with great dignity among my city neighbours by the name of Sir John Anvil. Being in my temper very ambitious, I was now bent upon making a family, and accordingly resolved that my descendants should have a dash of good blood in their veins. In order to this I made love to the Lady Mary Oddly, an indigent young woman of quality. To cut short the marriage treaty I threw her a *carte blanche*, as our newspapers call it, desiring her to write upon it her own terms. She was very concise in her demands, insisting only that the disposal of my fortune, and the regulation of my family, should be entirely in her hands. . . . . . She at first changed my name to Sir John Envil, and at present writes herself Mary Enville . . . . .

" She dictates to me in my own business, sets me right in a point of trade, and if I disagree with her about any of my ships at sea, wonders that I will dispute with her, when I know very well that her great-grandfather was a flag officer.

. . . " In short, Mr. Spectator, I am so much out of my natural element, that to recover my old way of life I would be content to begin the world again, and be plain Jack Anvil."

married to baronets—one to Sir John Hinde Cotton, who, besides being a politician, was also interested in ironworks in Yorkshire; and the process was completed when, in 1756, the daughter of John Crowley married the second Earl of Ashburnham, himself the scion of a line of Sussex iron-masters.[1] The same path was trodden by the Foleys, who became barons in the eighteenth century, by the Wortleys, from whom have descended the Earls of Wharncliffe, by the Hardys of Low Moor, afterwards Earls of Cranbrook, and by the Guests, from whom Lord Wimborne springs;[2] while one of the legitimated daughters of John Wilkinson married a Legh and became the mother of the first Lord Newton.[3]

But with the Quakers there was little of this movement from one social class to another : the discipline of the Friends and their hostility to marriages contracted " out of the Society " were sufficient to prevent it. There was thus no tendency towards the dissipation of capital. Quaker industry brought wealth into being; Quaker austerity and opposition to luxury led to the accumulation of that wealth; and Quaker aloofness and other-worldliness led to the constant re-invest-ment of that wealth in the business of iron production. If, however, it be true that the ethics of dissent—and of Quakerism in particular—often pointed the way to fortune, it is equally true that profits were sometimes sacrificed to principle. Robert Plumsted, a Quaker merchant of London, refused to export arms to America during the Seven Years' War, and endeavoured to persuade his correspondent not to seek elsewhere for them.[4] And lucrative government orders for cannon were refused by the Coalbrookdale Company during the period when its affairs were controlled by Richard Reynolds, whose Pacificism was also exhibited later in life by his refusal to pay the assessed taxes in 1798.[5] This attitude to war obviously closed what was certainly the easiest

---

1. Beaven, *Aldermen of London*, ii, 195; Surtees, *History of Durham*, ii, 168-170; *Surtees Collections*, cxxiv, 240.
2. *Records of Cardiff*, v, 319.
3. Palmer, *John Wilkinson*, 35.
4. Skeel, The Letter-Book of a Quaker Merchant (1756-8). *Eng. Hist. Rev.*, xxxi, 141.
5. Rathbone, *Memoir*, 28-29.

avenue to wealth that the industry could offer—an avenue which led the Wilkinsons and the Walkers within a few years from obscurity to an affluence far exceeding that of the Quaker ironmasters.[1]

Nor was the idea of right-dealing absent in the transaction of ordinary trade. That the eighteenth century Friend no less than the mediæval Catholic held firmly to some doctrine of Just Price may be exemplified in the action of the Ketley and Horsehay companies under the same direction. Speaking of Reynolds his biographer says : " At the beginning of the American War, when bar-iron rose to an extravagant price, and the makers of pig-iron could obtain their own terms, instead of taking an unreasonable advantage of the opportunity, he proposed to his customers that it should be left to one of themselves to name a fair price for pig-iron in the *then state* of the trade, and to determine the scale of proportionate reduction which should take place when the price of bar-iron should fall, as he foresaw that it would follow the *then* great and unsatisfied demand. The proposal was accepted, and by the scale that was then fixed his conduct was governed, so long as he remained in the iron trade."

This reasonableness in business matters may help to account for the high reputation which Reynolds acquired among other ironmasters and manufacturers, for at no time would he make use of the ordinary devices of businessmen in search of orders or popularity. A detailed examination of his letters and of those of a few similar spirits would provide an interesting study in social psychology, since it might throw light on the motives to industrial action and the qualities which, in the eighteenth century at least, were necessary to economic success. Those written to his son, Joseph, are full of admonition to frugality, thrift, and decorum in conduct. Writing in 1789 he refers to the levity of conversation at the quarterly meetings of the ironmasters, and cautions his son against " sitting longer amongst them than was absolutely

---

1. In 1796 Samuel Galton was disowned and expelled from the Society of Friends because he refused to cease business as a gun-maker, out of which he subsequently acquired a fortune of over £200,000. Hill and Dent, *Memorials*, 99.

necessary"; while in another letter he speaks of his own attendance at these meetings in earlier years, as times of "peculiar trial," and adds that he went to them "with fear as well as dislike."[1] Yet the men he met there were no libertines or hard-drinkers: the majority at least were sober-minded nonconformists whose attitude to life and whose standards of morality were not essentially different from his own. Nevertheless this aloofness did not cut Reynolds from social activities; by the schools he established at Ketley, by his agitation for the abolition of the slave-trade, and by his widespread charities he earned the title of philanthropist; and his interest in political questions, at least so far as they related to industry or to the poor, is attested by a large number of letters addressed in vigorous prose to members of both the Government and the Opposition of his day.

From the middle of the century Methodism began to be a force among the industrial classes; and that its appeal found a response among the ironmakers is proved by many references in the Journal of John Wesley.[2] In the early days, however, its influence was mainly confined to the working-classes, and though Wesley obtained sympathy and support from some of the Quaker ironmasters few, if any, became actual adherents. It required the passage of years for obscure workers to become capitalist-employers; but towards the end of the century the transmutation had, in numerous cases, been effected. It is at least a plausible hypothesis that Methodist conviction was one of the energising forces that had brought it about. Up and down the country there were ironmasters who were pillars of the connexion, and many ironworks became centres of propaganda for the new teaching. "In the afternoon we came to Barton Forge" [wrote Wesley in 1755[3]] "where a gentleman of Birmingham had set up a large iron-work, and fixed five or six families, with a serious man over them, who lost near all he had in the great riot at Wednesbury. Most of them are seeking to save their souls." In Yorkshire the

---

1. Rathbone, *op. cit.*, 179, 185-6.
2. *See, e.g.,* Wesley's *Journal* (ed. Curnock), iii, 119; v, 357, 517; vi, 226; vii, 150; viii 43, 51, 150, 368.
3. *Ibid.,* iv, 109. For a story of Methodism and suicide at Ledbrook Forge in Gloucestershire see *Aris's Birmingham Gazette,* 8 Apr. 1751.

Walker ironworks at Masborough was a similar beacon of Methodism, and all the partners in the Thorncliffe ironworks—Chambers, Newton, Maskew, Longden and the Scotts—were devout and active Wesleyan Methodists : the works themselves were opened with a religious service, and many of the subordinates in the firm were drawn from the chapels in Derbyshire which the partners visited as lay-preachers. That their spiritual creed was no mere incident but an integral part of life is shown by the curious admixture with business affairs of religious exhortation in the letters that passed between them; and when, in 1828, Scott wished to dissolve partnership, Dr. Adam Clarke, the well-known divine, was called in to act as arbitrator in the dispute which had arisen.[1]

In South Wales, again, the spiritual energies of the ironmasters found most general expression in the Methodist movement. The wealthiest of them all, Richard Crawshay, it is true, adhered to the Established Church; but his contemporaries, almost to a man, were followers of Wesley. In particular the Guests gave their weighty influence in support of his teaching, and several generations, beginning with John, the founder of the family, produced local preachers in the denomination.[2]

Samuel Walker's connection with Methodism has already been mentioned. For a time he adhered to the orthodox teaching, but when the controversy between Wesley and Whitfield resulted in open rupture, and the minister whose church he attended was expelled by Wesley, in 1762, he and his brother Aaron helped to establish at Rotherham a new chapel of the Independent type. Round this the chief activities of the Walker family henceforth centred; and Joshua, the son of Samuel, was largely responsible for the founding of the Independent College at Rotherham in 1795. Samuel himself perhaps suffered from religious melancholia, or at least his pastimes were hardly those of the lusty, natural man. He had built for himself at Masborough a mausoleum, " into which," says the historian of Rotherham,[3] " he often

1. Habershon, *Chapeltown Researches*, 168.
2. Baring-Gould, *A Book of South Wales*, 113.
3. Guest, Rotherham, 458, 500.

retired, with his excellent wife, to read the Word of God, and to meditate on that time which must one day come, when his mortal remains should be deposited there, and his spirit have returned to Him Who gave it."

But of the Independents in the industry perhaps the most remarkable was Joseph Dawson of the Low Moor Ironworks. Originally a Congregational minister, he became interested first in coal mines and later in ironsmelting ; and according to tradition was in the habit of paying wages to his workmen on Sunday morning before entering the pulpit. After the establishment of the Low Moor Company, his industrial and semi-scientific pursuits occupied the whole of his time, and he left the ministry to become a leading figure in the commercial life of Yorkshire, and chairman of the northern association of ironmasters.[1] To the same denomination belonged Dr. Roebuck, whose brother Benjamin was long connected with the Independent Nether Chapel in Sheffield.

The religious orientation of the Wilkinsons is more difficult to describe. Isaac and his son William were both members of the Presbyterian chapel in Wrexham, and William was buried in the dissenters' graveyard there. But, like many others of the same persuasion, they developed tendencies to Unitarianism, and Mary, the daughter of Isaac, married Dr. Priestley, the celebrated chemist, at that time an instructor in the Dissenters' College in Warrington, and afterwards a Unitarian minister in Birmingham. John Wilkinson, on the other hand, has been variously described as a Unitarian, a Churchman, a Methodist, and an unbeliever. Certain it is that he received his early training under Rotheram at Kendal ; that he was not without contact with the Established Church is indicated by the monument he erected in the parish church at Wrexham to the memory of his first wife, who died in 1756 ; and his association with Methodism in Staffordshire has been frequently related.[2] The Wesleyans of Bradley, many of whom were his own workers, persuaded him to erect for them a chapel in which the doors, the window-frames, and even the pulpit were of iron cast in the Bradley

1. For Dawson see Meade, *Coal and Iron Industries.*
2. Palmer, *History of the Older Nonconformity of Wrexham,* 135, 213.

works. And, according to one account, " Squire Wilkinson was well paid for his gift in the salvation of his soul. He attended one of the opening services to see how the cast-iron pulpit looked, and the word, preached by one of his own workmen, took hold of his heart."[1] If indeed there be any vital connection between creed and morality, Wilkinson's subsequent domestic life must have caused him to be regarded as, to say the least of it, a somewhat wayward member of the fold.[2] However that may be, it is probable that he was for a time sympathetic to the Methodists, and his bailiff, Samuel Ferriday, was a strong supporter of the movement in Bilston. Methodism indeed must have found abundant scope among the ironworkers and colliers of this district, where the inn-keepers boasted of brewing " men's fists and women's tongues." And the Methodist Conference of 1806 can hardly have turned a deaf ear to Ferriday's appeal for a small chapel in that previously inadequately-tended corner of the vineyard " in Hell Lane . . . near Ruffian Lane, leading to Dark Lane and Soddom."[3]

In character the ironmasters were compact of virtues which it is easier for the twentieth century to ridicule than to emulate : stress was laid on the primary virtues of industry and thrift; and however long the category of failings their enemies might indite, ostentation and indolence at least could find no place in it. To them mere outward show had few attractions : Benjamin Huntsman refused the proffered fellowship of the Royal Society, and James Watt would hear nothing of the proposal that an inscription in his honour should be placed on the engine he was erecting in Whitbread's brewery.[4] The frugality of the Quaker ironmasters has already been mentioned : that of the Methodists and other dissenters was no less clearly marked. As the latter had no scruples in undertaking the manufacture of cannon and arms, and many of them indeed breathed forth the fire of martial

1. Lawley. *History of Bilston*, 169.
2. For details see Randall, *The Wilkinsons*.
3. Lawley, *op. cit.*, 168.
4. Watt to S. Whitbread, 18 Feb. 1787.

patriotism,[1] they were able within a few years of war, in
many cases, to accumulate considerable fortunes. Even so,
the early habits of thrift and caution remained with them.
It is not surprising that the Walkers should have allowed
themselves only ten shillings a week each for the maintenance
of their families during the early days of their enterprise, but
that they should have retained the same penurious spirit in
later life is worthy of remark : in 1760 only £140 was divided
among the four partners in the enterprise; and even in the
subsequent years of affluence the daily menu was strictly
regulated in the interests of austerity and economy. The very
canal barges in which Samuel Walker's materials were carried
were named " Providence " and " Industry " to typify the
virtues on which the ironmaster himself had floated to fortune.

Far more a man of the world than the other figures in the
industry was Samuel Garbett : originally a brassworker, then
a chemist, he became a partner in the spinning enterprise of
John Wyatt and Lewis Paul, a joint-adventurer with Roebuck
in the Carron Works, and a shareholder along with Boulton
and Watt in the Albion Mills and in the copper mines of
Cornwall. There were indeed few sides of the industrial and
commercial life of his day that he did not touch. A type of
businessman more often found in the twentieth than in the
eighteenth century, his chief energies were thrown into the
politics of industry rather than into the detail of administration
and commerce. The later years of his life, in particular, were
spent in the manifold activities of arbitrator, prosecutor of
emigrant artisans, Guardian of the Birmingham Assay Office,
Chairman of the Commercial Committee, and spokesman to
Government on all questions affecting the interests of
employers and dealers of Birmingham and the Midlands.[3]
All these offices brought him into almost daily contact with
politicians and high-placed officers in the Civil Service. Yet,

---

1. It pervades the hymn composed by George Newton for the opening of
Mount Pleasant Chapel, near Chapeltown. *Sheffield Iris*, 11 May 1806.
    " Protected by our Country's Laws,
      Guarded from persecuting foes,
    Thus we can sing, and pray and praise,
      And bless the Lord for Gospel Days."
2. Guest, *op. cit.*, 487.
3. *Note on S. Garbett.* Birmingham.

throughout, he retained the simple habits of early life, and a foreign visitor was surprised to discover that his domestic establishment consisted of but one maid and a single blind man-servant.[1]

Other examples of Puritan frugality, sometimes indeed approaching meanness, might easily be given from the lives of industrialists who have figured in this book. Alone of them all Matthew Boulton appears to have "steered a true course between the Ascetic rocks and the Sensual whirlpools." When ironmasters like the Lloyds were opposing the project for a playhouse in Birmingham, he readily signed the petition in favour of a licence, subsequently justifying his conduct, it is true—as a broad-minded modern employer often justifies liberalities to his workers—on grounds of business interest.[2] Boulton's friends included many of the leaders of his generation, and his connection with the brilliant group that constituted the Lunar Society is too well-known to need re-telling here. Throughout, his correspondence breathes the genial, tolerant spirit of the best type of the educated English man of business; and that he was no less possessed of self-restraint and courage than the other ironmasters was proved on several occasions, and notably in his dealings with John Wilkinson. If the personality of Wilkinson in its hardness and obstinacy has often been described as cast iron, then that of Boulton in its flexibility and tenacity may be spoken of as finely tempered steel; and in the conflict of wills it was not the less refined metal that won.

The austerity of the ironmasters, whether cause or effect of their sectarianism, affected every side of their lives. Successful themselves, they were intolerant of what might appear weakness or inefficiency in others; and though their charities were numerous there was little of the milk of human kindness in their constitutions. At that time, more than any other, industrial leadership demanded men of an autocratic mould; and, individualists as they were both by nature and circum-

---

1. Bremmer, *Industries of Scotland*, 53.
2. " I have frequently given my designers, painters and modellers tickets to the play, in order to improve them in those arts whereby they are to live and gain reputation, and I have found my account in it." *Dartmouth MSS.*, App. I, Vol. 3, 234.

stance, they resented any attempt on the part of the workers
to determine, in any measure, the conditions of their working
life. In more than one, indeed, there was developed something
approaching contempt for the aspirations of labour. The
spectacle of "the French nation risen against tyrants,"
excited for a time the sympathy of the Birmingham group,
and many of them shared with Priestley the unpopularity
and physical danger which this involved. But when it came
to the application of the abstract principles of liberty, equality,
and fraternity, they preferred that the experiment should be
made on the other side of the English Channel. "We are
sorry to hear that you have had symptoms of Rioting in
your quarter" [wrote Watt to Wilkinson[1] in 1791] "the
madness seems very prevalent over all at present, and I doubt
will not be allayed without a copious bleeding. . . . This
comes of preaching up the Soveraingty (*sic*) and Majesty of
the people, we cannot say their Majesties are very gracious."
But most of the ironmasters had little time or inclination for
political speculation and their main concern was that industry
should be left alone : although there were among them philan-
thropists like Reynolds, and demagogues like Attwood, most
of them were, apparently, content to accept social conditions
as they found them.

Bold in their business operations, careful to a fault in the
administration of their gains, the industrialists found their
wealth steadily increasing ; and this was constantly re-invested,
whether in their own works, in mines of coal and ironstone,
or in Government stock. Early ironmasters like the Sitwells
found their principal outlet in the purchase of land. When
Lord Foley died in 1766 his fortune, derived mainly from
ironworks, consisted of real estate yielding £21,000 per
annum, mines worth £7,000 per annum, and no less than
£500,000 in the Funds.[2] And surely the *rentier* never
flowered more finely than in that millionaire descendant of the
Birmingham ironmaster, Humphrey Jennens, of whom it was
told that he always kept £50,000 in the hands of his banker
and never drew out the dividends from his holding in the

---

1. Watt to Wilkinson, 10 Apr. 1791.
2. *Aris's Birmingham Gazette*, 27 Jan. 1766.

Funds till half-a-year after they were due.[1] But not all successful producers who left the industry became mere *rentiers* : the instinct for affairs was too active in them to allow of repose ; and a restless energy, tempered by caution, led many from the path of iron-making into the less arduous avenues of finance.

The iron industry was by no means unique in this respect : in all parts of the country banks grew up in the soil of local industry, enriched by the accumulations of local · trade. Cotton produced a Rothschild ; wool and linen a Backhouse ; drapery a Barclay ; and so on. But though the iron industry was not exceptional, it possessed features which rendered the transmutation of surplus capital into banking credit relatively easy. Even in the eighteenth century iron production implied control over considerable resources ; for not only was the fixed capital required large in amount, but ironmaking necessitated a capacity for waiting and risk-bearing greater than that called forth by most other occupations. Situated as he was between two inferior economic classes, the ironmaster had usually to give cash or short-date bills for his raw materials, and, on the other hand, to grant long credit to his customer—whether the Office of Ordnance or the craftsman in the subsidiary metal trades. Thus from an early date he became accustomed to financing the operations of others, and it is not surprising that from time to time he attempted to " coin his credit."

An early illustration of the issue of a note currency by an ironmaster was that of Sir Ambrose Crowley. " I have found it pernicious to give any power to Draw money on me, for where the drawers, extravigantly given, the Remitter and my self run a great hazard. To prevent the said Evills, and to have a Sufficient Supply of Money in any place where my Occasions require, I have thought fitt to print Currant Bills to be Indented, and leaving a Counter part in the Book they are Cutt from, with other Characters and Numbers whereby the Counterfeiting may not be feared, and to the End they may be valued in all places better than Money I do resolve not to give out any of the Currant Bills, till money be first laid by, and Secured for the punctuall payment of them." The

1. *Birmingham Scrap Book*, vii, 319.

bills were to be payable on demand and in specie—not by
bank notes or by those of the goldsmiths—and Crowley's
expectation of the result of strictly following these principles
is indicated in the instructions to his agents : " The
Currency these Bills will have by Reason of Ready payments
you will soon find them in great Esteem, you are therefore to
use your Best Endeavours to get as much above the vallue as
you can for them."[1]

Since ironworks were often carried on in localities remote
from established banks—as in Furness—the ironmasters
sometimes found the provision of cash for the payment of
wages a matter of no small difficulty.   It was perhaps the
absence of a bank from which money of small denomination
could be obtained—combined with a desire for self-advertisement—that led John Wilkinson to issue his token coins
between 1787 and 1793.[2]   The coining of tokens was, of course,
by no means uncommon among industrialists at this time;
but Wilkinson went a step further than most when he printed
and put into circulation notes payable to bearer, in form
similar to those of any ordinary bank of issue.   These notes,
like the metallic tokens, appear to have been used in the
payment of wages, though as some were of relatively high
denomination they were probably also used in commercial
transactions of a larger scale.   At a time when the disastrous
experiments in currency made by the French were attracting
much attention, the issue was regarded in some quarters with
dislike; and since it was believed that Wilkinson was
sympathetically disposed towards the revolutionaries in
France, it was argued that there must be some sinister motive
behind his issue of notes.[3]   Accordingly steps were taken to

---

1. *Law-Book of the Crowley Ironworks.*
2. Tokens of small denomination were issued in 1787, '88, '89, '90, '92, and
'93, and in 1788 a silver token was manufactured which circulated at 3s. 6d.
3. *Hist. MSS. Comm., Kenyon MSS.,* xiv, App. IV, 536.   Peter Whitehall
Davis to Lord Kenyon :
1792 December 19, Broughton.—" I take the liberty to trouble your Lordship
with another letter, in which I have inclosed an *assignat,* made payable at
Bersham Furnace, endorsed ' Gilbert Gilpin '; I am informed he is the first
clerk of Mr. Wilkinson, whose sister married Doctor Priestley.   With what view
Mr. Wilkinson circulates *assignats,* is best known to himself.   It appears to me
that good consequences cannot arise from their being made currant, and that
very pernicious effects may.   Mr. Wilkinson, at his foundry at Bersham (where,
I am informed, he has now a very large number of cannon), and in his coal and

prevent their remaining in circulation, and the evolution of John Wilkinson from ironmaster to banker was temporarily arrested. At a later date other ironmasters printed notes of a similar character; but as the *assignats* had now collapsed and were forgotten, no hostility was aroused in the breast of any nervous patriot, and the issues were allowed to circulate without. molestation. Prior to 1811, for example, Popplewell, Pullan, and Shaw of the Royds Ironworks, made themselves responsible for paper that passed in the neighbourhood of Leeds; and between 1803 and 1826 the Low Moor Company of Bradford had a currency of their own consisting first of notes of a guinea, and afterwards of notes of one pound denomination.[1]

None of these firms engaged in banking in the modern sense of the word. But both before and after this period there were many instances of a complete transference of capital from ironmaking to banking. The first banking house in Sheffield was established by Benjamin Roebuck, brother of the founder of Carron; and though there is no evidence that Dr. Roebuck took an active part in the management, it is believed that the closing of the bank in 1778 was not unconnected with the financial difficulties of the ironmaster.[2] In 1778 the Broadbents of Sheffield, whose father had been a prominent ironmaster, founded a bank at Hartshead;[3] and a little later part of the wealth accumulated by Samuel Walker was used to establish the bank of Walker, Eyre, and Stanley of Sheffield and Rotherham. The descendants of Benjamin Huntsman have been connected with banking in Sheffield, and the steel

1. Ling Roth, *The Genesis of Banking in Halifax*, 3, 18.
2. Leader, *The Early Sheffield Banks*, 2.
3. Hunter-Gatty, *Hallamshire*, 170. The bank was short-lived, and disappeared in 1780.

---

lead mines, employs a considerable body of men. They are regularly paid every Saturday with *assignats*. The Presbyterian tradesmen receive them in payment for goods, by which intercourse they have frequent opportunities to corrupt the principles of that description of men, by infusing into their minds the pernicious tenets of Paine's *Rights of Man*, upon whose book, I am told, publick lectures are delivered to a considerable number in the neighbourhood of Wrexham, by a Methodist. The bad effects of them are too evident in that parish."

Note in the handwriting of Chief Justice Kenyon: " This letter occasioned the Act of Parliament, passed in January 1793, for preventing the negotiation of French paper money in England."

industry was also represented in the bank of Parker, Shore, and Bladelock. In 1805 the Reynolds of Ketley were at least contemplating the formation of a bank at Wellington,[1] and in South Wales iron production gave birth to the well-known house of Guest and Co., of Dowlais and London.[2]

Some of these institutions set up by the ironmasters were mere ephemera, destined to perish in one or other of the recurrent financial crises of the period. But more than one has stood the test of years and has survived to play its part in the finance of modern industry. In the early years of the eighteenth century the Spooners of Birmingham—like the Pembertons, who were goldsmiths even before they were ironmasters—combined their operations in the iron trade with the business of money-lending and the granting of accommodation to traders.[3] And before the century had come to an end they had instituted a specialised bank in Birmingham in conjunction with members of the Attwood family. The Attwoods, no less than the Spooners, had behind them a long connection with various branches of iron manu-facture. In the seventeenth century the family had become associated by marriage with the Foleys, and members of it had moved from Cleobury Mortimer to Halesowen, where Matthias Attwood made a fortune from steel-converting, the manufacture of nails, and the sale of Swedish iron. This enabled him to enter into partnership on equal terms with the wealthy Isaac Spooner; and in 1791 the business of Spooner, Attwood and Co., generally known as the Birmingham Bank, came into being. Several of the sons of Matthias were connected with banking and the iron trade: George, the eldest, directed financial affairs in Birmingham; Matthias, the second, was at the London office in Gracechurch Street, and afterwards helped to form the National Provincial Bank of Ireland; and Thomas, the third son, was the well-known Chartist Member for Birmingham, whose evidence against the

---

1. Rathbone, *Memoir*, 220. " I suppose my son Joe has consulted his brother Rathbone on his design of opening a bank at Wellington in which I shall willingly assist him." The bank was probably that of Eyton, Reynolds, and Wilkinson, which financed the Coalbrookdale Company.
2. *Records of Cardiff*, v, 317.
3. Hill and Dent, *Memorials*, 95.

Orders in Council has been cited,[1] and whose opposition
to the resumption of cash payments in 1819 showed him to
be no less heterodox in finance than in other departments of
economics and politics. Other brothers remained in the iron
and nail industries, and had association not only with
Staffordshire but also with the district around Newcastle,
where Charles Attwood became senior partner in the Weardale
Iron and Coal Company. In later years George Marshall,
of the Britannia Iron Foundry, became one of the partners
in the Birmingham Bank, which was ultimately absorbed by
Barclay, Bevan and Company.[2]

This was not by any means the only point of contact
between the iron trade and the group of banks now known
under the comprehensive title of Barclay's. Samuel Galton,
partner in the gun-smith business of Farmer and Galton,
became the husband of Lucy Barclay, an alliance which
possibly affected his future activities, for shortly afterwards
he joined with Paul James of Bristol—perhaps a member of
the family of ironmasters—to set up the banking establishment
of Galton and James.[3] A stream from a more distant source
was that of Gurney, Alexander and Company. In the 'forties
of the eighteenth century William Alexander, an ironmonger
of Needham Market, founded a bank at Ipswich, which in
the early years of the nineteenth century became connected
with that of the Spooners, and in quite recent times has
become merged in Barclay's Bank.[4]

But perhaps the best example of a family of ironmasters
which transferred its energies to finance is that of the Lloyds.
It was in 1698 that Sampson, brother of Charles Lloyd of
Dolobran, moved to Birmingham, and established himself as
an ironmaster and merchant in the town. In addition to the
slitting-mill in Bradford Street, he and his sons, Sampson and
Nehemiah, came to control forges at Burton-on-Trent and at
Powicke in Worcestershire. At this time it appeared that the
family might become leaders among the ironmasters of their

1. *Supra*, 149-150.
2. *Birmingham Weekly Post*, 31 Aug. 1889 : Notes and Queries, 2504;
Robinson, *The Attwood Family*, 33.
3. Hill and Dent, *Memorials*, 99.
4. *The Records of a Famous Banking House*, 47.—Guildhall Library.

day and that a business comparable to that of the Darbys might be established. But in 1765 a new turn was given to their activities, for Sampson entered into partnership with John Taylor, a prominent button-maker, to form the bank of Taylor and Lloyd—an institution which financed Matthew Boulton and other leading industrialists of the Birmingham district. Again matrimonial alliances played a part in business success: one daughter, Rachael, married David Barclay, and another, Mary, became the wife of Osgood Hanbury. In 1770 the younger Sampson took a leading part in the formation in London of the house of Taylor, Lloyd, Hanbury, and Bowman. But for long the banks in Birmingham and Lombard Street remained distinct institutions, and it was not until as late as 1889 that the two were amalgamated, and Lloyd's assumed the status of national, as distinct from local, bankers.[1]

A detailed study of the history of joint-stock banks would, no doubt, show that other ironmasters also made their contribution to the growth of British finance. But the illustrations already given should suffice to establish our generalisation. Like the thirsty lands of the Punjab, English industry to-day receives its vitalising supplies from five great rivers; and if the courses of these are followed it appears that two at least have received tributary aid from streams springing out of ferruginous soil. In the case of Barclay's these were, no doubt, subsidiary to the main current: but with Lloyd's the capital and enterprise derived from iron-making constituted the parent stream. From a tiny slitting-mill and two small forges in the Midlands has proceeded one of the greatest forces in modern finance.

1. Lloyd, *The Lloyds of Birmingham*, 26-32.

APPENDIX A.

AN ACCOUNT OF THE METHOD OF PRODUCING IRON AT THE END OF THE
SEVENTEENTH CENTURY.[1]

" When they have gotten their *Ore* before 'tis fit for the *furnace,*
they burn or calcine it upon the open ground, with small charcoal,
wood, or sea-cole, to make it break into small pieces, which will be
done in 3 days, and this they call *annealing* it, or fiting it for the
furnace. In the mean while they also heat their *furnace* for a weeks
time with charcoal without blowing it, which they call *seasoning* it,
and then they bring the *Ore* to the *furnace* thus prepared, and throw
it in with the charcole in baskets *vicissim i.e.,* a basket of *Ore,* and
then a basket of coal S.SS. where by two vast pair of *bellows* placed
behind the *furnace,* and compress'd alternatly by a large wheel turned
by water, the fire is made so intense, that after 3 days time the metall
will begin to run, still after increasing, till at length in fourteenights
time they can run a *Sow* and *piggs* once in 12 hours, which they do
in a bed of sand before the mouth of the *furnace,* wherein they make
one larger furrow than the rest, next the *Timp* (where the metall
comes forth) which is for the *Sow,* from whence they draw two or
three and twenty others (like the *labells* of a *file* in *Heraldry*) for the
piggs, all which too they make greater or lesser according to the
quantity of their Metall : into these when their *Receivers* are full
they let it forth, which is made so very fluid by the violence of the
fire, that it not only runs to the utmost distance of the *furrows* but
stands boiling in them for a considerable time : before it is cold, that
is when it begins to blacken at top, and the *red* to goe off, they break
the *Sow* and the *pigs* off from one another, and the *sow* into the same
length with the pigs, though in the running it is longer and bigger
much, which is now done with ease ; whereas if let alone till they are
quite cold, they will either not break at all, or not without difficulty."

*   *   *   *   *

" From the *Furnaces,* they bring their *Sows* and *pigs* of *Iron* when
broken asunder, and into lengths, to the *Forges;* which are of two
sorts, but commonly (as at *Cunsall*) standing together under the same
roof; one whereof they call the *Finery,* the other the *Chafery* : they
are both of them *open hearths,* upon which they place great heaps of
coal [*i.e.,* charcoal], which are blown by bellows like to those of the
Furnaces, and compressed the same way, but nothing near so large.

1. Plot, *Natural History of Staffordshire,* 161-4.

In these two *forges* they give the *Sow* and *piggs* 5 several *heats*, before they are perfectly wrought into *barrs*.   First in the *Finery* they are melted down as thin as lead, where the *Metall* in an hour thickens by degrees into a lump or mass, which they call a *loop*, this they bring to the great *Hammer* raised by the motion of a *water-wheel*, and first beat ît into a thick square, which they call a *half bloom*.   Then 2ly they put it into the Finery again for an hour, and then bring it again to the same *Hammer*, where they work it into a *bloom*, which is a square barr in the middle, and two square knobs at the ends, one much less then the other, the smaller being call'd the *Ancony* end, and the greater the *Mocket head*.   And this is all they doe at the *Finery*.   Then 3 the *Ancony end* is brought to the *Chafery*, where after it has been heated for a quarter of an hour, it is also brought to the *Hammer*, and there beat quite out to a *bar*, first at that end; and after that, the *Mocket head* is brought also 4. to the *chafery*, which being *thick*, requires two *heats*, before it can be wrought under the *Hammer* into bars of such shapes and sizes as they think fittest for *Sale*.

" Whereof, those they intend to be cut into *rodds*, are carryed to the *slitting Mills*, where they first break or cut them cold with the force of one of the *Wheels* into short lengths; then they are put into a *furnace* to be heated red hot to a good height, and then brought singly to the *Rollers*, by which they are drawn even, and to a greater length : after this another *Workman* takes them whilst hot and puts them through the *Cutters*, which are of divers sizes, and may be put on and off, according to pleasure : then another lays them straight also whilst hot, and when cold binds them into faggots, and then they are fitting for sale.

*   *   *   *   *

" Thus I say the *Iron-works* are exercised in their *perfection*, and all their principal *Iron* undergoes all the foremention'd preparations; not but that for several purposes, as for the *backs* of *Chimneys*, *Garden-rolls*, and such like; they use a sort of *cast-Iron* which they take out of the *Receivers* of the *Furnaces*, as soon as it is melted, in great *Ladles*, and pour it into *moulds* of fine sand, in like manner as they cast the other softer *Metalls*.   Thus the ingenious *Will. Chetwynd* of *Rugeley*, Esq; at *Madeley* furnace, cast *Iron-Rolls* for gardens, hollow like the *Mills* for *Sugar Canes*, of 5, 6, 7 or 800 weight a piece . . . . For such purposes as these, this serves well enough, but for others it will not, for it is so brittle, that being heated, with one blow of a hammer it will break all to pieces."

APPENDIX B.

SOME STATISTICS OF THE SUPPLIES OF IRON IN THE EARLY EIGHTEENTH
CENTURY.

According to a document cited by Mushet the total annual output
of pig iron in England and Wales about the year 1720 was only 17,350
tons, and that of bar iron 12,060. This statement, which was based
on the supposed output of 59 furnaces and 100 forges, has been
frequently cited as authoritative, but even a cursory study of the
industry at this period is sufficient to establish an under-estimate
here. [1] Perhaps a more accurate calculation is that made by
William Rea,[2] an ironmaster of Monmouth, who put the annual output
of pig iron for the same period at 25,000 tons, and that of bar at 18,000
tons. For the production of bar iron there is also the apparently
carefully compiled list of the author of *The Interest of Great Britain,*
according to whom in 1721 the output of the forges of England and
Wales was 12,190 tons. As, however, in this year the industry was
suffering from depression the writer's statement of the former output
of the same forges is probably a better guide when it is the productive

1. The list is printed by Mushet, *Papers on Iron and Steel,* 43 ; and also in
Scrivenor, *History,* 57. Scrivenor, however, enumerates only the furnaces, and
assigns the year 1740 to the document—an error which has been copied by
almost every writer since his time. The list is obviously defective in several
respects :
    i. Some bar iron was still made direct from the ore in bloomery forges,
without passing through the blast furnace at all. Thus in a paper written as
late as 1780 an account is given of an old man who produced malleable iron in
this way in Yorkshire, and it is probable that in the more remote parts of the
country the method was common during the early years of the century. Wyrall,
" Observations of the Iron Cinders found in the Forest of Dean." *Bristol and
Gloucester Arch. Coll.,* ii. 234.
    ii. No allowance is made for wares cast direct from the blast furnace, and
these, though small in volume, were not negligible.
    iii. Many large furnaces and forges are omitted from the list. Mushet
himself (*op. cit.,* 390) observes that the famous furnace at Tintern Abbey
is not included. That at Dolgan in Merioneth appears to have been
overlooked, as were also the large furnaces in the north of Lancashire and
Cumberland. (Fell, *Early Iron Industry passim* ; and Swedenborg, *op. cit.,* iii,
160, cited by Mantoux, *op. cit.,* 272.) As regards malleable iron the omission
of the small works of Surrey is probably not serious, but the compiler was
apparently ignorant also of larger forges in other parts of the country : in
Pembroke there were two which together produced 340 tons, in Northumberland
two producing 355 tons, and in Durham the forges of the Crowleys gave an
output of 250 tons per annum. (See *The Interests of Great Britain,* Appendix.)
It seems likely then that the output of both pig and bar at this time was
somewhat greater than has been imagined.
    2. *J.H.C.,* xxxii, 112.

capacity of the country that we have in mind, rather than the actual conditions in a particular and abnormal year; for this his figure is 19,585 tons—an estimate which does not diverge seriously from that of William Rea given above.

During the following twenty or thirty years production appears to have remained stationary, or even to have fallen slightly : according to Abraham Spooner, it did not exceed 12,000 or 15,000 tons in 1737, and Edward Knight put it at the lower of these figures.[1] But this again was at a time of special depression when thirty of the 125 forges were stopped; and in spite of the statement of Jonas Hanway[2] that the output of English iron was only 10,000 tons in 1750, there is no proof that a continued decline of any moment had taken place. In 1757, when the Bill for the extension of free importation from America was under consideration, it was estimated that the forges numbered 109, and that the output of bar iron was 18,000 tons per annum.   It would thus appear that by this time the tide had turned, and there is abundant evidence of steadily increasing production during the 'sixties.

Faulty as were some of these early lists of ironworks they nevertheless provide valuable information as to the geographical distribution of the industry at this time.   The compilation cited by Mushet and discussed above is summarised in the following table.[3]

TABLE I.

District.	County.	Furnaces.		Forges.	
South East	Kent	4		1	
	Sussex	10	15	8	11
	Hants.	1		1	
	Berks.	—		1	
South West	Gloucester	6		7	
	Hereford	3	11	5	20
	Monmouth	2		8	
Midlands	Shropshire	6		10	
	Worcester	2	12	10	36
	Warwick	2		4	
	Stafford	2		12	

1. *J.H.C.*, xxii, 854; xxiii, 110.
2. *British Trade over the Caspian Sea*, i, 457.
3. The classification of counties is based on that of Mantoux.

Chester and N. Wales	Chester	3 ⎫		3 ⎫	
	Flint	—		1	
	Denbigh	2 ⎬ 5		1 ⎬ 7	
	Montgomery	—		1	
	Cardigan	— ⎭		1 ⎭	

South Wales	Brecon	2 ⎫		1 ⎫	
	Glamorgan	2		1	
	Caermarthen	1 ⎬ 5		4 ⎬ 7	
	Pembroke	— ⎭		1 ⎭	

Sheffield District	York	6 ⎫		9 ⎫	
	Derby	4 ⎬ 11		4 ⎬ 17	
	Notts.	1 ⎭		4 ⎭	

North West	Lancs.	— —		1 ⎫ 2	
	Cumberland	—		1 ⎭	

Considered alone, these figures would give an exaggerated impression of the part played by the older centres of Southern England, for no reference is made to the size of each productive unit. But, in an appendix to his pamphlet, the author of *The Interest of Great Britain* makes a statement of the capacity of each of the 128 forges enumerated, and from this it is possible roughly to estimate the normal scale of operations in this branch of the industry, for each locality.

TABLE II.

Number of Forges of each size.   Total.

Output in Tons.	0 to 50	51 to 100	101 to 150	151 to 200	201 to 250	251 to 300	301 to 350	351 to 400	401 to	Forges	Output
South East	9	2	—	1	—	—	—	—	—	12	740
South West ...	1	5	—	8	1	3	1	—	1	20	3,950
Midlands	1	9	13	9	9	1	—	3	—	45	7,910
Chester & N. Wales	—	3	4	5	—	—	—	—	—	12	1,800
South Wales ...	—	6	1	1	2	—	—	—	—	10	1,370
Sheffield District ...	1	3	9	3	1	—	1	—	—	18	2,680
North West ...	1	2	2	1	—	—	—	—	—	6	630
North East	—	3	2	—	—	—	—	—	—	5	505
Total	13	33	31	28	13	4	2	3	1	128	19,585

The typical, or representative, forge produced between 51 and 200 tons of bar iron in a normal year, and the average output of the English forges was 153 tons. But in the year 1721, if our author's figures are reliable, 33 of these forges were closed, and the average output of those at work was only 128 tons.

The extent of foreign competition during this period varied from time to time and according to the type of iron. No *pig* iron was brought in from foreign countries, and only quite small quantities from the American Plantations : it was the forge master, therefore, rather than the furnace owner, who felt the burden of the importations, and even here the severity of the rivalry varied with the grade of iron. Exact information is lacking, but from the sometimes conflicting statements made by witnesses before the Committees of 1737 and 1738 it is possible to form a rough estimate of the part played by overseas supplies of bar iron at this time. It would appear that the importations had increased, between 1720 and 1737, from an average of about 17,000 tons per annum to something over 24,000 tons, of which about three-fourths came from Sweden.[1]

The highest grade of Swedish iron, of which 1,200 to 1,500 tons were imported, was sold at Bewdley for £17 or £18 and was purchased entirely by the English steel-makers : it was a special product and thus did not compete directly with English iron. Of the latter it is possible to distinguish four main grades, known respectively as *best tough, ordinary tough, blend,* and *cold-short.*

The first of these was subject to the competition of the second grade of Swedish, of *Government* and *Merchant Siberia,* as well as of Spanish iron; but as the English bars were somewhat softer, and so required less labour and fewer tools in manufacture, they sold for about £16 as against £15 paid for the Swedish iron. They were generally preferred for the making of " toys " and other wares of good, but not the best, steel.[2] The bulk of imports from Sweden were of this grade. Ordinary tough bar was used for general purposes, and was considered superior to the lower grades of Russian iron—known as Brinsco and Moscow—which were used as substitutes for it. English ordinary tough bar sold at this time for about £14, while the corresponding grades of Russian iron fetched £11 a ton.[3] Blend and cold-short English iron were inferior grades used almost exclusively for the making of nails, for which purpose also the lower grades of Russian iron were employed.

1. Scrivenor, *op. cit.,* Table V.
2. Yarranton contrasts the harder Spanish iron with that produced in the Forest of Dean : " The Forest Iron works easie, plyable, and soft ; the Spanish works tough, churlish and dogged." *England's Improvement,* Pt. I, 147.
3. *J.H.C.,* xxii, 852. Evidence of John Bannister.

APPENDIX C.

The Marketing of Charcoal Iron.

In earlier centuries much of the product of the industry was sold by the ironmasters at their own warehouses in the form of bars; and the chapmen who visited the warehouses distributed the metal to the consumers either direct, or through the organisation of fairs.[1] It was at the fair that the manorial bailiff of the middle ages purchased the bar iron that was subsequently worked into ploughshares and other implements by the local smith; and that even late in the seventeenth century consumers were being supplied through the same channel is indicated by contemporaries. " For here," [wrote Thomas Baskerville,[2] referring to Stourbridge Fair] " you shall see large streets and shops full of all the variety of wares that are to be sold in London, and great quantities of iron brought from several parts of the nation and elsewhere." But when this account was written the fairs were already beginning to lose their functions, and during the eighteenth century they were used not so much for the actual purchase and delivery of iron as for that of obtaining orders and collecting debts.[3] Like the modern exchange, the fair became a convenient meeting-place for business men, rather than a market in which the goods themselves changed hands.

Direct sales were still made by ironmasters through their own warehouses. Crowley had such in Greenwich and in Thames Street, London; the Backbarrow Company opened warehouses at Ulverston, Whitehaven, Penrith, Keswick, Kendal, Lancaster, Hawkshead, and other places, obviously to facilitate sale in small quantities to farmers and smiths.

1. See the letter of Thomas Kirkland, agent to the Earl of Rutland, who conducted ironworks at Rievaulx in 1582. *Hist. MSS. Comm., 12th Rept.,* iv, 138; cf. *ibid. 15th Rept.,* ii, 33; *V.C.H. Surrey,* ii, 275.
2. *Hist. MSS. Comm., 13th Rept.,* ii, 272.
3. Thus in the Coalbrookdale records, under date 29 Sept. 1718, occurs the following entry:

	£	s.	d.
Allow'd towards T. Goldneys Expenses to Chest[r] fair &c. : collect. m[o] for y[e] new Compa	1	00	00

And the same practice, it may be added, afterwards prevailed in the coke-iron industry. The Carron Company disposed of some of its goods through a London warehouse, though this was owned, in part, by others; prior to 1772 it was conducted by a William Adam and a John Wiggan, " who in co-partnership with the Carron Company bought the goods at one price and sold them at another," the co-partners and the company each receiving one-third of the profit on sales.[1]   A somewhat similar system was adopted by the Coalbrookdale Company, which sent some of its products to its warehouse in Bristol; and an account book of the firm shows that two prices were recorded, the first being that at which the goods were supplied to the warehouse, and the second that paid by the purchaser. Thus during the year 1st August 1804 to 31st July 1805 the amounts received for goods sold retail totalled £426 6s. 9d., and the wholesale value of these was £325 10s. 0d.

Notwithstanding these evidences of commercial dealings carried on by producers, it is certain that much of the pig and bar iron used in England passed through the hands of specialised merchants; and the statement of a modern writer [2] that the iron industry of the eighteenth century was "characterised by the want of definite middlemen " will hardly bear examinaion.

It is evident that the large quantities of bar iron brought in from abroad was the subject of commerce between merchants and dealers.   According to Edward Knight,[3] one of the largest ironmasters in Britain, American iron passed through the following hands before it was returned to the colonists in the form of manufactured wares :

" the Factor beyond Sea, the Importer, who sells it to the Bar Ironmonger that lies near the Manufactory; he sells it to the Manufacturer that employs the Workmen : Which Iron, when manufactured is sent to the London Ironmonger, who sells it to the Merchant, and he exports it; and a Factor disposes of it in America. . . . And, it is supposed all these different Hands will have a Profit of about £6 per Cent

1. *Information in Carron Co.* versus *Samuel Garbett*, 16 November 1778.
2. Westerfield, *Middlemen in English Industry*.
3. *J.H.C.*, xxiii, 109.

each, some more and some less; which will amount to about £40 per Cent exclusive of Carriage and Freight."

For that section of the trade with which we are here concerned the importing merchant and the bar ironmonger were the more important middlemen. But there were sometimes others not enumerated in Knight's account; and in particular, the owner of a slitting-mill, who received iron from the bar ironmonger, sometimes combined his industrial function with that of rod ironmonger, supplying the nail manufacturers, locksmiths, and other metal workers with their raw material.

The relatively large volume of iron imported from abroad naturally led to a localisation of marketing in the chief ports. Most of the supplies from Sweden and Russia were brought in through London and Newcastle; and London, Bristol, and, perhaps, Gainsborough, were the chief centres for the importation of American iron.[1] Much of the commerce arising out of the activities of English ironworks was also conducted by sea. From early times the bar iron of the Weald had been sent by way of the Channel ports to merchant houses in London, and ordnance was in the same way transported, when, indeed, it was not surreptitiously exported overseas. The route, however, appeared unnecessarily long, and was hazardous in time of war; hence an attempt, made in 1740, to improve the northward-flowing Medway in order to obtain a more direct and safe passage between the ironworks and the capital.[2] Iron, steel, and manufactured wares from Crowley's forges near Newcastle were also marketed in London, and at a later date the Carron Company ran a line of vessels between Scotland and the Metropolis to carry not only their own products but also passengers and general merchandise.[3] Similarly the iron of the Furness area was sent to Liverpool, Bristol, and Chepstow,[4] and trade in iron ore, as well as that

---

1. *J.H.C.*, xxiii, 110. For the trade through Gainsborough see Skeel, " The Letter-Book of a Quaker Merchant," *Eng. Hist. Rev.*, xxxi, 137.

2. *Sussex Arch. Coll.*, ii, 187. *J.H.C.*, xxiii, 443, 530.

3. See advertisement in *Aris's Birmingham Gazette*, 7 April 1766, announcing that a ship sails from Glasgow Wharf, London, for Carron, Bo-ness and Alloa every ten days, and that the proprietors will carry and insure goods delivered to their charge. The Carron Company still runs a line of steamships.

4. Fell, *op. cit.*, 300-319.

in finished products, did much to aid the development of such minor seaports as Whitehaven[1] and Cardiff.[2]

Even more important than the sea-borne traffic in iron was that of the river system of England. The foreign and American pig and bar iron, and Swedish iron sent round from London, were unloaded at Bristol and carried in trows or barges up the Severn to Bewdley or Bridgnorth, thence to be transported to the forges or smithies of the Black Country. And pig, bar, and cast iron wares from Coalbrookdale, Broseley, and other iron centres of Shropshire, were sent down the river to Bristol and so to their ultimate destination whether at home or abroad. Probably something over one-half of the domestic output came from works which had communication with the Severn, and the river hence became the principal highway of the industry. " There is no river that has such a length of navigation as the Severn [says Whitworth]; you may navigate a vessel of fifty tons, and not a lock the whole way, two hundred miles up to Welch Pool, except in an excessive drought. . . ."

Along both banks from time immemorial there had existed a right of way, and a narrow footpath was trodden by gangs of bow-hauliers—varying in number from five to forty or fifty—who dragged the laden trows up the river. As trade increased, this method of traction appeared inadequate : in 1761 the merchants of Bewdley, Stourbridge, Dudley, and Kidderminster sought to substitute horses for men, and petitioned for the construction of a horse-towing path from Bewdley to Worcester. Traders in Wolverhampton, Birmingham, and Manchester supported the proposal; and when, a little later, the matter was again raised, Richard Reynolds, the Quaker ironmaster, attacked the existing usage on the ground of social no less than of economic interest : it was degrading since it made men into beasts of burden; it led

1. The ironmaster, Anthony Bacon, took a part in improving the harbour at Whitehaven in 1740. *J.H.C.*, xxiii, 460.
2. Even at the end of the seventeenth century bar iron and cast wares were coming in through Cardiff in moderate quantities. As South Wales became a producing centre the imports came to consist largely of ore from Furness and Cumberland, and the port became also an important channel for exports : in 1788 the Collector of Customs writes of " three private Wharfs for Shipping and Landing Goods, chiefly Iron." *Records of Cardiff*, ii, 388, 409-420, 430.

to a congregating of bad characters; and it provided opportunities for theft.[1] Opposition to change came, however, from
local landowners, and from ironmongers who feared that
heavy tolls would be levied on the trows to maintain the
proposed towing path; and, despite the powers granted in
1772,[2] the old methods of haulage continued almost to the end
of the century.[3]

Of the bar iron moved in both directions the greater part
was unloaded at Wribbenhall, a suburb of Bewdley. Situated
on the outskirts of the Wyre Forest industry, at a spot where
the river was spanned by a bridge, and not far from the point
of confluence with the Stour, Bewdley was an obvious marketing centre for the forges and manufactories of Shropshire,
Worcestershire, and South Staffordshire.

" Wribbenhall, from its excellent quays and vicinity to
Bewdley, was long the principal part of Worcestershire
[says Nash[4]]. From Manchester, Stourbridge, Dudley,
and the iron works of the Stour, innumerable pack horses
came laden with the manufactures of these places to be put
on board the barges and sent to their various destinations. . .
At a spring tide I have been told 400 pack horses have been
for several nights together quartered in this neighbourhood,
and in consequence Bewdley was a rich and very trading
town."

Here dwelt many of the prominent merchants and ironmongers of the Midlands, and that the importance of the
market was not confined to this district is indicated by
witnesses before the Parliamentary Committees of 1737 and

1. *J.H.C.*, xxix, 85, 93. See also Whitworth, *Advantage of Inland Navigation*, 55, and Rathbone, *Memoir of Reynolds*, 45.

2. 12 Geo. III, 109. The Act applied only to that part of the river
between Bewdley and Coalbrookdale. For the opposition to the measure see
J.H.C., xxix, 194.

3. In 1799 Nash wrote: "Various have been the attempts to introduce
horses, but the banks are often so steep, the line way must so often change
sides . . . the laying a tax upon a free river, and many other objections have
rendered, and I trust always will render, this scheme abortive." *Worcestershire*,
46. In this very year the powers granted in 1772 were renewed by
39 Geo. II, c. 8, and were at length exercised. By 43 Geo. III, c. 129, the
towing path was extended to Worcester, and by 49 Geo. III, c. 121, upstream
to Shrewsbury. Finally, in 1811, a towing path was made from Worcester
to Gloucester, by 51 Geo. III. c. 148, and horse-drawn barges could pass
between Gloucester and Shrewsbury.

4. Nash, *op. cit.*, Supplement, 46, 47.

1738, for Bewdley prices were quoted by ironmasters from all parts of the country.[1] English, colonial, and foreign bars were all sold, and were carried by the purchasers to the mills of the Stour, where they were slit into nail-rods and sold to the nail-ironmongers, who in turn handed them over to the domestic workers. Of this commerce in nail-rods and manufactured wares, Birmingham naturally became the centre; and, as the making of iron moved eastward from Shropshire to Staffordshire, it became increasingly the market for bar iron also, while Bewdley steadily declined. In 1766 when Brindley planned the Wolverhampton Canal to join the Grank Trunk, he at first proposed to construct his basin near Bewdley. But the nearsightedness of the townspeople in opposing the scheme led him to adopt, as an alternative, the site of a tiny hamlet at the mouth of the Stour; and the trading classes of Bewdley must have watched with envy and regret the rapid rise of Stourport, nourished, after 1771, by the inland water-traffic between the Black Country and the seaports.

But long before these events Birmingham had become the home of many who made a living by dealings in iron. In 1702, Sampson Lloyd, son of Charles Lloyd of Dolobran, set up his slitting-mill on the tiny stream from which alone it was possible to obtain power in Birmingham, and shortly after he engaged also in a mercantile business. The famous Old Square, in which dwelt so many of the notabilities of the town at one time or another, was itself the creation of an ironmaster, John Pemberton. Abraham and Isaac Spooner, Randle Bradburn, Charles and Sampson Lloyd, Samuel Garbett—all ironmongers or merchants—had houses here; and the Square became the fashionable centre to which gravitated prosperous ironmasters who desired to transmute their wealth into social prestige—Richard Baddeley who owned a furnace at Rushall, Richard Parkes, of Wednesbury, his partner John Fidoe, William and Harry Hunt, who conducted the slitting-mill at Halesowen, and Samuel Garbett, who claimed to be the largest importer of Swedish bar iron, outside London.[2]

1. *J.H.C.*, xxii, 852, 853, xxiii, 115.
2. Lloyd, *The Lloyds of Birmingham*; Hill and Dent, *Memorials of the Old Square, Birmingham, passim*; *Cal. H.O. Papers* (1766-9), 82.

The only other large inland region of manufacture was
that of South Yorkshire and Derbyshire, and here most of the
iron used was either produced locally or imported for the use
of the cutlers from Sweden. In the former case it could be
sold direct to the users; in the latter, the chief mercantile
operation was performed outside the area itself, for most of the
Swedish iron required for steel-making reached Sheffield
through Hull. Direct communication between the two towns
by river was impossible, since in its upper courses the Don was
navigable only by very small boats; the route followed, therefore, was from the Humber by way of the Trent and the
Idle to Bawtry, and thence by land—a matter of twenty
miles—to Sheffield. Bawtry had hence early developed into
an inland port; from the sixteenth century, if not before, it
had been concerned with dealings in iron and steel, and
with the exportation of cutlery and finished wares.[1] And
through it also, on their way to the Barbadoes and elsewhere,
passed the cast and wrought iron wares from the furnaces of
the Sitwells and others of Derby and Nottingham.

But though Bawtry thus occupied in this area a position
similar to that of Bewdley in respect of the West Midlands, it
was less conveniently situated as a marketing centre; and
frequent attempts were made to secure a less expensive means
of communication with Hull.[2] In the year 1721 the Cutlers'
Company and the Corporation of Doncaster formulated a
scheme; and, in spite of the strong opposition of merchants
in Bawtry, Samuel Shore, ironmaster of Sheffield, and his
colleague John Smith were able to convince a House of
Commons Committee of the desirability of their proposals.
Accordingly Acts were passed in 1726 and 1727, the first
of which empowered the Cutlers' Company to improve the

1. The Memorandum Book of the Steward to the Earl of Shrewsbury
records the carrying from Bawtry to Sheffield of six barrels of steel in 1574.
Lloyd, *Cutlery Trades*, App. II.
2. For the earlier attempts to improve the navigation of the Don see
Jackman, *Transportation in Modern England*, i, 202. Iron for Staffordshire
was carried up the Trent to Burton. "When a number of ironworks were
established in our part of the country, my father, who is still living (upwards
of eighty years of age) bought the foreign bars at Burton upon Trent, before
the Birmingham Canal was made, and brought them by land carriage to
Birmingham." *Minutes of Evidence against the Orders in Council (1812)*, 24.—
Ev. of William Whitehouse.

river from Doncaster to Tinsley,[1] three miles from Sheffield, and the second enabled the Corporation of Doncaster to do the same for that part of the river lying between their town and Barnby.[2] In 1732 these bodies transferred their powers to the Company of Proprietors of the Navigation of the River Don, among the original shareholders in which were several wealthy ironmasters and steelmakers : Francis and William Sitwell, William and Joseph Steer, Samuel Shore, and the Crawshaws,[3] to all of whom the advantages of direct river communication with the Humber must have been enormous. The company, in turn, made over its powers to three adventurers, subject to a payment of £1,500 per annum.[4] Shortly afterwards complaints arose : the lessees were accused of granting preferential rates to merchants and manufacturers of Sheffield at the expense of those of Doncaster. But these and other difficulies were overcome; in 1739 further powers were obtained, and by the middle of the century much of the traffic had been deflected from Bawtry to the new route. Not, however, until 1819 did the opening of a canal between Tinsley and Sheffield complete the direct water route between the cutlery centre and the coast.

The volume of the import and export trade through Hull implies a concentration of merchants here : it was from Joseph Sykes and Sons, a well-known firm of importers, who later secured a virtual monopoly of the trade, that the Huntsmans obtained the supplies of Swedish iron necessary for the production of crucible steel.[5] In Sheffield specialised middle-men developed more slowly, and it was not until the later decades of the century that merchant firms were established here. These were concerned with finished wares rather than with iron, though blister, sheer, and cast steel were also bought and sold.[6]

1.   12 Geo. I, c. 38.
2.   13 Geo. I, c. 20.
3.   Hunter, *Hallamshire*, 155.
4.   *J.H.C.*, xxiii, 440.
5.   *Supra*, p. 57.
6.   According to Hunter it was between 1760 and 1770 that " some of the persons whose fathers had been manufacturers established themselves in the character of merchants and general dealers in the long list of articles made at Sheffield. They employed considerable capitals and opened extensive correspondencies immediately with houses on the Continent and in America." *Hallamshire*, 157.

APPENDIX D.

Copies of Minutes of Meetings of Ironmasters.

(a) *In Yorkshire—Thorncliffe MSS.*

At a meeting of the following persons at Sheffield Nov. 3d 1800—
Resolved

1. That all Iron sent to London, Newcastle or any other Distant place or at Hull itself we engage to deliver at Hull at the same price and oblige all our Customers to take the risque of the Sea upon themselves and pay the Freight and that the present price shall be £9 for No. 1, £8 10s. for No. 2, and £7 5s. for No. 3.

2. That we will sell in our own neighbourhoods as follows vizt. In the neighbourhood of Leeds No. 1 £9, No. 2 £8 10s., No. 3 at £7 5s. delivered at the Foundries and Forges and No. 1 £8 10s., No. 2 £8, and No. 3 at £6 5s. to £6 7s. in the neighbourhood of Sheffield on our furnace Hills the consumers paying the Carriage.

3. That in Case we send Metal to each other's neighbourhoods we will charge it not at a less price than that what it is sold at in that Neighbourhood as stated above.

4. That all Contracts now made shall be completed under the usual Regulations.

5. That we will not make any alterations in price without acquainting each other and new regulations being agreed upon.

> Jarratt Dawson & Hardy.
> Longden & Co.
> John Sturges & Co.
> John Darwin & Co.
> Booth & Co.
> John Scott.
> Ricd. Swallow Jr.

(b) *South Wales—Ebbw Vale MSS.*

At a Meeting of Ironmasters held at the King'shead Inn, Newport, Jany. 13th, 1809—

Mr. Fothergill's Letter to Mr. Reynold L. Waddenbrook having been read, as also replies thereto
Resolved—

That this Meeting is determined to support the price of Iron fixed at the last Gloucester Meeting.

That the Makers of South Wales are determined not to supply Iron to any Commission House or other person who shall resell at a less price than £14 5s. od. per ton at Bristol.

Present—

Taitt	Fothergill	
Oliver	Harrison	who were individually
Homfray	Blakemore	asked the question.
Hill	Frere	
Rose		

That the Makers of Bar Iron will not execute any order to be shipped by them for a less quantity than 5 tons.

Resolved—

That copies of these resolutions be transmitted to the absent Bar Iron Makers—stating that those present have individually agreed to them, and desiring their immediate determination : to be transmitted by letter to Mr. John Scale of Aberdare—who in case of the refusal of any Bar Iron Makers to accede to these resolutions, is requested to inform the other Bar Iron Makers thereof.

That one penny per ton on Pigs & also on Bars be paid by the Makers upon the last year's make, & be carried to the general Acct. & that the Treasurers do pay such part of the Two Hundred Pounds subscribed for defraying the expence of opposing the Bristol Dock Bill—as may be called for.

Mr. Crawshay's letter advising an advance upon Iron having been read, this Meeting returns him their best thanks for his opinion & advice; but as it does not conceive itself at liberty to make alterations without consulting the General Meeting at Glo'cester, the Chairman will request his further advice previous to that Meeting at Lady Day.

RD. FOTHERGILL, Chairman
for JNO. SCALE.

APPENDIX E.

The following letter was written by Abiah Darby, wife of the second Abraham Darby : it is undated but was probably written about 1775. It is a typical letter of an eighteenth-century Quakeress, but its principal value lies in the evidence it contains concerning the origin of smelting with coke. The writer asserts that it was the first Abraham Darby who devised the process, and there is no suggestion that her own husband, the second Abraham Darby, had any part in the discovery. It is claimed for the latter, however, that he was the first to fine coke-smelted pig iron into bars. The letter strengthens and indeed, renders superfluous, the argument developed in Chap. II, pp. 28—36. The original, which was seen by the author as the final proofs were being read, is in the possession of Alfred Darby, Esq., of Shrewsbury.

Sunniside.

Esteemed Friend,

Thy very acceptable favour of the 9th ulto. claim'd my earliest acknowledgments, which I should immediately have made, had not thy kind condescension in taking notice of my late honour'd Husband, and requesting to be inform'd of any circumstance which may be interesting relating him, caused my delay—to recollect what might occur concerning his transactions or improvements in the Manifactory of Iron, so beneficial to this nation.   But before I proceed further, I cannot help lamenting with thee in thy just observation, " that it has been universally observed, that the Destroyers of mankind are recorded and remembered, while the Benefactors are unnoticed and forgotten." This seems owing to the depravity of the mind, which centres in reaping the present advantages, and suffering obscurity to vail the original causes of such benefits; and even the very names of those to whom we are indebted for the important discoveries, to sink into oblivion.   Whereas if they were handed down to posterity, gratitude would naturally arise in the commemoration of their ingenuity, and the great advantages injoyed from their indefatigable labours—I now make free to communicate what I have heard my Husband say, and what arises from my own knowledge; also what I am inform'd from a person now living, whose father came here as a workman at the first beginning of these Pit Coal Works.

Then to begin at the original. It was my Husband's Father,

whose name he bore (Abraham Darby and who was the first that set on foot the Brass Works at or near Bristol) that attempted to mould and cast Iron pots, &c., in sand instead of Loam (as they were wont to do, which made it a tedious and more expensive process) in which he succeeded. This first attempt was tryed at an Air Furnace in Bristol. About the year 1709 he came into Shropshire to Coalbrookdale, and with other partners took a lease of the works, which only consisted of an old Blast Furnace and some Forges. He here cast Iron Goods in sand out of the Blast Furnace that blow'd with wood charcoal; for it was not yet thought of to blow with Pit Coal. Sometime after he suggested the thought, that it might be practable to smelt the Iron from the ore in the blast Furnace with Pit Coal : Upon this he first try'd with raw coal as it came out of the Mines, but it did not answer. He not discouraged, had the coal coak'd into Cynder, as is done for drying Malt, and it then succeeded to his satisfaction. But he found that only one sort of pit Coal would suit best for the purpose of making good Iron.—These were beneficial discoveries, for the moulding and casting in sand instead of Loam was of great service, both in respect to expence and expedition. And if we may compare little things with great—as the invention of printing was to writing, so was the moulding and casting in Sand to that of Loam. He then erected another Blast Furnace, and enlarged the Works. This discovery soon got abroad and became of great utillity.

This Place and its environs was very barren, little money stiring amongst the Inhabitants. So that I have heard they were Obliged to exchange their small produce one to another instead of money, until he came and got the Works to bear, and made Money Circulate amongst the different parties who were employed by him. Yet notwithstanding the Service he was of to the Country, he had opposers and ill-wishers, and a remarkable circumstance of awful Memory occurs; of a person who endeavour'd to hinder the horses which carried the Iron Stone and Coal to the Furnaces, from coming through a road that he pretended had a right to Oppose : and one time when he saw the horses going alone, he in his Passion, wished he might Never Speak More if they should Ever come that way again. And instantly his Speech was stop'd, and altho' he lived Several years after yet he Never Spoke More!

My Husband's Father died early in life; a religious good man, and an Eminent Minister amongst the people call'd Quakers.

My Husband Abraham Darby was but Six years old when his Father died—but he inherited his genius—enlarg'd upon his plan, and made many improvements. One of Consequence to the prosperity of these Works was as they very short of water that in the Summer or dry Seasons they were obliged to blow very slow, and generally blow out the furnaces once a year, which was attended with great loss.

But my Husband proposed the Erecting a Fire Engine to draw up the Water from the lower Works and convey it back into the upper pools, that by continual rotation of the Water the furnaces might be plentifully supplied; which answered Exceeding Well to these Works, and others have followed the Example.

But all this time the making of Barr Iron at Forges from Pit Coal pigs was not thought of. About 26 years ago my Husband conceived this happy thought—that it might be possible to make bar from pit coal pigs. Upon this he Sent some of our pigs to be tryed at the Forges, and that no prejudice might arise against them he did not discover from whence they came, or of what quality they were. And a good account being given of their working, he errected Blast Furnaces for Pig Iron for Forges. Edward Knight Esqr a capitol Iron Master urged my Husband to get a patent, that he might reap the benefit for years of this happy discovery : but he said he would not deprive the public of Such an Acquisition which he was Satisfyed it would be ; and so it has proved, for it soon spread, and Many Furnaces both in this Neighbourhood and Several other places have been errected for this purpose.

Had not these discoveries been made the Iron trade of our own produce would have dwindled away, for woods for charcoal became very Scarce and landed Gentlemen rose the prices of cord wood exceeding high—indeed it would not have been to be got. But from pit coal being introduced in its stead the demand for wood charcoal is much lessen'd, and in a few years I apprehend will set the use of that article aside.

Many other improvements he was the author of. One of Service to these Works here they used to carry all their mine and coal upon horses' backs but he got roads made and laid with Sleepers and rails as they have them in the North of England for carring them to the Rivers, and brings them to the Furnaces in Waggons. And one waggon with three horses will bring as much as twenty horses used to bring on horses' backs. But this laying the roads with wood begot a Scarcity and rose the price of it. So that of late years the laying of the rails of cast Iron was substituted ; which altho' expensive, answers well for Ware and Duration. We have in the different Works near twenty miles of this road which cost upwards of Eight hundred pounds a mile. That of Iron Wheels and axletrees for these waggons was I believe my Husband's Invention.

He kept himself confined to the Iron Trade and the Necessary Appendages annex'd thereto. He was just in his dealings—of universal benevolence and charity, living Strictly to the Rectitude of the Divine and Moral Law, held forth by his great Lord and Saviour, had an extraordinary command over his own spirit, which thro' the Assistance of Divine Grace enabled to bear up with fortitude above all opposition : for it may seem very strange, so valuable a man should have Antagonists, yet he had. Those called Gentlemen with an Envious Spirit could not bear to see him prosper; and others covetious; strove to make every advantage by raising their Rents of their collieries and lands in which he wanted to make roads; and endeavour'd to stop the works. But he surmounted all : and died in Peace beloved and Lamented by many.

INDEX.

Printed in Great Britain by
Butler & Tanner Ltd.,
Frome and London